ANALYTIC GEOMETRY
WITH VECTORS

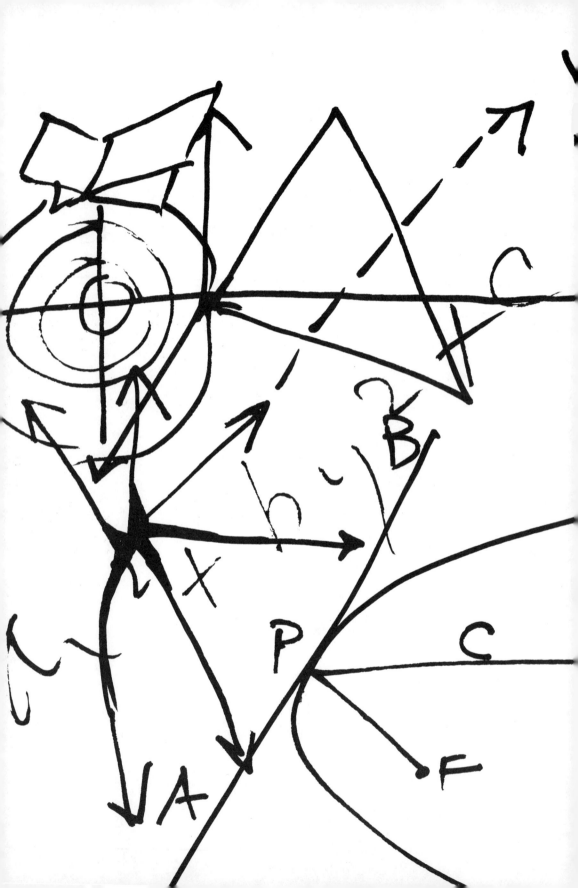

ANALYTIC GEOMETRY
WITH VECTORS

ANTHONY J. PETTOFREZZO
Southern Connecticut State College

MARCOANTONIO M. LACATENA
Montclair State College

SCOTT, FORESMAN AND COMPANY

PREFACE

The purpose of this book is to combine a traditional program in two-dimensional and three-dimensional analytic geometry with the modern concepts and methods of algebra. It is believed by the authors that the use of the concepts and methods of vector algebra and matrix algebra makes the study of analytic geometry a more integral part of the mathematics programs of today. Topics usually reserved for an introductory course in linear algebra are presented at a level suitable for students studying analytic geometry for the first time. This approach is consistent with recommendations made by such study groups as the Commission on Mathematics, the School Mathematics Study Group, the Committee on the Undergraduate Program in Mathematics, and the Cambridge Conference.

The use of vector and matrix techniques enables the reader to approach the study of analytic geometry in terms of a few fundamental ideas. It has long been the opinion of the authors that a vector approach to geometry is superior to the traditional approach. Furthermore, an earlier introduction to vectors and matrices will (i) better prepare the student of engineering, science, or mathematics to understand related courses in physics, engineering, statistics, and abstract linear algebra; (ii) make a major contribution to the general mathematical development of the reader.

Chapter 1 contains a complete and formal treatment of distance functions and general linear coordinate systems. Chapter 2 is fundamental to the rest of the book. This chapter is an introducton to two-dimensional and three-dimensional analytic geometry in vector language. The algebra of vectors is developed as a study of ordered pairs and ordered triples of real numbers. Each operation and concept is then interpreted geometrically in terms of directed line segments. The concept of the scalar product of two vectors and the concept of a set of linearly independent vectors are stressed. Chapter 3 contains a treatment of the equations and properties of lines in a plane. The coordinate forms of the equations of lines subject to certain specific geometric conditions are derived subsequent to the derivation of the vector forms of the equations. The use of direction numbers of a line is emphasized. Parametric forms of an equation of a line are introduced here. Polar coordinates are treated briefly in Chapter 4. An introduction to the circle and some of its properties is made via vectors. Chapter 5 contains a vector approach to the derivations of the equations of planes and lines in space. This chapter represents a substantial introduction to three-dimensional analytic geometry. Chapter 6 contains the usual treatment of conic sections and their equations in standard, or canonical, forms. The synthetic approach to the conics motivates their definitions as loci in the plane. The polar coordinate forms of the conic sections are considered. A discussion of the general properties of graphs, such as symmetry, intercepts, and extent, is presented here. Chapter 7 is a self-contained introduction to the elementary theory of square matrices, including the basic definitions, fundamental operations, and important properties. In Chapter 8, matrices are used to represent or define particular types of transformations. The rigid motion transformations are characterized in terms of the properties of the matrices representing them. Every rigid motion transformation of the plane is shown to be a product of rotations, reflections, and translations. The general equation of the conic sections is presented in matrix form. By means of the rigid motion transformations of the plane, the general equation of the conic sections is transformed to a canonical form. The classification of the conics in terms of the eigenvalues of the matrix of the conic is made. The standard forms of the equations of the seventeen types of quadric surfaces, along with their properties, are presented in Chapter 9. The development parallels the discussion of the conics in Chapter 6. By means of the rigid motion transformations of space, the general equation of the quadric surfaces is transformed to a canonical form in Chapter 10. This chapter contains a detailed presentation of the classification of the quadric surfaces according to the invariant properties of the surfaces.

More than 140 detailed illustrative examples are included as an aid to the reader in his mastery of the concepts and methods presented. There are over 1,100 exercises, many of which have several parts, that range from problems with numerical solutions to those that require the proof of a particular theorem. Answers to selected exercises are included.

The only prerequisite required of the reader is an understanding of the material usually presented in the introductory courses in plane synthetic geometry and intermediate algebra at the high school level. The book contains more than enough material for a full semester course in analytic geometry. A one quarter course in two-dimensional analytic geometry can be completed by omitting Chapters 5, 9, and 10 and those aspects of three-dimensional analytic geometry contained in the remaining chapters. An abbreviated course in two-dimensional and three-dimensional analytic geometry would consist of the study of Chapters 1 through 6.

We wish to express our appreciation to Mr. Robert Wesner, Program Director of Mathematics and Science of Scott, Foresman and Company, for his continued encouragement during the development of the manuscript, to Mr. Nat Weintraub for his invaluable editorial comments and suggestions, and to the entire editorial and production staff of Scott, Foresman and Company for their efforts and contributions towards the publication of the book. We also acknowledge our appreciation and gratitude to Mrs. Betty Pettofrezzo who gave willingly of her time and ability to type the various drafts of the manuscript.

A. J. P.

M. M. L.

CONTENTS

COORDINATE SYSTEMS

1.1 DISTANCE FUNCTIONS

The basic concept of analytic geometry is that of a *linear coordinate system*. In this section we shall begin our study of linear coordinate systems by studying a special type of function called a *distance function*.

Let P and Q be any two points of a set S.* We shall assume that there exists at least one function d, called a *distance function*, which associates with the pair of points P and Q a real number $d(P, Q)$ in such a way that:

(i) $d(P, Q) \geq 0$,

(ii) $d(P, Q) = 0$ if and only if $P = Q$,

(iii) $d(P, Q) = d(Q, P)$.

Furthermore, if R is a third point of the set S,

(iv) $d(P, R) \leq d(P, Q) + d(Q, R)$.

Note that the domain of a distance function is the Cartesian set $S \times S$ where S is the set of points. The range of a distance function is some subset of the set of nonnegative real numbers.

In terms of properties (i), (ii), (iii), and (iv), there are many distance functions. The following examples illustrate two such distance functions.

> **Example 1.** Let S be the set of points on a line. A function d is defined such that if P and Q are any two points on the line, then
>
> $$d(P, Q) = \begin{cases} 0 & \text{if} \quad P = Q \\ 1 & \text{if} \quad P \text{ and } Q \text{ are distinct points.} \end{cases}$$
>
> Prove that d is a distance function.

---

* By "any two points" we mean that P and Q may be distinct points or the same point. Whenever we wish P and Q to be distinct points, it will be necessary for us to write "any two distinct points."

Property (i) is satisfied since P and Q must be either the same point or distinct points; in either case, $d(P, Q) \geq 0$. If $P = Q$, then $d(P, Q) = 0$; if $P \neq Q$, then $d(P, Q) \neq 0$. Hence $d(P, Q) = 0$ if and only if $P = Q$, and property (ii) is satisfied. By definition,

$$d(Q, P) = \begin{cases} 0 & \text{if } Q = P \\ 1 & \text{if } Q \text{ and } P \text{ are distinct points.} \end{cases}$$

If P and Q are the same point, then $d(P, Q) = 0$, $d(Q, P) = 0$, and $d(P, Q) = d(Q, P)$; if P and Q are distinct points, then $d(P, Q) = 1$, $d(Q, P) = 1$, and $d(P, Q) = d(Q, P)$. Hence $d(P, Q) = d(Q, P)$, and property (iii) is satisfied. Let R be any third point on the line, and consider the following cases:

If $P = Q = R$, then $d(P, R) = 0$, $d(P, Q) = 0$, $d(Q, R) = 0$, and $d(P, R) \leq d(P, Q) + d(Q, R)$ since $0 \leq 0 + 0$.

If $P = Q \neq R$, then $d(P, R) = 1$, $d(P, Q) = 0$, $d(Q, R) = 1$, and $d(P, R) \leq d(P, Q) + d(Q, R)$ since $1 \leq 0 + 1$.

If $P = R \neq Q$, then $d(P, R) = 0$, $d(P, Q) = 1$, $d(Q, R) = 1$, and $d(P, R) \leq d(P, Q) + d(Q, R)$ since $0 \leq 1 + 1$.

If $P \neq Q = R$, then $d(P, R) = 1$, $d(P, Q) = 1$, $d(Q, R) = 0$, and $d(P, R) \leq d(P, Q) + d(Q, R)$ since $1 \leq 1 + 0$.

If $P, Q,$ and R are distinct points, then $d(P, R) = 1$, $d(P, Q) = 1$, $d(Q, R) = 1$, and $d(P, R) \leq d(P, Q) + d(Q, R)$ since $1 \leq 1 + 1$.

Therefore, since property (iv) is also satisfied, the function d is a distance function.

It should be mentioned that the "points" of the set S in the definition of a distance function may themselves be real numbers, as in Example 2.

Example 2. Let S be the set of real numbers. A function d is defined such that if $a, b \in S$, then $d(a, b) = |b - a|$. Prove that d is a distance function.

Recall from elementary algebra that $|b - a| \geq 0$ for every pair of real numbers a and b; therefore, $d(a, b) \geq 0$ and property (i) is satisfied. If $a = b$, then $b - a = 0$, $|b - a| = 0$, and $d(a, b) = 0$; if $a \neq b$, then $|b - a| \neq 0$ and $d(a, b) \neq 0$. Hence $d(a, b) = 0$ if and only if $a = b$, and property (ii) is satisfied. Since $b - a = -(a - b)$, then $|b - a| = |a - b|$ and $d(a, b) = d(b, a)$; that is, property (iii) is satisfied. Let c be a real number, and consider the following cases:

If $a \leq b \leq c$, then $d(a, c) = |c - a| = c - a$,
$$d(a, b) = |b - a| = b - a,$$
$$d(b, c) = |c - b| = c - b,$$
and $d(a, c) \leq d(a, b) + d(b, c)$
since $c - a \leq (b - a) + (c - b)$. (Why?)

If $b \leq a \leq c$, then $d(a, c) = |c - a| = c - a$,
$$d(a, b) = |b - a| = a - b,$$
$$d(b, c) = |c - b| = c - b,$$
and $d(a, c) \leq d(a, b) + d(b, c)$
since $c - a \leq (a - b) + (c - b)$. (Why?)

In a similar manner, $d(a, c) \leq d(a, b) + d(b, c)$ if $a \leq c \leq b$, $b \leq c \leq a$, $c \leq a \leq b$, or $c \leq b \leq a$. These cases are left to the reader as Exercise 1. Thus property (iv) is satisfied, and the function d is a distance function.

Exercises

1. Let $d(a, b) = |b - a|$ as in Example 2, where $a, b \in S$ and S is the set of real numbers. Show that property (iv) of a distance function is satisfied where   (a) $a \leq c \leq b$;   (b) $b \leq c \leq a$;   (c) $c \leq a \leq b$; (d) $c \leq b \leq a$.

Let S be the set of real numbers, and let $a, b \in S$. Determine whether or not each of the following functions d is a distance function. If d is not a distance function, indicate which properties are not satisfied.

2. $d(a, b) = \pi|b - a|$.

3. $d(a, b) = (a - b)^2$.

4. $d(a, b) = \dfrac{|b - a|}{1 + |b - a|}$ · Show also that $0 \leq d(a, b) < 1$.

5. $d(a, b)$ equals the minimum of 1 and $|b - a|$.

6. $d(a, b)$ equals the maximum of 1 and $|b - a|$.

1.2 COORDINATE SYSTEMS ON LINES

In this section we shall define what we mean, in general, by a coordinate system on a line in terms of a distance function. Then in §1.3 we shall choose a particular distance function to define familiar coordinate systems.

Throughout our discussion we shall assume on the part of the reader a familiarity with the intuitive notion of *betweenness* for points on a line, including the properties of betweenness for points. For example, if A, B, and C are any three distinct points on a line, then one and only one of them is between the other two. If B is between A and C, then B is between C and A. Furthermore, if B is between A and C, then A, B, and C are three distinct collinear points.

Let d be any distance function. A coordinate system for the set of points on a line can be established in the following manner. Choose any two distinct points O and N on the line ℓ and arbitrarily assign $d(O, N) = 1$, as shown in Figure 1.1.* The distance $d(O, N)$ is called the *unit distance*.

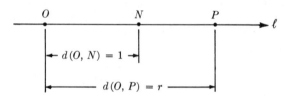

Figure 1.1

Note that O determines two half-lines: the half-line that contains N and the half-line that does not contain N. We shall note the importance of the half-line that contains N by using an arrowhead on that half-line only, as indicated in Figure 1.1. Let P be any point on line ℓ, and let r be the ratio of the distance $d(O, P)$ to $d(O, N)$. Then r is the distance from O to P since

$$r = \frac{d(O, P)}{d(O, N)} = \frac{d(O, P)}{1} = d(O, P).$$

If the point O is not between N and P, as shown in Figure 1.1, then associate the nonnegative real number r with the point P. If the point O is between N and P, as shown in Figure 1.2, then associate the negative real number

---

* In certain cases the distance function must be modified in order to make this arbitrary assignment. Otherwise, a coordinate system cannot be defined in terms of that particular distance function.

$-r$ with the point P. In this manner, each point on the line ℓ is assigned a real number called the *coordinate* of the point. However, it should be mentioned that, in general, not every real number is the coordinate of a point, as we shall illustrate in Example 2. This association of a subset of the set of real numbers with the set of points on the line ℓ is called a *coordinate system on the line*. A coordinate system on a line is therefore a function whose domain is the set of points on a line and whose range is a subset of the set of real numbers.

Figure 1.2

Example 1. Find the coordinates of the points O and N in any coordinate system.

Since O is not between N and O, then by definition the coordinate of the point O is r where

$$r = \frac{d(O, O)}{d(O, N)} = \frac{0}{1} = 0;$$

that is, the coordinate of the point O is 0. Since O is not between N and N, then by definition the coordinate of the point N is r where

$$r = \frac{d(O, N)}{d(O, N)} = \frac{1}{1} = 1;$$

that is, the coordinate of the point N is 1.

Example 2. Consider the distance function defined in Example 1 of §1.1 to establish a coordinate system on a line. (Recall that $d(O, P) = 0$ if $O = P$, and $d(O, P) = 1$ if O and P are distinct points.) Find the coordinate of any point P where (a) O is between P and N; (b) O is not between P and N.

(a) If O is between P and N, then the coordinate of P is $-r$ where

$$r = \frac{d(O, P)}{d(O, N)} = \frac{1}{1} = 1;$$

that is, the coordinate of P is -1.

(b) If O is not between P and N, and O and P are distinct points, then the coordinate of P is r where

$$r = \frac{d(O, P)}{d(O, N)} = \frac{1}{1} = 1;$$

that is, the coordinate of P is 1. If $O = P$, then by the results of Example 1 of this section the coordinate of P is 0.

Note that the range of the coordinate system in this example is the set $\{-1, 0, 1\}$. Furthermore, -1 and 1 are each associated with infinitely many points on the line, while 0 is the coordinate of only one point.

1.3 LINEAR COORDINATE SYSTEMS

The coordinate system on a line illustrated in Example 2 of §1.2 is of trivial importance beyond its identification. Since infinitely many distance functions exist, it is possible to describe infinitely many such trivial coordinate systems on a given line. However, one of the purposes of our study is to describe coordinate systems which can serve as models for our interpretation of real physical space and its subspaces.

In your study of elementary algebra you used coordinate systems on a line in which there are one-to-one correspondences between the points on the line and the real numbers; that is, each point on the line has a coordinate, and each real number is the coordinate of one and only one point on the line. One such coordinate system is indicated in Figure 1.3. Further-

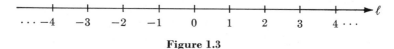

Figure 1.3

more, the coordinate systems you used possess another property with respect to the distance function:

(v)   Let P, Q, and R be three distinct points. Then

$$d(P, R) = d(P, Q) + d(Q, R)$$

if and only if P, Q, and R are collinear and Q is between P and R.

The addition of property (v) to our list of properties for a distance function enables us to characterize those nontrivial distance functions which lead to the familiar coordinate systems on a line.

Let d be a distance function with properties (i)–(v). Let A and B be any two distinct points on a line with coordinates a and b respectively. In order to determine the form of the distance function, we need only consider four cases.

Case 1: Let $a > 0$ and $b > 0$. Then $d(O, A) = a$, $d(O, B) = b$, and A and B are on the same half-line determined by O. Now, either A is between O and B or B is between O and A. If A is between O and B, as shown in Figure 1.4, then by property (v)

$$d(O, B) = d(O, A) + d(A, B),$$
$$d(A, B) = d(O, B) - d(O, A)$$
$$= b - a.$$

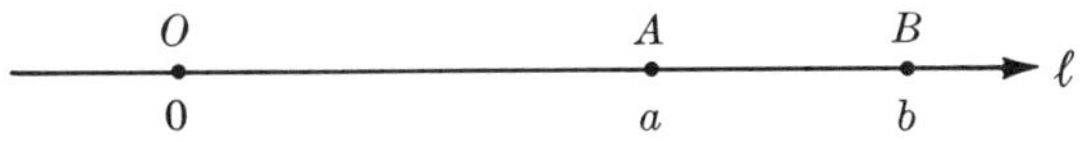

Figure 1.4

If B is between O and A, as shown in Figure 1.5, then by property (v)

$$d(O, A) = d(O, B) + d(B, A),$$
$$d(B, A) = d(O, A) - d(O, B) = a - b,$$
$$d(A, B) = a - b. \qquad \text{(Why?)}$$

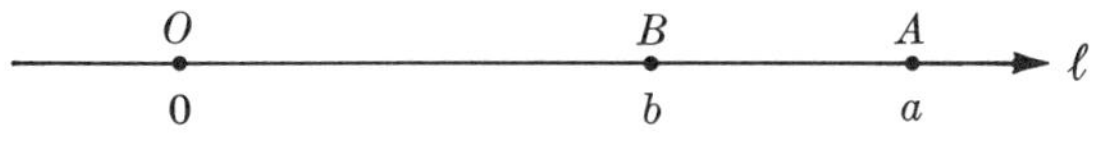

Figure 1.5

Regardless of whether A is between O and B or B is between O and A,

$$d(A, B) = |b - a|;$$

that is, the distance between the points A and B is equal to the absolute value of the difference of their coordinates.

Case 2: Let $a < 0$ and $b < 0$. Then $d(O, A) = -a$, $d(O, B) = -b$, and A and B are on the same half-line determined by O. If A is between O and B, as shown in Figure 1.6, then by property (v)

$$d(O, B) = d(O, A) + d(A, B),$$
$$d(A, B) = d(O, B) - d(O, A) = -b - (-a)$$
$$= a - b.$$

Figure 1.6

If B is between O and A, as shown in Figure 1.7, then by property (v)

$$d(O, A) = d(O, B) + d(B, A),$$
$$d(B, A) = d(O, A) - d(O, B) = -a - (-b)$$
$$= b - a,$$
$$d(A, B) = b - a.$$

Figure 1.7

Once again, regardless of whether A is between O and B or B is between O and A,

$$d(A, B) = |b - a|.$$

Case 3: Let $a < 0$ and $b > 0$. Then $d(O, A) = -a$, $d(O, B) = b$, and O is between A and B, as shown in Figure 1.8. By property (v)

$$d(A, B) = d(A, O) + d(O, B)$$
$$= -a + b = b - a$$
$$= |b - a|.$$

Figure 1.8

Case 4: Let $a > 0$ and $b < 0$. Then $d(O, A) = a$, $d(O, B) = -b$, and O is between A and B, as shown in Figure 1.9. By property (v)

$$d(A, B) = d(A, O) + d(O, B)$$
$$= a + (-b) = a - b$$
$$= |b - a|.$$

Figure 1.9

In each of the four cases considered, the distance $d(A, B)$ between the two distinct points A and B with coordinates a and b respectively is given by

$$d(A, B) = |b - a|. \qquad (1.1)$$

It should be obvious that if A and B are not distinct points, the distance between A and B may also be represented by (1.1). Thus any distance function d used hereafter to establish a coordinate system on a line must be such that (1.1) is satisfied. Any coordinate system on a line in terms of a distance function such that (1.1) is satisfied will be called a *linear coordinate system*. Furthermore, in order for the distance function to satisfy our intuitive concept of physical distance, it will be assumed that the points with integral coordinates are "uniformly" spaced on the line. In abstract space this need not be the situation.

> **Example 1.** Consider the collinear points P, Q, R, and S with coordinates -4, -2, 3, and 8 respectively. Find (a) $d(R, S)$; (b) $d(P, Q)$; (c) $d(P, R)$.
>
> (a) $d(R, S) = |8 - 3| = 5$;
>
> (b) $d(P, Q) = |-2 - (-4)| = 2$;
>
> (c) $d(P, R) = |3 - (-4)| = 7$.
>
> **Example 2.** Show that the assignment of the coordinates 1, 3, and 2 to the collinear points A, B, and C respectively, as shown in Figure 1.10, is not permitted in a linear coordinate system.

Figure 1.10

> Note that B is between A and C. Property (v) is not satisfied if the distance function is such that (1.1) is satisfied since
>
> $$d(A, B) = |3 - 1| = 2,$$
> $$d(B, C) = |2 - 3| = 1,$$
> $$d(A, C) = |2 - 1| = 1,$$
>
> and
>
> $$d(A, C) \neq d(A, B) + d(B, C).$$

If x, y, and z are any three distinct real numbers, then y is *between* x and z if either $x < y < z$ or $z < y < x$. The results of Example 2 suggest the following property of any linear coordinate system on a line.

Theorem 1.1. *Let A, B, and C be any three distinct collinear points with coordinates x, y, and z respectively. Then B is between A and C if and only if y is between x and z.*

Proof: If y is between x and z, then either $x < y < z$ or $z < y < x$. If $x < y < z$, then

$$\begin{aligned}
d(A, B) + d(B, C) &= |y - x| + |z - y| \\
&= (y - x) + (z - y) \\
&= z - x = |z - x| \\
&= d(A, C).
\end{aligned}$$

Hence by property (v) the point B is between A and C. If $z < y < x$, then it can be shown in a similar manner that the point B is again between A and C. The proof of this is left to the reader as Exercise 7.

Conversely, if B is between A and C, then by property (v)

$$d(A, B) + d(B, C) = d(A, C);$$

that is,

$$|y - x| + |z - y| = |z - x|.$$

This equation is equivalent to one of eight equations, depending upon whether each of the expressions $y - x$, $z - y$, and $z - x$ is a positive or negative real number:

$$\begin{aligned}
(1) \quad & (y - x) + (z - y) = z - x, \\
(2) \quad & (y - x) + (z - y) = x - z, \\
(3) \quad & (y - x) + (y - z) = z - x, \\
(4) \quad & (y - x) + (y - z) = x - z, \\
(5) \quad & (x - y) + (z - y) = z - x, \\
(6) \quad & (x - y) + (z - y) = x - z, \\
(7) \quad & (x - y) + (y - z) = z - x, \\
(8) \quad & (x - y) + (y - z) = x - z.
\end{aligned}$$

Equations (2) and (7) imply $x = z$, equations (3) and (6) imply $y = z$, and equations (4) and (5) imply $x = y$. However, none of these cases are possible since A, B, and C are distinct points. Equation (1) is obtained when $x < y < z$, and equation (8) is obtained when $z < y < x$; hence in both cases, y is between x and z.

Example 3. Show that the assignment of the coordinate 5 to each of two distinct points A and B, as shown in Figure 1.11, is not permitted in a linear coordinate system.

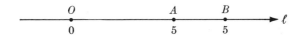

Figure 1.11

Note that A is between O and B. Property (ii) is not satisfied if the distance function is such that (1.1) is satisfied: $d(A, B) = 0$; however, $A \neq B$.

It is interesting to note in passing that property (v) is satisfied:

$$d(O, A) = |5 - 0| = 5,$$

$$d(A, B) = |5 - 5| = 0,$$

$$d(O, B) = |5 - 0| = 5,$$

so that

$$d(O, A) = d(O, A) + d(A, B).$$

Example 3 suggests that in a linear coordinate system on a line, the correspondence between the points on the line and the real numbers is one-to-one, as stated in Theorem 1.2.

Theorem 1.2. *Let A and B be any two points on a line with coordinates a and b respectively. The distance function d such that $d(A, B) = |b - a|$ establishes a one-to-one correspondence between the points on the line and the real numbers.*

Proof: We have already shown that any distance function can be used to assign a coordinate (real number) to each point on the line. Assume that A and B are distinct points having the same coordinate; that is, $a = b$. Then $d(A, B) = 0$, and property (ii) is not satisfied. Hence two distinct points have different coordinates. It remains to be proved that every real number is the coordinate of some point on the line.

Let x be any real number, and consider the expression $|x - 0|$. Since d is such that $d(A, B) = |b - a|$, there exists a point X such that $d(O, X) = |x - 0| = |x|$. If x is positive, the point X is x units from the origin on the half-line containing N; if x is negative, the point X is $-x$ units from the origin on the other half-line.

Theorem 1.1 implies that there are at least two different linear coordinate systems on a line. Given the point O with coordinate 0 on a line, there are two different linear coordinate systems with the same unit distance but with opposite orientation, as shown in Figures 1.12 and 1.13. As a matter of choice, we shall generally prefer to use the orientation indicated in Figure 1.12.

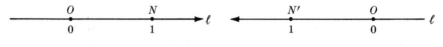

Figure 1.12   Figure 1.13

It should be mentioned that there are infinitely many linear coordinate systems on a line since the point O with coordinate 0 and the point N which determines the unit distance can be arbitrarily chosen. Once a linear coordinate system has been established on a line, the line is usually referred to as a *real number line, coordinate line,* or *coordinate axis*. The line is a geometric representation of the real numbers. The point O is called the *origin* of the coordinate system. The half-line determined by the point O that contains the point N is called the *positive half* of the coordinate axis; the other half-line is called the *negative half* of the coordinate axis. Since there is a one-to-one correspondence between the points on the line and the real numbers, it is usually convenient to refer to "the point x" instead of "the point whose coordinate is x."

Exercises

1. Let P, Q, R, and S be points on a line with coordinates -3, -1, 2, and 5 respectively, and let $d(A, B) = |b - a|$. Find
    (a) $d(P, S)$;   (c) $d(R, Q)$;   (e) $d(S, P)$;
    (b) $d(R, S)$;   (d) $d(P, R)$;   (f) $d(Q, P)$.

2. Determine which of the following assignments of coordinates to the distinct collinear points A, B, and C is possible in a linear coordinate system if B is between A and C.*
    (a) $A:(3)$, $B:(4)$, $C:(6)$;   (d) $A:(5)$, $B:(4)$, $C:(3)$;
    (b) $A:(-3)$, $B:(0)$, $C:(-2)$;   (e) $A:(3)$, $B:(3)$, $C:(4)$.
    (c) $A:(\frac{1}{4})$, $B:(\frac{1}{3})$, $C:(\frac{1}{2})$;

3. Consider the distance function of Example 1 of §1.1. Let P, Q, and R be distinct points. Show that property (v) is not satisfied.

4. Show that property (v) is not satisfied for the distance function d where
    $$d(a, b) = \frac{|b - a|}{1 + |b - a|}$$
    and a, b, and c are real numbers.

---

* The point P with coordinate x will be denoted by $P:(x)$.

5. Repeat Exercise 4 for the distance function d where $d(a, b)$ equals the minimum of 1 and $|b - a|$.

6. Show that property (v) is satisfied for the distance function d where $d(a, b) = \pi|b - a|$ and a, b, and c are real numbers.

7. Complete the proof of Theorem 1.1 by showing that if $z < y < x$, then the point B is between A and C.

1.4 LINEAR COORDINATE SYSTEMS FOR PLANES

Any two intersecting lines ℓ_1 and ℓ_2 determine a plane. The point of intersection can be used as the origin of linear coordinate systems to be established on each line, as shown in Figure 1.14. Consider the arbitrary selection of points N and N' on ℓ_1 and ℓ_2 respectively and the assignment of unit distances to $d(O, N)$ and $d(O, N')$. Note that the unit distance on ℓ_1 need not be the same as the unit distance on ℓ_2; that is, line segments ON and ON' need not be congruent.

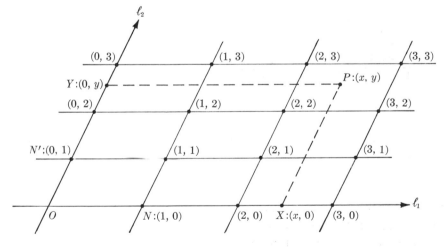

Figure 1.14

A linear coordinate system for the plane can be obtained by associating an ordered pair of real numbers with each point P not on ℓ_1 or ℓ_2 in the following manner. Construct a pair of lines that contain point P and are parallel to lines ℓ_2 and ℓ_1 respectively, as shown in Figure 1.14. The pair of lines intersect ℓ_1 and ℓ_2 at points X and Y, whose coordinates are x and y respectively in the coordinate systems established on ℓ_1 and ℓ_2. The ordered pair of real numbers (x, y) is associated with the point P; the real numbers x and y are the *coordinates* of P. The ordered pair of real numbers $(x, 0)$ is associated with the point X; $(0, y)$ is associated with the point Y; $(0, 0)$ is associated with the origin O. This association of the ordered pairs of real numbers with the points in the plane is a one-to-one correspondence called a *linear coordinate system for the plane*. The plane is often referred to as a *coordinate plane*.

Example. Consider a linear coordinate system for the plane in which the coordinate lines ℓ_1 and ℓ_2 intersect to form an angle whose measure is $\pi/6$. Let the ratio of the unit distances along ℓ_1 and ℓ_2 be equal to $\sqrt{2}$, as in Figure 1.15. Locate the points A, B, C, and D, whose coordinates are $(1, 0)$, $(1, 3)$, $(3, 2)$, and $(2, 1)$ respectively in the figure.

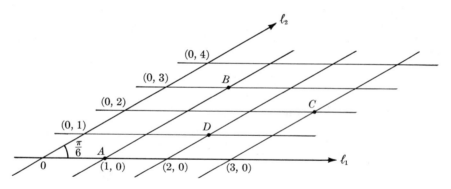

Figure 1.15

It will be convenient at this time to introduce a change of notation. Instead of denoting the distance from point A to point B by $d(A, B)$, we shall write $|AB|$; that is,

$$d(A, B) = |AB|.$$

If the line segment determined by A and B is denoted simply by AB, then the measure of its length is denoted by $|AB|$.

Consider a linear coordinate system for the plane in which the unit distance along ℓ_2 is twice the unit distance along ℓ_1, as in Figure 1.16. Let P, R, and S have coordinates $(1, 1)$, $(3, 1)$, and $(3, 3)$ respectively. By the law of cosines,

$$|PS|^2 = |PR|^2 + |RS|^2 - 2|PR|\,|RS|\cos(\pi - \theta).$$

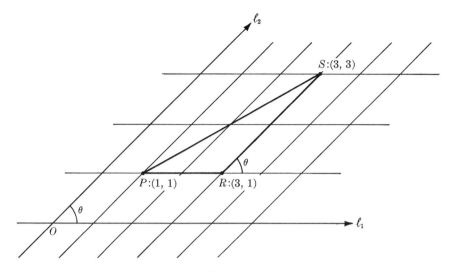

Figure 1.16

Let $\theta = \pi/4$. Then

$$|PS|^2 = |3 - 1|^2 + |3 - 1|^2 - 2|3 - 1|\ |3 - 1| \cos (3\pi/4);$$

$$|PS| = \sqrt{8 + 4\sqrt{2}} = 2\sqrt{2 + \sqrt{2}}.$$

Now, consider another orientation of the triangle PRS in the plane. For example, suppose the triangle is positioned in the plane in such a manner that the vertices P, R, and S have coordinates $(5, 2)$, $(5, 1)$, and $(1, 1)$ respectively, as in Figure 1.17.

Then, by the law of cosines,

$$|PS|^2 = |5 - 1|^2 + |2 - 1|^2 - 2|5 - 1|\ |2 - 1| \cos (3\pi/4);$$

$$|PS| = \sqrt{17 + 4\sqrt{2}}.$$

The measures for the same line segment PS are different; thus the measure of the length of a line segment is dependent on the position of the line segment in the plane.

In the study of two-dimensional physical space it is usually not sufficient to establish just any coordinate system for the plane. Certain properties of the coordinate system are desirable. For example, once a linear coordinate system has been established, it is desirable that the measure of the length of a line segment be independent of its orientation in the plane. In general, we want the size and shape of a geometric figure to be preserved under certain movements in the plane; that is, the measures of lengths, areas, and related properties of a geometric figure should not depend upon

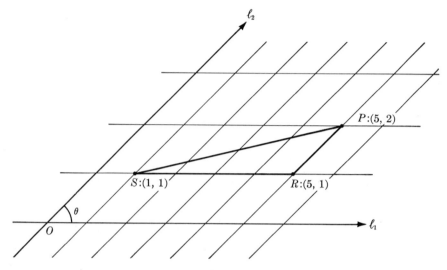

Figure 1.17

the position of the figure in the plane with respect to the coordinate axes. In §1.5 we shall discuss the condition under which the measure of the length of a line segment is independent of the orientation of the segment.

Exercises

1. Consider a linear coordinate system for the plane in which the unit distance along ℓ_2 is twice the unit distance along ℓ_1. Let ℓ_1 and ℓ_2 intersect to form an angle whose measure is $\pi/3$. Let the coordinates of the vertices of triangle PRS be $P:(2, 2)$, $R:(6, 2)$, and $S:(6, 8)$; let the coordinates of the vertices of triangle $P'R'S'$ be $P':(2, 2)$, $R':(14, 2)$, and $S':(14, 4)$.
   (a) Find the measures of the lengths of the line segments PS and $P'S'$ and compare them. Discuss the results.
   (b) What can be done to the unit distances on ℓ_1 and ℓ_2 to make the measures of the lengths of the line segments PS and $P'S'$ the same?

2. Consider a linear coordinate system for the plane in which the unit distance along ℓ_1 is twice the unit distance along ℓ_2. Let ℓ_1 and ℓ_2 intersect to form an angle whose measure is $3\pi/4$. Let the coordinates of the vertices of quadrilateral $ABCD$ be $A:(1, 1)$, $B:(1, 2)$, $C:(2, 2)$, and $D:(2, 1)$.

(a) Sketch the quadrilateral. Find the measures of the lengths of the line segments AB, BC, CD, and DA. What kind of quadrilateral is $ABCD$?

(b) Rotate the quadrilateral $ABCD$ clockwise about vertex A through an angle whose measure is $3\pi/4$. Sketch the quadrilateral. Find the new coordinates of the points B, C, and D. Determine the measures of the lengths of the line segments AB, BC, CD, and DA.

(c) Keep the quadrilateral $ABCD$ fixed. Repeat part (a) of this exercise with the unit distance along ℓ_1 equal to the unit distance along ℓ_2.

1.5 CARTESIAN COORDINATE SYSTEMS

It is desirable to have a measure of the length of a line segment which is independent of the orientation of the segment. This is possible if the unit distance along ℓ_2 is chosen to be equal to the unit distance along ℓ_1. For example, let the unit distance along ℓ_2 in Figure 1.16 be the same as the unit distance along ℓ_1. Then the coordinates of the vertices of triangle PRS are $P:(1, 2)$, $R:(3, 2)$, and $S:(3, 6)$ respectively, as in Figure 1.18, and by the

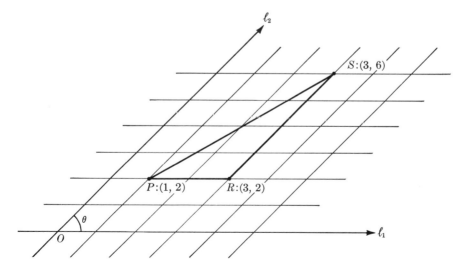

Figure 1.18

law of cosines

$$|PS|^2 = |3 - 1|^2 + |6 - 2|^2 - 2|3 - 1|\,|6 - 2|\cos(3\pi/4);$$

$$|PS| = \sqrt{20 + 8\sqrt{2}}.$$

Similarly, let the unit distance along ℓ_2 in Figure 1.17 be the same as the unit distance along ℓ_1. Then the coordinates of the vertices of triangle PRS are S:(1, 2), R:(5, 2), and P:(5, 4) respectively, as in Figure 1.19, and by the law of cosines

$$|PS|^2 = |5 - 1|^2 + |4 - 2|^2 - 2|5 - 1|\,|4 - 2|\cos(3\pi/4);$$

$$|PS| = \sqrt{20 + 8\sqrt{2}}.$$

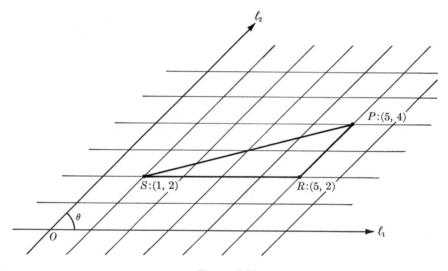

Figure 1.19

The line segment PS has the same measure in both Figure 1.19 and Figure 1.18; that is, the line segment PS has the same measure regardless of orientation if the unit distance along ℓ_2 is the same as the unit distance along ℓ_1.

A linear coordinate system for the plane in which the units of distance along the coordinate axes are the same is called a *Cartesian coordinate system*. The plane is often referred to as a *Cartesian plane;* the coordinates of any point in the plane are called the *Cartesian coordinates* of the point.

> **Example 1.** Consider a Cartesian coordinate system in which the reference lines ℓ_1 and ℓ_2 intersect to form an angle whose measure is $2\pi/3$, as shown in Figure 1.20. Determine the distance between the points A:(2, 1) and B:(4, 4).

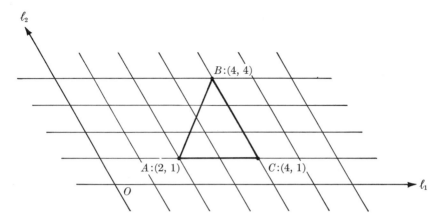

Figure 1.20

Using the law of cosines, we have

$$|AB|^2 = |AC|^2 + |CB|^2 - 2|AC|\,|CB|\cos(\pi/3)$$
$$= |4 - 2|^2 + |4 - 1|^2 - 2|4 - 2|\,|4 - 1|(\tfrac{1}{2}) = 7;$$

$$|AB| = \sqrt{7}.$$

In general, if A and B are any two points in a plane whose Cartesian coordinates are (x_0, y_0) and (x_1, y_1) respectively, then the distance $|AB|$ can be expressed by the equation

$$|AB|^2 = (x_1 - x_0)^2 + (y_1 - y_0)^2 + 2(x_1 - x_0)(y_1 - y_0)\cos\theta \quad (1.2)$$

where θ is the measure of the angle formed by the positive halves of the coordinate axes ℓ_1 and ℓ_2. The distance formula (1.2) takes on its simplest form when $\theta = \pi/2$, that is, when ℓ_1 is perpendicular to ℓ_2. Under that condition,

$$|AB|^2 = (x_1 - x_0)^2 + (y_1 - y_0)^2; \quad (1.3)$$

$$|AB| = \sqrt{(x_1 - x_0)^2 + (y_1 - y_0)^2}. \quad (1.4)$$

Whenever ℓ_1 is perpendicular to ℓ_2 and the unit distances along ℓ_1 and ℓ_2 are the same, the linear coordinate system is called a *rectangular Cartesian coordinate system*. Hereafter, unless otherwise specified, by "a coordinate system for the plane" we mean a rectangular Cartesian coordinate system. In a rectangular Cartesian coordinate system for the plane, the first member of the ordered pair (x, y) is called the *x coordinate*, or *abscissa;* the second member is called the *y coordinate*, or *ordinate*. Furthermore, the lines ℓ_1 and ℓ_2 are called the *x axis* and the *y axis* respectively and are labeled X and Y.

It is interesting to note that it is possible to establish a relationship between the coordinates of any point P in a linear coordinate system and the coordinates of P in a rectangular Cartesian coordinate system. Let the positive halves of two coordinate axes ℓ_1 and ℓ_2 intersect to form an angle whose measure is θ, as in Figure 1.21. Let the unit distances $|OP_1|$ and

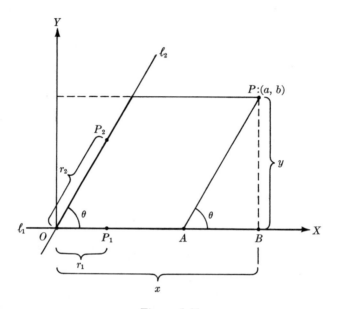

Figure 1.21

$|OP_2|$ along ℓ_1 and ℓ_2 be equal to r_1 and r_2 respectively in the rectangular Cartesian coordinate system whose x axis is ℓ_1 and whose y axis is obtained by rotating ℓ_2 counterclockwise about its origin through an angle whose measure is $\pi/2 - \theta$. If (a, b) and (x, y) are the coordinates of P in the linear coordinate system and the rectangular Cartesian coordinate system respectively, then

$$x = |OA| + |AB|$$
$$= r_1 a + |AP| \cos \theta = r_1 a + r_2 b \cos \theta;$$
$$y = |BP|$$
$$= |AP| \sin \theta = r_2 b \sin \theta.$$

By using these formulas it is possible to show that the distance between any two points P and P' whose coordinates are (a, b) and (c, d) respectively in a linear coordinate system can be expressed by the equation

$$|PP'|^2 = r_1^2(c - a)^2 + r_2^2(d - b)^2 + 2r_1 r_2(c - a)(d - b) \cos \theta. \quad (1.5)$$

The derivation of equation (1.5) is left to the reader as Exercise 7.

Example 2. Use equation (1.5) to show that the distance $|PS|$ in Figure 1.16 is the same as the distance $|PS|$ in Figure 1.17.

In Figure 1.16, let $(a, b) = (1, 1)$, $(c, d) = (3, 3)$, $r_1 = 1$, $r_2 = 2$, and $\theta = \pi/4$. Then by equation (1.5)

$$|PS|^2 = 1^2(3 - 1)^2 + 2^2(3 - 1)^2$$
$$+ 2(1)(2)(3 - 1)(3 - 1) \cos (\pi/4)$$
$$= 4 + 16 + 8\sqrt{2} = 20 + 8\sqrt{2};$$
$$|PS| = \sqrt{20 + 8\sqrt{2}}.$$

In Figure 1.17, let $(a, b) = (1, 1)$, $(c, d) = (5, 2)$, $r_1 = 1$, $r_2 = 2$, and $\theta = \pi/4$. Then by equation (1.5)

$$|PS|^2 = 1^2(5 - 1)^2 + 2^2(2 - 1)^2$$
$$+ 2(1)(2)(5 - 1)(2 - 1) \cos (\pi/4)$$
$$= 16 + 4 + 8\sqrt{2} = 20 + 8\sqrt{2};$$
$$|PS| = \sqrt{20 + 8\sqrt{2}}.$$

Exercises

In Exercises 1–4 let the unit distances along ℓ_1 and ℓ_2 be the same, and let θ be the measure of the angle between ℓ_1 and ℓ_2. Determine the distance $|AB|$ where:

1. $\theta = \pi/4$; $A:(2, 1)$ and $B:(6, -3)$.

2. $\theta = \pi/3$; $A:(-2, 0)$ and $B:(4, 8)$.

3. $\theta = 4\pi/3$; $A:(2, 5)$ and $B:(6, 9)$.

4. $\theta = 3\pi/4$; $A:(-2, -2)$ and $B:(4, 0)$.

5. Determine the rectangular Cartesian coordinates of the points whose coordinates in the linear coordinate system of Example 1 are (a) $A:(2, 2)$; (b) $B:(\sqrt{3}/2, \sqrt{3})$; (c) $C:(5, 0)$; (d) $D:(0, 4)$.

6. Derive equation (1.2).

7. Derive equation (1.5).

8. Use equation (1.5) to show that the distances $|PS|$ and $|P'S'|$ in Exercise 1 of §1.4 are the same.

9. Let the rectangular Cartesian coordinates of the vertices of triangle ABC be $A:(-r, 0)$, $B:(r, 0)$, and $C:(0, s)$.
   (a) Show that the triangle is isosceles.
   (b) Under what conditions is the triangle equilateral?

10. The rectangular Cartesian coordinates of three vertices of a parallelogram are $A:(-1, 2)$, $B:(3, 1)$, and $C:(1, 5)$. Find the coordinates of the fourth vertex D.

Let S be the set of points in a plane. Let $P_1:(x_1, y_1)$ and $P_2:(x_2, y_2)$ be any two points in the plane. Determine whether or not each of the following functions d is a distance function. If d is not a distance function, indicate which properties are not satisfied.

11. $d(P_1, P_2) = \sqrt{(x_2 - x_1)^2 + (y_2 - y_1)^2}$.

12. $d(P_1, P_2) = |x_2 - x_1| + |y_2 - y_1|$.

13. $d(P_1, P_2)$ equals the maximum of $|x_2 - x_1|$ and $|y_2 - y_1|$.

1.6 LINEAR COORDINATE SYSTEMS FOR SPACE

A linear coordinate system for space can be established by considering three noncoplanar lines ℓ_1, ℓ_2, and ℓ_3 which intersect in a common point O. Points N, N', and N'' on ℓ_1, ℓ_2, and ℓ_3 respectively determine the unit distances. Through any point P, not on ℓ_1, ℓ_2, or ℓ_3, construct planes parallel to the planes determined by ℓ_2 and ℓ_3, ℓ_3 and ℓ_1, and ℓ_1 and ℓ_2 respectively. These planes intersect lines ℓ_1, ℓ_2, ℓ_3 at the points X, Y, and Z whose coordinates are x, y, and z respectively, as in Figure 1.22. The ordered triple of real numbers (x, y, z) is associated with the point P; the real numbers x, y, and z are the *coordinates* of P. The ordered triple of real numbers $(x, 0, 0)$ is associated with the point X; $(0, y, 0)$ is associated with the point Y; $(0, 0, z)$ is associated with the point Z; $(0, 0, 0)$ is associated with the origin O. This association of the ordered triples of real numbers with the points in space is a one-to-one correspondence called a *linear coordinate system for space*. The space is often referred to as a *coordinate space*.

As in the case of the coordinate plane, the measure of the length of a line segment in space will depend on its orientation in space. As in the case of the plane, this measure can be made to be independent of orientation if the unit distances along ℓ_1, ℓ_2, and ℓ_3 are the same. Furthermore, the simplest form of the distance function is obtained if ℓ_1, ℓ_2, and ℓ_3 are pairwise mutually perpendicular, as in Figure 1.23. The formula for the distance between two points A and B whose coordinates are (x_0, y_0, z_0) and (x_1, y_1, z_1)

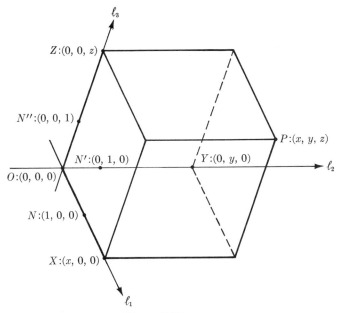

Figure 1.22

respectively can be expressed by the equation

$$|AB|^2 = (x_1 - x_0)^2 + (y_1 - y_0)^2 + (z_1 - z_0)^2; \qquad (1.6)$$

$$|AB| = \sqrt{(x_1 - x_0)^2 + (y_1 - y_0)^2 + (z_1 - z_0)^2}. \qquad (1.7)$$

The linear coordinate system in Figure 1.23 is called a *rectangular Cartesian coordinate system for space*. Hereafter, unless otherwise specified,

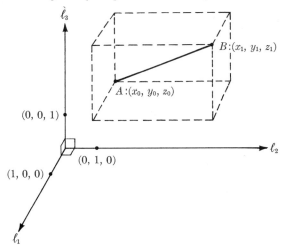

Figure 1.23

by "a coordinate system for space" we mean a rectangular Cartesian coordinate system. In a rectangular Cartesian coordinate system for space, the first member of the ordered triple (x, y, z) is called the x *coordinate*, the second member is called the y *coordinate*, and the third member is called the z *coordinate*. Furthermore, the lines ℓ_1, ℓ_2, and ℓ_3 are called the x *axis*, the y *axis*, and the z *axis* respectively and are labeled X, Y, and Z. The planes determined by lines ℓ_2 and ℓ_3, ℓ_3 and ℓ_1, and ℓ_1 and ℓ_2 are called the yz *plane*, the zx *plane*, and the xy *plane* respectively.

Example 1. Find the distance between $A:(4, -1, 2)$ and $B:(7, 2, -3)$ in a rectangular Cartesian coordinate system.

$$|AB| = \sqrt{(7-4)^2 + (2-(-1))^2 + (-3-2)^2}$$
$$= \sqrt{3^2 + 3^2 + (-5)^2} = \sqrt{43}.$$

Example 2. Show that the triangle with vertices $P:(0, 0, 0)$, $R:(2, 2, 4)$, and $S:(4, -6, 7)$ is a right triangle.

Since $|PR| = 2\sqrt{6}$, $|RS| = \sqrt{77}$, and $|PS| = \sqrt{101}$, then $|PS|^2 = |PR|^2 + |RS|^2$. Hence triangle PRS is a right triangle.

Exercises

1. Consider a linear coordinate system for space where ℓ_1, ℓ_2, and ℓ_3 are pairwise mutually perpendicular, the unit distances along ℓ_1 and ℓ_2 are the same, and the unit distance along ℓ_3 is twice the unit distance along ℓ_1. Let $P:(1, 1, 0)$, $R:(1, 5, 0)$, and $S:(1, 5, 2)$ be three points in the coordinate space.
   (a) Find the measure of the length of the line segment PS.
   (b) Rotate the triangle PRS about the line PR through an angle whose measure is $\pi/2$ such that the size and shape of the triangle is preserved and the coordinates of the vertices become $P':(1, 1, 0)$, $R':(1, 5, 0)$, and $S':(5, 5, 0)$ respectively. What is the measure of the length of the line segment $P'S'$?
   (c) How can the measures of the lengths of the line segments PS and $P'S'$ be made equal?

Let ℓ_1, ℓ_2, and ℓ_3 define a rectangular Cartesian coordinate system for space.

2. Find $|PR|$ where $P:(4, -1, 2)$ and $R:(7, 2, -3)$.

3. Find $|PR|$ where $P:(3, -1, 2)$ and $R:(-1, -1, 4)$.

4. Describe the position of the points $P:(x, y, z)$ for which   **(a)** $x = 3$; **(b)** $x > 3$;   **(c)** $x < 3$.

5. Describe the position of the points $P:(x, y, z)$ for which $|x| \leq 1$, $|y| \leq 1$, and $|z| \leq 1$.

6. Determine the distance of the point $P:(x, y, z)$ from the   **(a)** x axis; **(b)** y axis;   **(c)** z axis;   **(d)** yz plane;   **(e)** zx plane;   **(f)** xy plane.

7. Show that the triangle whose vertices are $P:(0, 0, 0)$, $R:(2, 2, 1)$, and $S:(1, -1, 0)$ is a right triangle.

8. Show that the quadrilateral whose vertices are $P:(1, 0, 0)$, $R:(2, 2, 0)$, $S:(2, 2, \sqrt{5})$, and $T:(1, 0, \sqrt{5})$ is a square.

9. Find the length of the projection of line segment AB, where $A:(1, -2, 2)$ and $B:(4, 2, 5)$, on the   **(a)** x axis;   **(b)** xy plane.

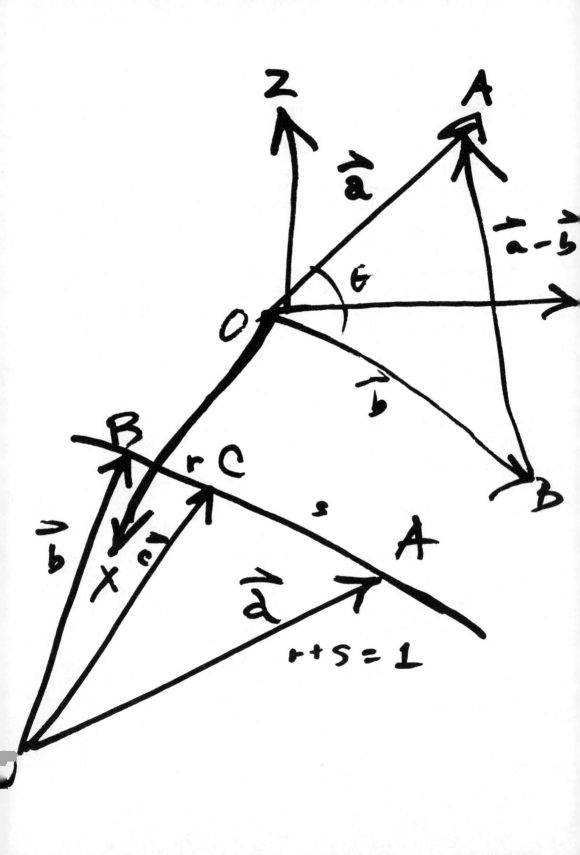

VECTORS

2.1 DIRECTED LINE SEGMENTS

It was mentioned in §1.3 that, as a result of Theorem 1.1, two possible orientations of the real number line are possible. Let us review this concept once more. Let R and S be any two distinct points on a line with coordinates r and s respectively. Then either S is to the left of R if $r - s > 0$, as shown in Figure 2.1, or S is to the left of R if $s - r > 0$, as shown in Figure 2.2.

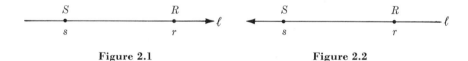

Figure 2.1   Figure 2.2

It was noted in §1.3 that we generally prefer to use the orientation indicated in Figure 2.1. Hereafter, we adopt the following convention to be used throughout the book.

> The point S with coordinate s is to the left of the point R with coordinate r if and only if $r - s > 0$.

This convention determines a definite ordering of the points on a line according to the algebraic ordering of their coordinates. Such an ordering of the points on a line enables us to assign a *directed distance* to a line segment on a line.

Let R and S be any two points on a line ℓ. Then $\overrightarrow{SR}$ will be used to denote the *directed line segment* from S to R, as shown in Figure 2.3. While we do not make any distinction between the endpoints of line segment SR, a distinction is made between the endpoints of the directed line segment $\overrightarrow{SR}$. The point S is called the *initial point* of $\overrightarrow{SR}$; the point R is called the *terminal point of $\overrightarrow{SR}$.*

Figure 2.3

There are two basic properties of a directed line segment that are of interest to us:

(i)   magnitude (length);

(ii)   direction.

Recall that the distance between the two points R and S on line ℓ is given by the absolute value of the difference of their coordinates; that is, $|SR| = |r - s|$. In terms of the convention for ordering the points on a line, the directed distance from S to R is given by the expression $|r - s|$ if and only if S is to the left of R, as in Figure 2.4. The directed distance from S to R is given by the expression $-|r - s|$ if and only if R is to the left of S, as in Figure 2.5. Since $|r - s| = r - s$ if $r > s$ and $-|r - s| = r - s$ if $r < s$, the *directed distance* from S to R is given by the number $r - s$. Therefore:

(i)   the magnitude (length) of $\overrightarrow{SR}$ is equal to $|r - s|$;

(ii)   the direction of $\overrightarrow{SR}$ on a real number line is denoted by the directed distance $r - s$.

Figure 2.4   Figure 2.5

Since the properties of magnitude and direction of a directed line segment $\overrightarrow{SR}$ on a line can be characterized, represented, or described by the single real number $r - s$, it is convenient to write

$$\overrightarrow{SR} = [r - s].$$

Example 1. Let R and S be two points on a line whose coordinates are 3 and -5 respectively. Write an expression for the directed line segment   **(a)** $\overrightarrow{SR}$;   **(b)** $\overrightarrow{RS}$.

(a) $\overrightarrow{SR} = [3 - (-5)] = [+8]$;

(b) $\overrightarrow{RS} = [-5 - 3] = [-8]$.

Note that the magnitude of each directed line segment is 8 and that the directed line segments have opposite directions.

Consider the directed line segment $\overrightarrow{SR}$ in Figure 2.6, where S and R have coordinates (x_0, y_0) and (x_1, y_1) respectively. The real numbers $x_1 - x_0$ and $y_1 - y_0$ denote the change required in each coordinate to move from the point S to the point R. Each real number denotes a directed distance with respect to a coordinate axis, and in this sense they describe the direction of $\overrightarrow{SR}$. The magnitude of $\overrightarrow{SR}$ is given by $\sqrt{(x_1 - x_0)^2 + (y_1 - y_0)^2}$. Since the properties of magnitude and direction of $\overrightarrow{SR}$ are dependent upon the ordered pair of real numbers $x_1 - x_0$ and $y_1 - y_0$, it is convenient to write

$$\overrightarrow{SR} = [x_1 - x_0, y_1 - y_0].$$

The real numbers $x_1 - x_0$ and $y_1 - y_0$ are called the *components* of $\overrightarrow{SR}$.

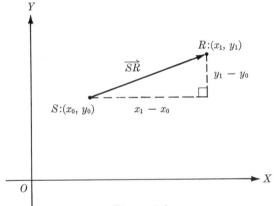

Figure 2.6

Example 2. Show that the magnitudes of $\overrightarrow{AB}$ and $\overrightarrow{CD}$ are equal if A, B, C, and D have coordinates $(2, 3)$, $(3, 6)$, $(4, 0)$, and $(7, 1)$ respectively. Sketch the directed line segments.

$$\overrightarrow{AB} = [3 - 2, 6 - 3] = [1, 3];$$

$$\overrightarrow{CD} = [7 - 4, 1 - 0] = [3, 1].$$

The magnitudes of $\overrightarrow{AB}$ and $\overrightarrow{CD}$ are denoted by $|AB|$ and $|CD|$ respectively:

$$|AB| = \sqrt{1^2 + 3^2} = \sqrt{10};$$

$$|CD| = \sqrt{3^2 + 1^2} = \sqrt{10}.$$

Hence $|AB| = |CD|$.

Note that $\overrightarrow{AB}$ and $\overrightarrow{CD}$ have different components and different directions.

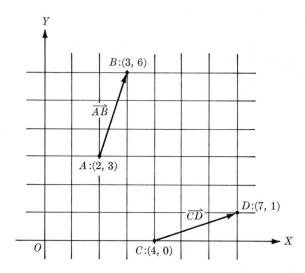

Figure 2.7

Example 3. Determine the coordinates of B given $A:(2, -1)$ and $\overrightarrow{AB} = [3, 4]$.

Let the coordinates of B be (x, y). Then

$$\overrightarrow{AB} = [3, 4] = [x - 2, y - (-1)].$$

Hence $x = 5$ and $y = 3$; that is, the coordinates of B are $(5, 3)$.

Let S and R be any two points in space whose coordinates are (x_0, y_0, z_0) and (x_1, y_1, z_1) respectively. In a fashion analogous to the situations on a line and in a plane, the properties of magnitude and direction of the directed line segment $\overrightarrow{SR}$ in space can be characterized, represented, or described by an ordered triple of real numbers $[x_1 - x_0, y_1 - y_0, z_1 - z_0]$. Each real number denotes a directed distance with respect to the x axis, y axis, and z axis respectively. The magnitude of $\overrightarrow{SR}$ is given by

$$\sqrt{(x_1 - x_0)^2 + (y_1 - y_0)^2 + (z_1 - z_0)^2}.$$

Therefore, we write

$$\overrightarrow{SR} = [x_1 - x_0, y_1 - y_0, z_1 - z_0].$$

The real numbers $x_1 - x_0$, $y_1 - y_0$, and $z_1 - z_0$ are called the *x component*, the *y component*, and the *z component* respectively of the directed line segment $\overrightarrow{SR}$.

Remark. The coordinates of a point are given within parenthesis. For example, $A:(5)$ denotes a point on a line, $B:(1, 3)$ denotes a point in a plane, and $C:(4, -1, 2)$ denotes a point in space. This notation is not to be confused with the bracket notation for a directed line segment. The real numbers (components) within the square brackets are associated with directed distances. For example, [5], [1, 3], and [4, -1, 2] denote directed line segments on a line, in a plane, and in space respectively.

Exercises

Write expressions for the directed line segments $\overrightarrow{SR}$ and $\overrightarrow{RS}$ where R and S are given. Sketch the directed line segments.

1. $R:(3)$ and $S:(-4)$.   **4.** $R:(-3)$ and $S:(-8)$.

2. $R:(-3, 1)$ and $S:(2, -3)$.   **5.** $R:(-3, 0)$ and $S:(0, 4)$.

3. $R:(1, 0, -3)$ and $S:(2, 1, 5)$.   **6.** $R:(0, 0, 0)$ and $S:(-1, 1, -1)$.

Show that the magnitudes of $\overrightarrow{AB}$ and $\overrightarrow{CD}$ are equal where A, B, C, and D are given. Sketch each directed line segment.

7. $A:(-1)$, $B:(3)$, $C:(8)$, and $D:(4)$.

8. $A:(2, 0)$, $B:(0, 2)$, $C:(8, 1)$, and $D:(6, 3)$.

9. $A:(1, 1, -1)$, $B:(-2, 5, -6)$, $C:(4, 3, 0)$, and $D:(0, -2, 3)$.

10. $A:(-5, 0, 5)$, $B:(-6, -1, 4)$, $C:(4, 8, 12)$, and $D:(3, 7, 11)$.

2.2 DIRECTION NUMBERS

Let A, B, C, and D be the points on a real number line whose coordinates are 0, 2, 4, and 7 respectively. Then $\overrightarrow{AB}$ and $\overrightarrow{CD}$ are two directed line segments such that $\overrightarrow{AB} = [2]$ and $\overrightarrow{CD} = [3]$, as shown in Figure 2.8. Now, it is evident that the directions of $\overrightarrow{AB}$ and $\overrightarrow{CD}$ are the same. In general we note that the directions of any two directed line segments whose respective components are both positive or both negative are the same. In this

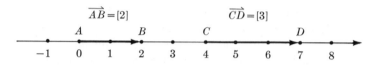

$$\overrightarrow{AB} = [2] \qquad \overrightarrow{CD} = [3]$$

Figure 2.8

sense, the component of a directed line segment on a real number line (or any positive multiple of that component) represents the direction of the segment and is called a *direction number* of the segment. For example, any number of the form $2t$ where $t > 0$ is a direction number of the directed line segment [2]. Indeed, on a real number line any positive number is a direction number of a directed line segment whose direction is "to the right"; any negative number is a direction number of a directed line segment whose direction is "to the left."

Consider two directed line segments $\overrightarrow{AB}$ and $\overrightarrow{AC}$ with the same initial point, but with different terminal points, both on the same line in a plane. Furthermore, let the point B be between the points A and C, as shown in Figure 2.9. Intuitively, we want to consider the directions of $\overrightarrow{AB}$ and $\overrightarrow{AC}$ to be the same. If the coordinates of A, B, and C are (x_0, y_0), (x_1, y_1), and (x_2, y_2) respectively, then

$$\overrightarrow{AB} = [x_1 - x_0, y_1 - y_0] \qquad \text{and} \qquad \overrightarrow{AC} = [x_2 - x_0, y_2 - y_0].$$

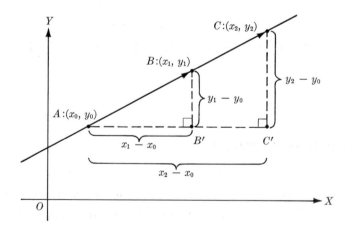

Figure 2.9

The components of $\overrightarrow{AB}$ and $\overrightarrow{AC}$ are *direction numbers* of each segment respectively. In general, the components of any directed line segment (or any positive multiple of the components) are its *direction numbers*. Since triangle ABB' is similar to triangle ACC', and B is between A and C, it follows that the directed distance $x_2 - x_0$ is the same positive multiple of $x_1 - x_0$ that $y_2 - y_0$ is of $y_1 - y_0$; that is,

$$\begin{cases} x_2 - x_0 = t(x_1 - x_0) \\ y_2 - y_0 = t(y_1 - y_0), \end{cases}$$

where t is a positive real number. This argument motivates the following definition.

> Two directed line segments have the same direction if and only if each direction number of one segment is the same positive multiple of the corresponding direction number of the other segment.

Example 1. Find $\overrightarrow{AB}$ and $\overrightarrow{CD}$ given $A:(1, 2)$, $B:(4, 4)$, $C:(3, -1)$, and $D:(9, 3)$. Show that $\overrightarrow{AB}$ has the same direction as $\overrightarrow{CD}$. Sketch the directed line segments.

$$\overrightarrow{AB} = [4 - 1, 4 - 2] = [3, 2];$$
$$\overrightarrow{CD} = [9 - 3, 3 - (-1)] = [6, 4].$$

Since each component of $\overrightarrow{CD}$ is twice the corresponding component of $\overrightarrow{AB}$, the directed line segments have the same direction (Figure 2.10). Note that the magnitude of $\overrightarrow{CD}$ is twice the magnitude of $\overrightarrow{AB}$.

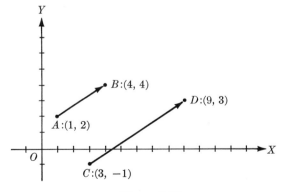

Figure 2.10

Since each component of $\overrightarrow{CD}$ in Example 1 is twice the corresponding component of $\overrightarrow{AB}$, it is convenient to write $\overrightarrow{CD} = 2\overrightarrow{AB}$; that is,

$$[6, 4] = 2[3, 2] = [2 \cdot 3, 2 \cdot 2] = [6, 4].$$

In general, if $\overrightarrow{RS} = [a, b]$, then we define $t\overrightarrow{RS}$, where t is a real number, to be $[ta, tb]$. In particular, if $t = -1$, then $(-1)\overrightarrow{RS} = [-a, -b] = \overrightarrow{SR}$. The components of $\overrightarrow{RS}$ are the negatives of the components of $\overrightarrow{SR}$, and the two directed line segments have opposite directions. Hence any directed line segment with the same direction as $\overrightarrow{RS}$ has an opposite direction to $\overrightarrow{SR}$. This argument motivates the following definition.

> Two directed line segments have opposite directions if and only if each direction number of one segment is the same negative multiple of the corresponding direction number of the other segment.

Example 2. Show that $\overrightarrow{AB}$ and $\overrightarrow{CD}$ have opposite directions given $A:(0, 1)$, $B:(3, 7)$, $C:(4, 3)$, and $D:(3, 1)$. Sketch the directed line segments.

$$\overrightarrow{AB} = [3 - 0, 7 - 1] = [3, 6];$$
$$\overrightarrow{CD} = [3 - 4, 1 - 3] = [-1, -2].$$

Since $\overrightarrow{AB} = -3\overrightarrow{CD}$, the directed line segments have opposite directions, as shown in Figure 2.11. Note that the magnitude of $\overrightarrow{AB}$ is three times the magnitude of $\overrightarrow{CD}$. Furthermore, note that $\overrightarrow{AB}$ and $\overrightarrow{CD}$ lie on parallel lines.

It should be evident that the properties of directed line segments in a plane which have been discussed thus far can be extended to a discussion of directed line segments in space.

Example 3. Show that the directed line segments $\overrightarrow{AB}$ and $\overrightarrow{CD}$ in space have the same direction where $\overrightarrow{AB} = [2, 2, -1]$ and $\overrightarrow{CD} = [6, 6, -3]$. How are the magnitudes of the two directed line segments related?

The directed line segment $\vec{CD}$ has the same direction as $\vec{AB}$ since $\vec{CD} = 3\vec{AB}$; that is,

$$[6,\ 6,\ -3] = 3[2,\ 2,\ -1] = [6,\ 6,\ -3].$$

The magnitude of $\vec{CD}$ is three times the magnitude of $\vec{AB}$ since

$$|CD| = \sqrt{6^2 + 6^2 + (-3)^2} = \sqrt{81} = 9;$$
$$|AB| = \sqrt{2^2 + 2^2 + (-1)^2} = \sqrt{9} = 3.$$

In general, if $\vec{CD} = t\vec{AB}$, where t is any real number, then $|CD| = |t|\,|AB|$.

It is sometimes necessary to distinguish between the components of a directed line segment and a set of direction numbers of the segment. Hereafter, it will be convenient to write $(ta : tb : tc)$, where t is any positive real number, as a set of direction numbers of the directed line segment $[a,\ b,\ c]$.

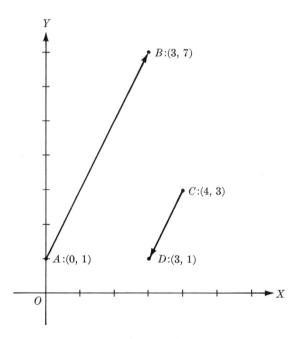

Figure 2.11

Exercises

In Exercises 1–8 determine whether the directed line segments $\overrightarrow{AB}$ and $\overrightarrow{CD}$ have the same direction or opposite directions. Compare the magnitudes of the two directed line segments.

1. $A:(2)$, $B:(4)$, $C:(-3)$, and $D:(-5)$.

2. $A:(1, 3)$, $B:(3, 5)$, $C:(-1, 1)$, and $D:(1, 3)$.

3. $A:(3, 1)$, $B:(-3, -5)$, $C:(-1, 1)$, and $D:(1, 3)$.

4. $A:(0, 1)$, $B:(5, 4)$, $C:(3, 2)$, and $D:(-7, -4)$.

5. $A:(1, 0, 1)$, $B:(2, 2, 2)$, $C:(5, 3, 1)$, and $D:(7, 7, 3)$.

6. $A:(-1, 1, -5)$, $B:(0, 2, 0)$, $C:(3, 2, 6)$, and $D:(5, 4, 16)$.

7. $A:(1, 1, 1)$, $B:(2, 3, -1)$, $C:(4, 3, 1)$, and $D:(5, 5, 0)$.

8. $A:(2, 3, 1)$, $B:(4, 5, 3)$, $C:(\frac{1}{2}, \frac{1}{4}, \frac{1}{3})$, and $D:(\frac{1}{4}, 0, \frac{1}{12})$.

9. Find several sets of direction numbers of each directed line segment.
    (a) $\overrightarrow{RS} = [2]$; (d) $\overrightarrow{RS} = [-1, 0]$;
    (b) $\overrightarrow{RS} = [-1]$; (e) $\overrightarrow{RS} = [2, 2, 1]$;
    (c) $\overrightarrow{RS} = [3, 1]$; (f) $\overrightarrow{RS} = [3, 7, -2]$.

10. The *direction cosines* of a directed line segment are those direction numbers for which the sum of their squares is equal to 1. Find the direction cosines of $\overrightarrow{RS}$ where:
    (a) $R:(1)$ and $S:(3)$; (d) $R:(2, 4)$ and $S:(5, 8)$;
    (b) $R:(4)$ and $S:(-2)$; (e) $R:(3, -2, 6)$ and $S:(4, 0, 8)$;
    (c) $R:(1, 0)$ and $S:(0, 1)$; (f) $R:(-2, -4, 3)$ and $S:(4, 2, 10)$.

11. Show that a set of direction cosines of the directed line segment $\overrightarrow{AB} = [a, b, c]$ is $(ta : tb : tc)$ where $t = 1/|AB|$.

12. Consider the directed line segment $\overrightarrow{OP}$ where $O:(0, 0, 0)$ and $P:(x, y, z)$. Let the angles that $\overrightarrow{OP}$ forms with the positive halves of the coordinate axes be α, β, and γ respectively, as shown in Figure 2.12. (These angles are called the *direction angles* of $\overrightarrow{OP}$.)
    (a) Find $\cos \alpha$, $\cos \beta$, and $\cos \gamma$.
    (b) Show that $(\cos \alpha : \cos \beta : \cos \gamma)$ is the set of direction cosines of $\overrightarrow{OP}$.

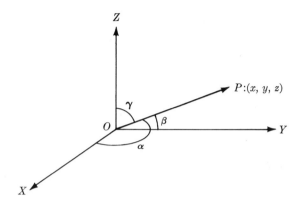

Figure 2.12

13. Let the direction angles of the directed line segment $\overrightarrow{OP}$ be $\alpha = \pi/3$, $\beta = \pi/4$, and $\gamma = \pi/3$. If $|OP| = 24$, find the coordinates of the point P.

14. Find $A:(x,\ y,\ z)$ such that $|OA| = 1$ and the measures of the angles $\overrightarrow{OA}$ forms with the positive halves of the coordinate axes are equal.

15. The direction numbers of a line in a plane or in space are defined to be the direction numbers of any parallel directed line segment.
    (a) Show that every line has two sets of direction cosines.
    (b) Find the sets of direction cosines of line AB where $A:(3, 4)$ and $B:(5, 2)$.
    (c) Find the sets of direction cosines of line AB where $A:(-1, 2, -7)$ and $B:(2, 6, 5)$.

2.3 GEOMETRIC VECTORS

In §2.2, as a matter of convenience, we wrote $\overrightarrow{CD} = t\overrightarrow{AB}$, provided that each component of $\overrightarrow{CD}$ was the product of t and the corresponding component of $\overrightarrow{AB}$. Let $\overrightarrow{AB} = [a,\ b,\ c]$ and $\overrightarrow{CD} = [ta,\ tb,\ tc]$ where t is a positive real number. Then $\overrightarrow{AB}$ and $\overrightarrow{CD}$ have the same direction, and

$$|AB| = \sqrt{a^2 + b^2 + c^2}\,;$$
$$|CD| = \sqrt{(ta)^2 + (tb)^2 + (tc)^2} = \sqrt{t^2(a^2 + b^2 + c^2)} = t|AB|.$$

If $t = 1$, then $|CD| = |AB|$; that is, *two directed line segments have the same magnitude and the same direction if corresponding components are equal.* Since the properties of magnitude and direction are the only basic properties of directed line segments with which we are concerned, it is convenient to adopt the point of view that $\overrightarrow{AB}$ is equivalent to $\overrightarrow{CD}$, and we write $\overrightarrow{CD} = \overrightarrow{AB}$. Indeed, we know very well that the two directed line segments are not identically the same since their location in space may differ. However, this difference of location is generally disregarded.

For example, the directed line segments shown in Figure 2.13 are equivalent in that they have the same magnitude and direction, and thus each directed line segment can be represented by the same ordered pair of real numbers [3, 2]. In general, the set consisting of a totality of equivalent directed line segments may be regarded as a single entity and is called a *geometric vector.* Each of the directed line segments $\overrightarrow{AB}$, $\overrightarrow{CD}$, $\overrightarrow{DE}$, $\overrightarrow{FG}$, and $\overrightarrow{HJ}$ in Figure 2.13 is merely a different representation of a single vector. This interpretation of the relationship between directed line segments and vectors is analogous to the representation of a rational number by equivalent fractions. For example, "one-third" is represented by any member of the infinite set of equivalent fractions $\{\frac{1}{3}, \frac{2}{6}, \frac{3}{9}, \frac{4}{12}, \ldots\}$.

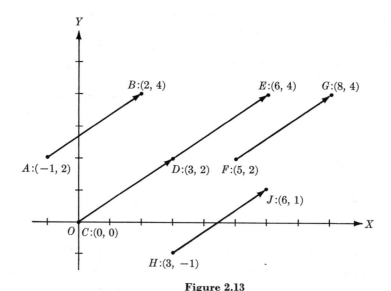

Figure 2.13

Hereafter, it will be convenient to refer to a directed line segment simply as a vector unless it is necessary to make a distinction between the two. We shall also find it convenient to refer to $\overrightarrow{CD} = \overrightarrow{AB}$ as the *equality of two geometric vectors.* On occasion it may be more convenient to denote vectors by single lowercase letters beneath a half-arrow, for example, $\vec{a}, \vec{b}, \vec{c}, \ldots$ If $\overrightarrow{AB} = \vec{n}$, the magnitude of $\overrightarrow{AB}$ may be denoted by $|AB|$ or $|\vec{n}|$.

Example. Given $A:(-1, -1)$, $B:(1, 3)$, $C:(2, -2)$, and $D:(4, 2)$, show that $\overrightarrow{AB} = \overrightarrow{CD}$.

$$\overrightarrow{AB} = [1 - (-1), 3 - (-1)] = [2, 4];$$

$$\overrightarrow{CD} = [4 - 2, 2 - (-2)] = [2, 4].$$

Since the corresponding components of $\overrightarrow{AB}$ and $\overrightarrow{CD}$ are identical, the vectors are equal; that is, $\overrightarrow{AB} = \overrightarrow{CD}$. Note in Figure 2.14 that the magnitudes of $\overrightarrow{AB}$ and $\overrightarrow{CD}$ are equal and that the directions are the same.

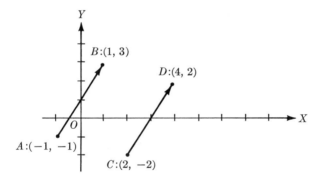

Figure 2.14

The vector $[a, b]$ can be represented in a plane by any geometric vector $\overrightarrow{MN}$ for which the difference of the x coordinates of N and M is equal to a and the difference of the y coordinates is equal to b. The geometric vector $\overrightarrow{OP}$, whose initial point is the origin and whose terminal point is $P:(a, b)$, is called the *position vector* $[a, b]$. Similarly in space, any geometric vector whose initial point is the origin is called a position vector. Every vector in a plane or in space is equal to some position vector.

Exercises

In Exercises 1–6 determine whether or not the vectors $\overrightarrow{AB}$ and $\overrightarrow{CD}$ are equal.

1. $A:(2)$, $B:(-3)$, $C:(0)$, and $D:(-5)$.

2. $A:(0, 1)$, $B:(1, 0)$, $C:(2, 0)$, and $D:(3, -1)$.

3. $A:(1, 2)$, $B:(2, 1)$, $C:(1, 2)$, and $D:(2, 1)$.

4. $A:(1, 1)$, $B:(-1, -1)$, $C:(-1, -1)$, and $D:(1, 1)$.

5. $A:(-3, 0, 1)$, $B:(0, 0, 0)$, $C:(0, 3, 3)$, and $D:(3, 6, 5)$.

6. $A:(1, -1)$, $B:(-1, 1)$, $C:(2, -2)$, and $D:(-2, 2)$.

7.   Given $A:(3, 2)$ and $B:(x, y)$, find x and y such that the vector $\overrightarrow{AB}$ is equal to the vector $\overrightarrow{CD} = [9, 3]$.

8.   The coordinates of three vertices of a parallelogram are $A:(3, 0, 4)$, $B:(6, 3, 7)$, and $C:(0, 5, 3)$. Find the coordinates of the fourth vertex D.

9.   Let $A:(1, 3)$, $B:(2, 4)$, $C:(0, 0)$, and $D:(-1, 1)$. Determine which of the vectors $\overrightarrow{AB}, \overrightarrow{BA}, \overrightarrow{AC}, \overrightarrow{CA}, \overrightarrow{CD}, \overrightarrow{DC}, \overrightarrow{CB}$, and $\overrightarrow{BC}$ are position vectors.

10.   Find $P:(x, y, z)$ such that the position vector $\overrightarrow{OP}$ is equal to $\overrightarrow{AB}$ where $A:(2, 3, -1)$ and $B:(-2, -1, -1)$.

2.4   ELEMENTARY OPERATIONS OF VECTOR ALGEBRA

In this section we shall formally define a vector and operations over a set of vectors from an algebraic point of view. The examples in this section illustrate the geometric interpretation of the vector operations in terms of directed line segments (geometric vectors).

Definition 2.1. *A two-dimensional vector $\vec{n}$ is an ordered pair of real numbers a and b: $\vec{n} = [a, b]$.*

A three-dimensional vector $\vec{n}$ is an ordered triple of real numbers a, b, and c: $\vec{n} = [a, b, c]$.

The definitions and properties of vectors that follow are stated and illustrated for two-dimensional vectors only. It is a simple matter to introduce a third component for each vector in order to obtain analogous statements for three-dimensional vectors.

Definition 2.2. (Equality of Vectors) *Let* $\vec{m} = [m_1,\ m_2]$
and $\vec{n} = [n_1,\ n_2]$. *Then* $\vec{m} = \vec{n}$ *if and only if* $m_1 = n_1$ *and*
$m_2 = n_2$.

Three properties of the equality of vectors follow directly from the
definition.

Theorem 2.1. *Let* $\vec{m}, \vec{n},$ *and* $\vec{p}$ *be arbitrary vectors. Then*

(i) $\vec{n} = \vec{n}$ *for every vector* $\vec{n};$ (2.1)

(ii)   *if* $\vec{m} = \vec{n},$ *then* $\vec{n} = \vec{m};$ (2.2)

(iii)   *if* $\vec{m} = \vec{n}$ *and* $\vec{n} = \vec{p},$ *then* $\vec{m} = \vec{p}.$ (2.3)

Definition 2.3. (Addition of Vectors) *If* $\vec{m} = [m_1,\ m_2]$ *and*
$\vec{n} = [n_1,\ n_2],$ *then* $\vec{m} + \vec{n} = [m_1 + n_1,\ m_2 + n_2].$

Consider the directed line segments $\vec{AB}$ and $\vec{CD}$ where $A:(0,\ 0)$,
$B:(2,\ 3)$, $C:(5,\ 6)$, and $D:(8,\ 4)$, as shown in Figure 2.15. The vector $\vec{CD}$
is equivalent to the vector $\vec{BE}$, where $E:(5,\ 1)$, since the magnitudes of $\vec{CD}$
and $\vec{BE}$ are equal and they have the same direction. In physics, a displacement is a movement of a given distance in a given direction. Now, the
result of a movement from point A to B followed by a movement from B

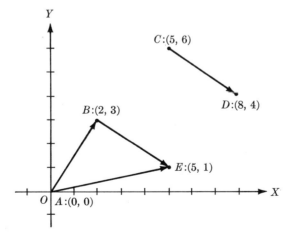

Figure 2.15

to E is equivalent to the sum of the two displacements represented by $\overrightarrow{AB}$ and $\overrightarrow{CD}$; that is,

$$\overrightarrow{AB} + \overrightarrow{CD} = \overrightarrow{AB} + \overrightarrow{BE}.$$

The resulting displacement is a movement from A to E. Thus

$$\overrightarrow{AB} + \overrightarrow{CD} = \overrightarrow{AB} + \overrightarrow{BE} = \overrightarrow{AE}.$$

If $\vec{m} = \overrightarrow{AB} = [2 - 0,\ 3 - 0] = [2,\ 3]$ and $\vec{n} = \overrightarrow{CD} = [8 - 5,\ 4 - 6] = [3,\ -2]$, then by Definition 2.3

$$\vec{m} + \vec{n} = [2,\ 3] + [3,\ -2] = [5,\ 1].$$

This result is precisely $\overrightarrow{AE}$ since $\overrightarrow{AE} = [5 - 0,\ 1 - 0] = [5,\ 1]$. Thus this interpretation of the addition of directed line segments (geometric vectors) is consistent with our algebraic definition of the addition of vectors.

The proofs of the following properties of vector addition are based upon the properties of real numbers. They are left to the reader as Exercises 6 and 7 respectively.

Theorem 2.2. *Vector addition is commutative; that is,*

$$\vec{m} + \vec{n} = \vec{n} + \vec{m}. \tag{2.4}$$

Theorem 2.3. *Vector addition is associative; that is,*

$$(\vec{m} + \vec{n}) + \vec{p} = \vec{m} + (\vec{n} + \vec{p}). \tag{2.5}$$

A geometric interpretation of Theorem 2.3 is shown in the two parts of Figure 2.16.

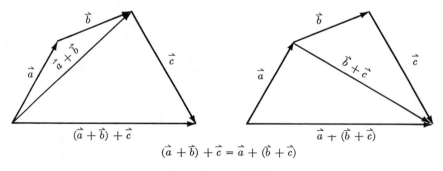

$$(\vec{a} + \vec{b}) + \vec{c} = \vec{a} + (\vec{b} + \vec{c})$$

Figure 2.16

Definition 2.4. *The vector* $\vec{0}$ *where* $\vec{0} = [0, 0]$ *is called the zero vector, or null vector.*

Note that for any vector $\vec{n}$

$$\vec{n} + \vec{0} = \vec{0} + \vec{n} = \vec{n}. \tag{2.6}$$

A geometric vector is a zero vector if its initial and terminal points coincide. The zero vector is the only geometric vector without a specified direction.

Definition 2.5. *The magnitude of the vector* $\vec{n}$, *where* $\vec{n} = [a, b]$, *is equal to* $\sqrt{a^2 + b^2}$ *and is denoted by* $|\vec{n}|$; *that is,*

$$|\vec{n}| = \sqrt{a^2 + b^2}.$$

Definition 2.6. *A vector whose magnitude is equal to 1 is called a unit vector.*

Definition 2.7. (Multiplication of a Vector by a Real Number) *If* $\vec{n} = [a, b]$ *and* t *is any real number, then*

$$t\vec{n} = [ta, tb].$$

In terms of directed line segments, we have already noted that vector $t\vec{n}$ is parallel to $\vec{n}$ with the same orientation if $t > 0$; vector $t\vec{n}$ is parallel to $\vec{n}$ with the opposite orientation if $t < 0$. As an example, vectors $\vec{a}$, $2\vec{a}$, $\frac{1}{2}\vec{a}$, $-\vec{a}$, and $-\frac{2}{3}\vec{a}$ are shown in Figure 2.17.

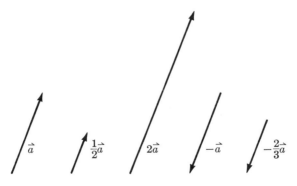

Figure 2.17

The multiplication of a vector by a real number satisfies certain "associative" and "distributive" laws.

Theorem 2.4. *Let r and s be any real numbers, and let $\vec{m}$ and $\vec{n}$ be any two vectors. Then*

$$\text{(i)} \quad r(s\vec{m}) = (rs)\vec{m}; \tag{2.7}$$

$$\text{(ii)} \quad (r + s)\vec{m} = r\vec{m} + s\vec{m}; \tag{2.8}$$

$$\text{(iii)} \quad r(\vec{m} + \vec{n}) = r\vec{m} + r\vec{n}. \tag{2.9}$$

Proof of (i): Let $\vec{m} = [m_1, m_2]$. Then

$$
\begin{aligned}
r(s\vec{m}) &= r(s[m_1, m_2]) \\
&= r[sm_1, sm_2] &&\text{(Definition 2.7)} \\
&= [r(sm_1), r(sm_2)] &&\text{(Definition 2.7)} \\
&= [(rs)m_1, (rs)m_2]; &&\text{(Associative property of multi-} \\
& &&\text{plication of real numbers)}
\end{aligned}
$$

$$
\begin{aligned}
(rs)\vec{m} &= (rs)[m_1, m_2] \\
&= [(rs)m_1, (rs)m_2]. &&\text{(Definition 2.7)}
\end{aligned}
$$

Hence $r(s\vec{m}) = (rs)\vec{m}$.

The proofs of (ii) and (iii) are left to the reader as Exercises 16 and 17 respectively.

Definition 2.8. *If $\vec{n} = [a, b]$, then $-\vec{n} = [-a, -b]$, and the vector $-\vec{n}$ is called the negative of $\vec{n}$.*

Definition 2.9. (Subtraction of Vectors) *If $\vec{m} = [m_1, m_2]$ and $\vec{n} = [n_1, n_2]$, then $\vec{m} - \vec{n} = [m_1 - n_1, m_2 - n_2]$; that is,*

$$\vec{m} - \vec{n} = \vec{m} + (-\vec{n}). \tag{2.10}$$

If two geometric vectors $\vec{m}$ and $\vec{n}$ have a common initial point, then the difference $\vec{m} - \vec{n}$ is a vector whose initial point is the terminal point of $\vec{n}$ and whose terminal point is the terminal point of $\vec{m}$, as shown in Figure 2.18, since

$$
\begin{aligned}
\vec{n} + (\vec{m} - \vec{n}) &= \vec{n} + (\vec{m} + (-\vec{n})) = \vec{n} + ((-\vec{n}) + \vec{m}) \\
&= (\vec{n} + (-\vec{n})) + \vec{m} = \vec{0} + \vec{m} \\
&= \vec{m}.
\end{aligned}
$$

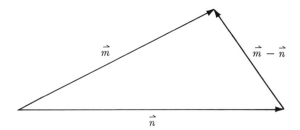

Figure 2.18

The elementary operations of vector algebra can be applied to the solutions of problems in plane geometry, as illustrated by the following two examples.

Example 1. Prove that the line segment joining the midpoints of two sides of a triangle is parallel to the third side and is equal to one-half its length.

Let M and N be the midpoints of sides AB and CB respectively, as shown in Figure 2.19. Then

$$\overrightarrow{MN} = \overrightarrow{MB} + \overrightarrow{BN} = \tfrac{1}{2}\overrightarrow{AB} + \tfrac{1}{2}\overrightarrow{BC}$$
$$= \tfrac{1}{2}(\overrightarrow{AB} + \overrightarrow{BC}) = \tfrac{1}{2}\overrightarrow{AC}.$$

Therefore, $|MN| = \tfrac{1}{2}|AC|$, and the line segment MN is parallel to side AC.

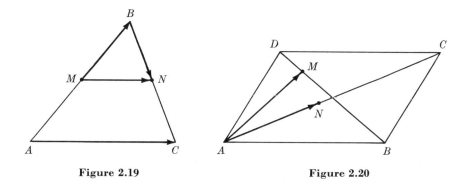

Figure 2.19   **Figure 2.20**

Example 2. Prove that the diagonals of a parallelogram bisect each other.

Let $ABCD$ be any parallelogram, as shown in Figure 2.20.

Then $\overrightarrow{AD} = \overrightarrow{BC}$ and $\overrightarrow{AB} = \overrightarrow{DC}$. Let M be the midpoint of diagonal DB; let N be the midpoint of diagonal AC. Then

$$
\begin{aligned}
\overrightarrow{AM} &= \overrightarrow{AD} + \overrightarrow{DM} = \overrightarrow{AD} + \tfrac{1}{2}\overrightarrow{DB} \qquad & \overrightarrow{AN} &= \tfrac{1}{2}\overrightarrow{AC} \\
&= \overrightarrow{AD} + \tfrac{1}{2}(\overrightarrow{AB} - \overrightarrow{AD}) & &= \tfrac{1}{2}(\overrightarrow{AB} + \overrightarrow{BC}) \\
&= \overrightarrow{AD} + \tfrac{1}{2}\overrightarrow{AB} - \tfrac{1}{2}\overrightarrow{AD} & &= \tfrac{1}{2}\overrightarrow{AB} + \tfrac{1}{2}\overrightarrow{BC} \\
&= \tfrac{1}{2}\overrightarrow{AB} + \tfrac{1}{2}\overrightarrow{AD}; & &= \tfrac{1}{2}\overrightarrow{AB} + \tfrac{1}{2}\overrightarrow{AD}.
\end{aligned}
$$

Therefore, $\overrightarrow{AM} = \overrightarrow{AN}$ and points M and N coincide. The only point that the diagonals DB and AC have in common is their point of intersection. Thus the diagonals bisect each other.

Exercises

1. Find $\vec{a} + \vec{b}$ where $\vec{a} = [3, 6, 1]$ and $\vec{b} = [1, -1, 3]$.

2. Find the vector sum $\overrightarrow{AB} + \overrightarrow{CD}$ where $A:(0, 0)$, $B:(1, 1)$, $C:(3, 4)$, and $D:(8, 5)$. Sketch the vectors $\overrightarrow{AB}$, $\overrightarrow{CD}$, and $\overrightarrow{AB} + \overrightarrow{CD}$.

3. If $|\vec{m}| = 5$, $|\vec{n}| = 6$, and $\vec{m}$ and $\vec{n}$ have the same direction, determine (a) the magnitude of $\vec{m} + \vec{n}$; (b) the magnitude of $\vec{m} - \vec{n}$; (c) the direction of $\vec{m} - \vec{n}$.

4. Simplify (a) $\overrightarrow{AB} + \overrightarrow{BC} + \overrightarrow{CD} + \overrightarrow{DE}$; (b) $\overrightarrow{AB} + \overrightarrow{BC} + \overrightarrow{CA}$; (c) $\overrightarrow{OA} - \overrightarrow{OB} + \overrightarrow{AC}$; (d) $\overrightarrow{AB} + \overrightarrow{AB}$.

5. Verify that vector addition is associative by taking $\vec{m} = [3, 1, 2]$, $\vec{n} = [1, -4, 0]$, and $\vec{p} = [5, 3, -1]$.

6. Prove Theorem 2.2.

7. Prove Theorem 2.3.

8. Show geometrically that $|\vec{a} + \vec{b}| \leq |\vec{a}| + |\vec{b}|$.

9. When a unit vector is obtained from a given vector by using an appropriate real number multiple, the given vector is said to be *normalized*. Show that every nonzero vector $\vec{a}$ can be normalized by using the real number multiple $1/|\vec{a}|$.

10. Normalize the vector $[6, -6, 7]$.

11. Let $\vec{a}$ be a unit position vector in the xy plane making an angle whose measure is θ with the positive half of the x axis. Find the components of $\vec{a}$.

12. Find $\vec{a} - \vec{b}$ where $\vec{a} = [3, -2, 5]$ and $\vec{b} = [-1, 4, -3]$.

13. Let $\vec{m} = [3, \ 2, \ 1]$ and $\vec{n} = [-3, \ 1, \ 2]$. Find (a) $3\vec{m} - 2\vec{n}$; (b) $4(\vec{m} + \vec{n})$.

14. Let $\vec{m} = [1, 3, 6]$ and $\vec{n} = [2, 1, 0]$. Find r such that (a) $r(\vec{m} + \vec{n}) = [6, 8, 12]$; (b) $r(\vec{m} + \vec{n}) = [0, 0, 0]$.

15. Let $\vec{m} = [3, \ -2]$ and $\vec{n} = [2, 5]$. Find numbers r and s such that (a) $r\vec{m} + s\vec{n} = [2, -14]$; (b) $r\vec{m} + s\vec{n} = [0, 0]$.

16. Prove part (ii) of Theorem 2.4. 17. Prove part (iii) of Theorem 2.4.

18. Prove that the median of a trapezoid is parallel to the bases and is equal to one-half the sum of their lengths.

19. Prove that the diagonals of a parallelepiped bisect each other.

2.5 LINEAR FUNCTIONS OF VECTORS

An expression such as $m_1\vec{a}_1 + m_2\vec{a}_2 + \cdots + m_n\vec{a}_n$ obtained by the addition of n real multiples of n vectors is called a *linear function* of the n vectors $\vec{a}_1, \vec{a}_2, \ldots, \vec{a}_n$. Consider the position vectors $\vec{a} = [-1, 2]$, $\vec{b} = [3, 2]$, and $\vec{c} = [4, 4]$ in the plane, as shown in Figure 2.21. It is possible to write $\vec{c}$ as a linear function of $\vec{a}$ and $\vec{b}$; that is, real numbers r and s exist such that $\vec{c} = r\vec{a} + s\vec{b}$. The real numbers r and s can be determined by considering this relation in terms of the components:

$$\begin{aligned}[4, 4] &= r[-1, 2] + s[3, 2] \\ &= [-r, 2r] + [3s, 2s] \\ &= [-r + 3s, 2r + 2s],\end{aligned}$$

whereby

$$\begin{cases} 4 = -r + 3s \\ 4 = 2r + 2s. \end{cases}$$

Solving this system of equations, we obtain $r = \frac{1}{2}$ and $s = \frac{3}{2}$. Hence $\vec{c} = \frac{1}{2}\vec{a} + \frac{3}{2}\vec{b}$. In Figure 2.22, the vector $\frac{1}{2}\vec{a} + \frac{3}{2}\vec{b}$ is constructed and verified equal to $\vec{c}$.

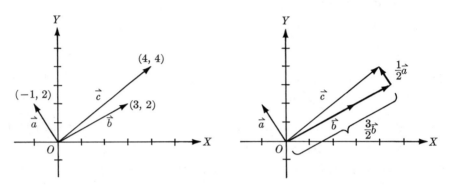

Figure 2.21   Figure 2.22

The question arises whether or not it is always possible to express a vector in the plane as a linear function of two given vectors. Consider the two parallel vectors $\vec{a} = [1, 2]$ and $\vec{b} = [2, 4]$. Let $\vec{c} = [3, 1]$. If $\vec{c} = r\vec{a} + s\vec{b}$, then

$$[3, 1] = r[1, 2] + s[2, 4]$$
$$= [r, 2r] + [2s, 4s]$$
$$= [r + 2s, 2r + 4s],$$

whereby

$$\begin{cases} 3 = r + 2s \\ 1 = 2r + 4s. \end{cases}$$

If $r + 2s = 3$, then $2r + 4s = 6$. However, no values of r and s exist such that $2r + 4s = 6$ and $2r + 4s = 1$ simultaneously. Hence we cannot express $\vec{c}$ as a linear function of $\vec{a}$ and $\vec{b}$.

Theorem 2.5. *If $\vec{a}$ and $\vec{b}$ are nonzero, nonparallel vectors in a plane, then any vector $\vec{c}$ in the same plane can be expressed as a linear function of $\vec{a}$ and $\vec{b}$; that is, $\vec{c} = r\vec{a} + s\vec{b}$ where r and s are real numbers.*

Proof: If $\vec{c}$ is parallel to $\vec{a}$, then $\vec{c} = r\vec{a}$ and $s = 0$; if $\vec{c}$ is parallel to $\vec{b}$, then $\vec{c} = s\vec{b}$ and $r = 0$. Now, consider the case where $\vec{c}$ is not parallel to $\vec{a}$ or $\vec{b}$. Since $\vec{a}$ and $\vec{b}$ are nonzero, nonparallel vectors, there exists a parallelogram $KLMN$ with sides parallel to $\vec{a}$ and $\vec{b}$ and whose diagonal can be associated with $\vec{c}$, as shown in Figure 2.23. Vectors parallel to $\vec{a}$ or $\vec{b}$ can be expressed as multiples of each respectively. Thus $\overrightarrow{KL} = r\vec{a}$ and $\overrightarrow{LM} = s\vec{b}$ for some real numbers r and s. Since $\vec{c} = \overrightarrow{KL} + \overrightarrow{LM}$, then $\vec{c} = r\vec{a} + s\vec{b}$ by substitution.

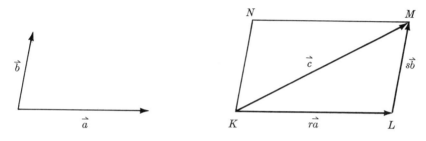

Figure 2.23

The vectors $\vec{a}$ and $\vec{b}$ in Theorem 2.5 form a *basis* for the set of vectors in the plane; that is, the two nonzero, nonparallel vectors serve as a set of reference vectors in that every vector of the plane is a linear function of them. The vectors $\vec{a}$ and $\vec{b}$ are called *base vectors*. Infinitely many pairs of vectors may form a basis for the set of two-dimensional vectors.

In a similar manner, any three nonzero, noncoplanar vectors constitute a basis for the set of three-dimensional vectors. Thus if $\vec{a}$, $\vec{b}$, and $\vec{c}$ are nonzero, noncoplanar vectors, and $\vec{d}$ is any given vector in space, then real numbers r, s, and t exist such that

$$\vec{d} = r\vec{a} + s\vec{b} + t\vec{c}.$$

Example 1. Let $\vec{a} = [3, 0]$ and $\vec{b} = [0, 1]$. Express $\vec{c}$, where $\vec{c} = [3, 1]$, as a linear function of $\vec{a}$ and $\vec{b}$.

Let $\vec{c} = r\vec{a} + s\vec{b}$. Then

$$\begin{aligned}
[3, 1] &= r[3, 0] + s[0, 1] \\
&= [3r, 0] + [0, s] \\
&= [3r, s],
\end{aligned}$$

whereby $r = 1$ and $s = 1$. Thus $\vec{c} = \vec{a} + \vec{b}$.

The base vectors of a set of two-dimensional or three-dimensional vectors constitute a set of *linearly independent* vectors. Two nonzero, non-parallel vectors form a set of linearly independent vectors in the sense that neither vector can be written as a linear function of the other. Any three coplanar vectors form a set of *linearly dependent* vectors in that at least one of the three can be expressed as a linear function of the other two vectors. For example, in Figure 2.24, $\vec{a}$, $\vec{b}$, or $\vec{c}$ can be expressed as a linear function of the other two vectors. Thus the three vectors constitute a set of linearly dependent vectors. Note in Figure 2.25 that while $\vec{a}$ cannot be expressed as a linear function of $\vec{b}$ and $\vec{c}$, both $\vec{b}$ and $\vec{c}$ can be expressed as a linear function of each other and of vector $\vec{a}$. Thus this set of vectors $\vec{a}$, $\vec{b}$, and $\vec{c}$ is also a set of linearly dependent vectors.

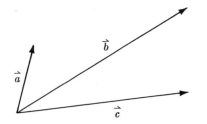

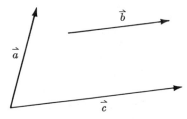

Figure 2.24   **Figure 2.25**

In a similar manner, three nonzero, noncoplanar vectors form a set of linearly independent vectors in the sense that none of them can be written as a linear function of the others. Any four vectors in space form a set of linearly dependent vectors.

Definition 2.10. *A set of n vectors $\vec{a}_1$, $\vec{a}_2$, . . . , $\vec{a}_n$ is a set of linearly independent vectors if $m_1\vec{a}_1 + m_2\vec{a}_2 + \cdots + m_n\vec{a}_n = \vec{0}$ implies that $m_1 = m_2 = \cdots = m_n = 0$. If there exist real numbers m_1, m_2, . . . , m_n not all zero such that $m_1\vec{a}_1 + m_2\vec{a}_2 + \cdots + m_n\vec{a}_n = \vec{0}$, then the n vectors $\vec{a}_1$, $\vec{a}_2$, . . . , $\vec{a}_n$ form a set of linearly dependent vectors.*

Theorem 2.6. *If $\vec{a}$ and $\vec{b}$ are linearly independent vectors in a plane, then any vector $\vec{c}$ in the same plane can be expressed as a linear function of $\vec{a}$ and $\vec{b}$ in only one way; that is, every vector in the plane is a unique linear function of $\vec{a}$ and $\vec{b}$.*

Proof: By Theorem 2.5, every vector $\vec{c}$ in the plane determined by the nonzero, nonparallel vectors $\vec{a}$ and $\vec{b}$ is a linear function of $\vec{a}$ and $\vec{b}$. Assume that there exists more than one representation of $\vec{c}$ in terms of $\vec{a}$ and $\vec{b}$:

$$\vec{c} = r\vec{a} + s\vec{b} \qquad \text{and} \qquad \vec{c} = u\vec{a} + v\vec{b}.$$

Then

$$(r\vec{a} + s\vec{b}) - (u\vec{a} + v\vec{b}) = \vec{0},$$

$$(r - u)\vec{a} + (s - v)\vec{b} = \vec{0}.$$

Since $\vec{a}$ and $\vec{b}$ are linearly independent vectors,

$$r - u = 0 \qquad \text{and} \qquad s - v = 0;$$

that is, $r = u$ and $s = v$. Hence the representation of $\vec{c}$ in terms of $\vec{a}$ and $\vec{b}$ is unique.

Example 2. Let the vectors $\vec{i}$, $\vec{j}$, and $\vec{k}$ denote the unit position vectors along the positive halves of the x, y, and z axes respectively. Express the position vector $\overrightarrow{OP}$, where P:(3, 2, 6), as a linear function of $\vec{i}$, $\vec{j}$, and $\vec{k}$.

Since $\vec{i} = [1, 0, 0]$, $\vec{j} = [0, 1, 0]$, and $\vec{k} = [0, 0, 1]$,

$$\overrightarrow{OP} = [3, 2, 6] = 3[1, 0, 0] + 2[0, 1, 0] + 6[0, 0, 1]$$
$$= 3\vec{i} + 2\vec{j} + 6\vec{k}.$$

Example 3. Let $\vec{a}$, $\vec{b}$, and $\vec{c}$ denote position vectors such that $\vec{a} = [1, 1, 0]$, $\vec{b} = [0, 0, 1]$, and $\vec{c} = [-1, 1, 0]$. Express the position vector $\overrightarrow{OP}$, where P:(1, 0, 1), as a linear function of $\vec{a}$, $\vec{b}$, and $\vec{c}$.

Let $\overrightarrow{OP} = r\vec{a} + s\vec{b} + t\vec{c}$. Then

$$[1, 0, 1] = r[1, 1, 0] + s[0, 0, 1] + t[-1, 1, 0]$$
$$= [r, r, 0] + [0, 0, s] + [-t, t, 0]$$
$$= [r - t, r + t, s],$$

whereby

$$\begin{cases} 1 = r - t \\ 0 = r + t \\ 1 = s. \end{cases}$$

Thus $r = \frac{1}{2}$, $s = 1$, $t = -\frac{1}{2}$, and $\overrightarrow{OP} = \frac{1}{2}\vec{a} + \vec{b} - \frac{1}{2}\vec{c}$.

Exercises

1. Let $\vec{a} = [1, 0]$ and $\vec{b} = [0, 2]$. Express $\vec{c}$, where $\vec{c} = [3, 1]$, as a linear function of $\vec{a}$ and $\vec{b}$.

2. Let $\vec{a} = [1, 0]$ and $\vec{b} = [-2, 0]$. Can you express $\vec{c}$, where $\vec{c} = [5, 2]$, as a linear function of $\vec{a}$ and $\vec{b}$? Explain your answer.

3. Let $\vec{c} = [1, 1]$. Find three different sets of base vectors $\vec{a}$ and $\vec{b}$ such that $\vec{c} = r\vec{a} + s\vec{b}$. Determine the values of r and s for each basis.

4. Let $\vec{a} = [2, 0, 0]$, $\vec{b} = [0, 3, 0]$, and $\vec{c} = [0, 0, 1]$.
    (a) Express the position vector $\overrightarrow{OP}$, where $P:(4, 1, -2)$, as a linear function of $\vec{a}$, $\vec{b}$, and $\vec{c}$.
    (b) Express $\overrightarrow{AB}$, where $A:(2, 6, 1)$ and $B:(3, 9, -2)$, as a linear function of $\vec{a}$, $\vec{b}$, and $\vec{c}$.

5. Let $\vec{i}$, $\vec{j}$, and $\vec{k}$ be the unit vectors of Example 2.
    (a) Express the position vector $\overrightarrow{OP}$, where $P:(4, 1, -2)$, as a linear function of $\vec{i}$, $\vec{j}$, and $\vec{k}$.
    (b) Express $\overrightarrow{AB}$, where $A:(2, 6, 1)$ and $B:(3, 9, -2)$, as a linear function of $\vec{i}$, $\vec{j}$, and $\vec{k}$.

In Exercises 6–9 determine whether each set of vectors is a set of linearly independent vectors or a set of linearly dependent vectors.

6. $\vec{a} = [-1, 2]$ and $\vec{b} = [3, 1]$.

7. $\vec{a} = [2, 1]$ and $\vec{b} = [6, 3]$.

8. $\vec{a} = [1, 1, 1]$, $\vec{b} = [0, -1, 1]$, and $\vec{c} = [2, 8, -4]$.

9. $\vec{a} = [0, 0, 2]$, $\vec{b} = [1, 1, -2]$, and $\vec{c} = [6, 8, 2]$.

10. Describe a basis for the set of vectors on a line.

11. Prove that if $\vec{a}$, $\vec{b}$, and $\vec{c}$ are nonzero, noncoplanar vectors, then any vector $\vec{d}$ in space can be expressed as a linear function of $\vec{a}$, $\vec{b}$, and $\vec{c}$.

12. Prove that the representation of $\vec{d}$ as a linear function of $\vec{a}$, $\vec{b}$, and $\vec{c}$ in Exercise 11 is unique.

13. Prove that if $\vec{a}$ and $\vec{b}$ are nonzero and nonparallel vectors, then $x\vec{a} + y\vec{b} = \vec{0}$ implies that $x = y = 0$.

14. Prove that if $\vec{a}$, $\vec{b}$, and $\vec{c}$ are nonzero, noncoplanar vectors, then $x\vec{a} + y\vec{b} + z\vec{c} = \vec{0}$ implies that $x = y = z = 0$.

2.6 DIVISION OF A LINE SEGMENT

Let $\vec{a}$, $\vec{b}$, and $\vec{c}$ be three position vectors with collinear terminal points A, B, and C, as shown in Figure 2.26. Furthermore, consider that C divides the line segment BA into two segments in the ratio r to s where $r + s = 1$. Now,

$$\vec{c} = \overrightarrow{OB} + \overrightarrow{BC} = \overrightarrow{OB} + r\overrightarrow{BA}$$
$$= \overrightarrow{OB} + r(\overrightarrow{OA} - \overrightarrow{OB}) = r\overrightarrow{OA} + (1 - r)\overrightarrow{OB}$$
$$= r\vec{a} + (1 - r)\vec{b}.$$

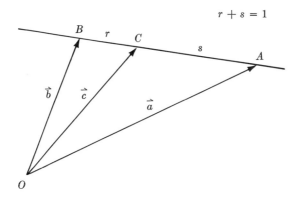

Figure 2.26

Conversely, if $\vec{c} = r\vec{a} + (1 - r)\vec{b}$, then

$$\overrightarrow{OC} = r\overrightarrow{OA} + (1 - r)\overrightarrow{OB} = r\overrightarrow{OA} + \overrightarrow{OB} - r\overrightarrow{OB}$$
$$= r(\overrightarrow{OA} - \overrightarrow{OB}) + \overrightarrow{OB} = r\overrightarrow{BA} + \overrightarrow{OB},$$
$$\overrightarrow{OC} - \overrightarrow{OB} = r\overrightarrow{BA},$$
$$\overrightarrow{BC} = r\overrightarrow{BA}.$$

Thus if $\vec{c} = r\vec{a} + (1 - r)\vec{b}$, then the terminal points A, B, and C of vectors $\vec{a}, \vec{b},$ and $\vec{c}$ are collinear. We have proved the following important theorem.

Theorem 2.7. *The terminal points A, B, and C of the three position vectors $\vec{a}$, $\vec{b}$, and $\vec{c}$ respectively are collinear if and only if*

$$\vec{c} = r\vec{a} + (1 - r)\vec{b},$$

where r is a real number.

Example 1. Find the coordinates of the point of trisection of line segment MN nearest to M where $M:(2, 6, -1)$ and $N:(5, -9, 8)$.

Let $P:(x, y, z)$ be the point of trisection of the line segment MN nearest to M. Since P divides the line segment MN in the ratio 1 to 2, that is, $\frac{1}{3}$ to $\frac{2}{3}$, then by Theorem 2.7

$$\overrightarrow{OP} = \tfrac{1}{3}\overrightarrow{ON} + \tfrac{2}{3}\overrightarrow{OM},$$
$$[x, y, z] = \tfrac{1}{3}[5, -9, 8] + \tfrac{2}{3}[2, 6, -1]$$
$$= [\tfrac{5}{3}, -3, \tfrac{8}{3}] + [\tfrac{4}{3}, 4, -\tfrac{2}{3}] = [3, 1, 2].$$

Thus P has coordinates $(3, 1, 2)$.

Example 2. Let M and N be the midpoints of sides AB and CD respectively of parallelogram $ABCD$. Prove that $AMCN$ is a parallelogram.

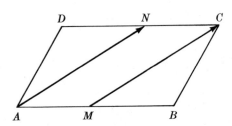

Figure 2.27

Since M is the midpoint of the line segment AB, then $\overrightarrow{CM} = \tfrac{1}{2}\overrightarrow{CA} + \tfrac{1}{2}\overrightarrow{CB}$ and $\overrightarrow{MC} = \tfrac{1}{2}\overrightarrow{AC} + \tfrac{1}{2}\overrightarrow{BC}$. Since N is the midpoint of the line segment CD, then $\overrightarrow{AN} = \tfrac{1}{2}\overrightarrow{AC} + \tfrac{1}{2}\overrightarrow{AD}$. Now, $\overrightarrow{AD} = \overrightarrow{BC}$ since opposite sides of parallelogram $ABCD$

are congruent and parallel. Thus $\overrightarrow{AN} = \overrightarrow{MC}$. Therefore, $AMCN$ is a parallelogram since two opposite sides are congruent and parallel.

Example 3. Prove that the medians of a triangle are concurrent at a point two-thirds of the distance from each vertex to the midpoint of the opposite side.

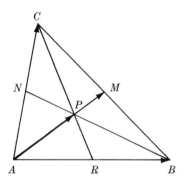

Figure 2.28

Let M and N be the midpoints of sides BC and AC respectively. Furthermore, let P be the point of intersection of medians AM and BN. By Theorem 2.7

$$\overrightarrow{AM} = \tfrac{1}{2}\overrightarrow{AB} + \tfrac{1}{2}\overrightarrow{AC} = \tfrac{1}{2}\overrightarrow{AB} + \overrightarrow{AN}.$$

Since A, P, and M are collinear, $\overrightarrow{AP} = t\overrightarrow{AM}$ where t is some real number. By substitution

$$\overrightarrow{AP} = t\left(\frac{1}{2}\overrightarrow{AB} + \overrightarrow{AN}\right)$$

$$= \frac{t}{2}\overrightarrow{AB} + t\overrightarrow{AN}.$$

Since B, P, and N are collinear, the sum of the real multiples of $\overrightarrow{AB}$ and $\overrightarrow{AN}$ must equal 1. Thus $t/2 + t = 1$ implies $t = \tfrac{2}{3}$, and thus $\overrightarrow{AP} = \tfrac{2}{3}\overrightarrow{AM}$; that is, P is two-thirds of the distance from vertex A to the midpoint of the opposite side. By a similar argument, the point P must be two-thirds of the distance from vertex B to the midpoint of the opposite side. Consider the medians CR and AM. Since their point of intersection must divide them in the ratio 2 to 1 by the same argument, median CR passes through P.

Exercises

1. Determine whether or not the points A, B, and C are collinear.
   (a) $A:(3, -1, 5)$, $B:(9, 2, 14)$, and $C:(5, 0, 8)$;
   (b) $A:(4, 2, 0)$, $B:(3, 3, 3)$, and $C:(1, 5, 6)$;
   (c) $A:(3, 1, -2)$, $B:(1, 0, 0)$, and $C:(-1, -1, 1)$;
   (d) $A:(3, 6, 4)$, $B:(-4, -5, -1)$, and $C:(2, 0, 6)$.

2. Find the coordinates of the point that divides the line segment AB, where $A:(-3, 2, 1)$ and $B:(5, -14, 13)$, in the ratio 1 to 3.

3. Prove that if M is the midpoint of line segment BC, and A is any point in space, then $\vec{AB} + \vec{AC} = \vec{AM} + \vec{AM}$.

4. Prove that if the points A, B, and C of Theorem 2.7 are such that C is between A and B, then $0 < r < 1$; if A is between B and C, then $r > 1$; if B is between A and C, then $r < 0$.

5. Find the coordinates of the points that divide the line segment MN, where $M:(6, 3, -4)$ and $N:(-2, 1, 2)$, in the ratios (a) 1 to 2; (b) 2 to 3; (c) -2 to 1; (d) 3 to -1.

6. Determine the coordinates of the *centroid* (point of intersection of the medians) of the triangle with vertices at $A:(x_1, y_1, z_1)$, $B:(x_2, y_2, z_2)$, and $C:(x_3, y_3, z_3)$.

7. Prove that the line segments joining the midpoints of the consecutive sides of a quadrilateral form a parallelogram.

8. Prove that the line segment joining one vertex of a parallelogram to the midpoint of an opposite side trisects a diagonal.

2.7 THE SCALAR PRODUCT

The way in which the product of two vectors is defined is quite arbitrary. The following definition of the multiplication of two vectors is useful in terms of the geometric properties that result.

> **Definition 2.11.** *If $\vec{a} = [a_1, a_2]$ and $\vec{b} = [b_1, b_2]$, then the scalar product of $\vec{a}$ and $\vec{b}$, denoted by $\vec{a} \cdot \vec{b}$, is the real number $a_1 b_1 + a_2 b_2$.*

The scalar product of two three-dimensional vectors is defined in an analogous fashion. Thus if $\vec{a} = [a_1, a_2, a_3]$ and $\vec{b} = [b_1, b_2, b_3]$, then

$$\vec{a} \cdot \vec{b} = a_1 b_1 + a_2 b_2 + a_3 b_3. \tag{2.11}$$

In this section, properties of the scalar product that follow from Definition 2.11 are stated and illustrated for two-dimensional vectors only. The proofs that are omitted are left to the reader as Exercises 9, 10, and 11. Analogous statements may be easily obtained for three-dimensional vectors.

Theorem 2.8. *The scalar product of two vectors is commutative; that is,*

$$\vec{a} \cdot \vec{b} = \vec{b} \cdot \vec{a}. \tag{2.12}$$

Theorem 2.9. *The scalar product of a vector with itself equals the square of its magnitude; that is,*

$$\vec{a} \cdot \vec{a} = |\vec{a}|^2. \tag{2.13}$$

Proof: Let $\vec{a} = [a_1, a_2]$. Then by definition

$$\begin{aligned} \vec{a} \cdot \vec{a} &= [a_1, a_2] \cdot [a_1, a_2] \\ &= a_1{}^2 + a_2{}^2 = (\sqrt{a_1{}^2 + a_2{}^2})^2 \\ &= |\vec{a}|^2. \end{aligned}$$

Theorem 2.10. *The scalar product is distributive with respect to the addition of vectors; that is,*

$$\vec{a} \cdot (\vec{b} + \vec{c}) = \vec{a} \cdot \vec{b} + \vec{a} \cdot \vec{c}. \tag{2.14}$$

Proof: Let $\vec{a} = [a_1, a_2]$, $\vec{b} = [b_1, b_2]$, and $\vec{c} = [c_1, c_2]$. Then

$$\begin{aligned} \vec{a} \cdot (\vec{b} + \vec{c}) &= [a_1, a_2] \cdot ([b_1, b_2] + [c_1, c_2]) \\ &= [a_1, a_2] \cdot [b_1 + c_1, b_2 + c_2] \\ &= a_1(b_1 + c_1) + a_2(b_2 + c_2) \\ &= a_1 b_1 + a_1 c_1 + a_2 b_2 + a_2 c_2; \end{aligned}$$

$$\begin{aligned} \vec{a} \cdot \vec{b} + \vec{a} \cdot \vec{c} &= [a_1, a_2] \cdot [b_1, b_2] + [a_1, a_2] \cdot [c_1, c_2] \\ &= a_1 b_1 + a_2 b_2 + a_1 c_1 + a_2 c_2 \\ &= a_1 b_1 + a_1 c_1 + a_2 b_2 + a_2 c_2. \end{aligned}$$

Hence $\vec{a} \cdot (\vec{b} + \vec{c}) = \vec{a} \cdot \vec{b} + \vec{a} \cdot \vec{c}$.

Theorem 2.11. *If t is any real number, then*

$$t(\vec{a} \cdot \vec{b}) = (t\vec{a}) \cdot \vec{b} = \vec{a} \cdot (t\vec{b}). \tag{2.15}$$

Let $\vec{a} = \overrightarrow{OA}$ and $\vec{b} = \overrightarrow{OB}$. The angle between the geometric vectors $\vec{a}$ and $\vec{b}$ is defined as the angle AOB where θ, the measure of the undirected angle, is such that $0 \leq \theta \leq \pi$. A most useful property of the scalar product $\vec{a} \cdot \vec{b}$ is related to the angle between the two vectors, as stated in the following theorem.

Theorem 2.12. *If $\vec{a}$ and $\vec{b}$ are nonzero vectors, then*

$$\vec{a} \cdot \vec{b} = |\vec{a}| \, |\vec{b}| \, \cos \theta$$

where θ is the measure of the angle between the vectors.

Proof: Let $\vec{a}$ and $\vec{b}$ be the position vectors $\overrightarrow{OA}$ and $\overrightarrow{OB}$, as shown in Figure 2.29. Then $\overrightarrow{BA} = \vec{a} - \vec{b}$. By the law of cosines

$$|BA|^2 = |OA|^2 + |OB|^2 - 2|OA| \, |OB| \cos \theta;$$

that is,

$$(\vec{a} - \vec{b}) \cdot (\vec{a} - \vec{b}) = |\vec{a}|^2 + |\vec{b}|^2 - 2|\vec{a}| \, |\vec{b}| \cos \theta.$$

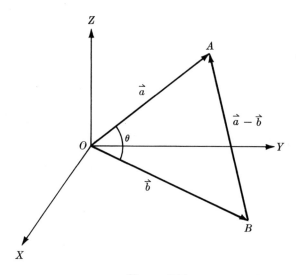

Figure 2.29

By the distributive property of the scalar product with respect to the addition of vectors, and by the commutative property of the scalar product,

$$\vec{(a} - \vec{b}) \cdot (\vec{a} - \vec{b}) = \vec{a} \cdot \vec{a} - 2\vec{a} \cdot \vec{b} + \vec{b} \cdot \vec{b}$$
$$= |\vec{a}|^2 + |\vec{b}|^2 - 2\vec{a} \cdot \vec{b}.$$

Thus

$$|\vec{a}|^2 + |\vec{b}|^2 - 2\vec{a} \cdot \vec{b} = |\vec{a}|^2 + |\vec{b}|^2 - 2|\vec{a}|\,|\vec{b}|\cos\theta,$$

and

$$\vec{a} \cdot \vec{b} = |\vec{a}|\,|\vec{b}|\cos\theta. \qquad (2.16)$$

Example 1. Determine the measure of the angle between the vectors $\vec{a}$ and $\vec{b}$ where $\vec{a} = [6, -4, 12]$ and $\vec{b} = [3, 5, -8]$.

By Theorem 2.12, $\vec{a} \cdot \vec{b} = |\vec{a}|\,|\vec{b}|\cos\theta$ implies that

$$\cos\theta = \frac{\vec{a} \cdot \vec{b}}{|\vec{a}|\,|\vec{b}|}.$$

Since $\vec{a} \cdot \vec{b} = (6)(3) + (-4)(5) + (12)(-8) = -98$, $|\vec{a}| = \sqrt{6^2 + (-4)^2 + 12^2} = 14$, and $|\vec{b}| = \sqrt{3^2 + 5^2 + (-8)^2} = 7\sqrt{2}$, then

$$\cos\theta = \frac{-98}{(14)(7\sqrt{2})} = -\frac{1}{\sqrt{2}}.$$

By definition, $0 \le \theta \le \pi$. Therefore, $\theta = 3\pi/4$.

Note that the quantity $|\vec{b}|\cos\theta$ is the component of $\vec{b}$ along $\vec{a}$; that is, $|\vec{b}|\cos\theta$ is the directed magnitude of the projection of $\vec{b}$ on $\vec{a}$, as shown in Figure 2.30. The center diagram in the figure suggests the following theorem.

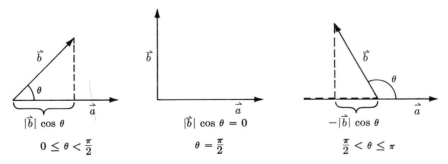

Figure 2.30

Theorem 2.13. *If two nonzero vectors $\vec{a}$ and $\vec{b}$ are perpendicular, then $\vec{a} \cdot \vec{b} = 0$.*

Proof: By Theorem 2.12, $\vec{a} \cdot \vec{b} = |\vec{a}| |\vec{b}| \cos \theta$. If $\vec{a}$ and $\vec{b}$ are perpendicular, then $\theta = \pi/2$ and $\cos \theta = 0$. Hence

$$\vec{a} \cdot \vec{b} = |\vec{a}| |\vec{b}|(0) = 0.$$

Note that if $\vec{a} \cdot \vec{b} = 0$, we cannot conclude that $\vec{a}$ is perpendicular to $\vec{b}$ unless we know that $\vec{a} \neq \vec{0}$ and $\vec{b} \neq \vec{0}$.

Theorem 2.14. *If $\vec{a}$ and $\vec{b}$ are nonzero vectors and $\vec{a} \cdot \vec{b} = 0$, then $\vec{a}$ and $\vec{b}$ are perpendicular.*

The properties of the scalar product stated in Theorems 2.13 and 2.14 can be applied to the solutions of problems in plane geometry, as illustrated in the following two examples.

Example 2. Prove that the diagonals of a rhombus are perpendicular.

Let $ABCD$ be a rhombus. Let $\vec{a} = \vec{AB} = \vec{DC}$ and $\vec{b} = \vec{AD} = \vec{BC}$, as shown in Figure 2.31. Since $ABCD$ is a rhombus, $|\vec{a}| = |\vec{b}|$. The vectors $\vec{a} - \vec{b}$ and $\vec{a} + \vec{b}$ can be associated with the diagonals DB and AC respectively. Then

$$(\vec{a} + \vec{b}) \cdot (\vec{a} - \vec{b}) = (\vec{a} + \vec{b}) \cdot \vec{a} - (\vec{a} + \vec{b}) \cdot \vec{b}$$
$$= \vec{a} \cdot \vec{a} + \vec{b} \cdot \vec{a} - \vec{a} \cdot \vec{b} - \vec{b} \cdot \vec{b}.$$

Since $\vec{a} \cdot \vec{b} = \vec{b} \cdot \vec{a}$,

$$(\vec{a} + \vec{b}) \cdot (\vec{a} - \vec{b}) = \vec{a} \cdot \vec{a} - \vec{b} \cdot \vec{b}$$
$$= |\vec{a}|^2 - |\vec{b}|^2 = 0.$$

Since $\vec{a} + \vec{b} \neq \vec{0}$ and $\vec{a} - \vec{b} \neq \vec{0}$, the vectors $\vec{a} + \vec{b}$ and $\vec{a} - \vec{b}$ are perpendicular. Hence the diagonals of the rhombus are perpendicular.

Example 3. Prove that an angle inscribed in a semicircle is a right angle.

Let P be any point on the circle with diameter AB, as shown in Figure 2.32. If O is the center of the circle, then $\vec{PA} = \vec{OA} - \vec{OP}$, $\vec{PB} = \vec{OB} - \vec{OP}$, and

$$\vec{PA} \cdot \vec{PB} = (\vec{OA} - \vec{OP}) \cdot (\vec{OB} - \vec{OP})$$
$$= \vec{OA} \cdot \vec{OB} - \vec{OP} \cdot \vec{OB} - \vec{OA} \cdot \vec{OP} + \vec{OP} \cdot \vec{OP}.$$

Since $\vec{OA} = -\vec{OB}$ and the scalar product is commutative,

$$\vec{PA} \cdot \vec{PB} = -\vec{OB} \cdot \vec{OB} + \vec{OP} \cdot \vec{OP}$$
$$= -|\vec{OB}|^2 + |\vec{OP}|^2.$$

Since $\vec{OB}$ and $\vec{OP}$ are associated with the radii, $|\vec{OB}| = |\vec{OP}|$, so that $\vec{PA} \cdot \vec{PB} = 0$. Therefore, if P does not coincide with either A or B, then the angle APB is inscribed in a semicircle and is a right angle.

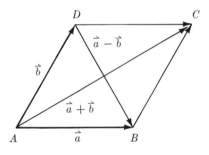

Figure 2.31

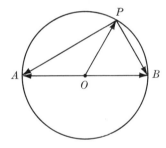

Figure 2.32

Exercises

1. Find $\vec{a} \cdot \vec{b}$ where $\vec{a} = [6, 3]$ and $\vec{b} = [2, -1]$.

2. Using $\vec{a} = [3, 1, 6]$, $\vec{b} = [2, 0, 4]$, and $\vec{c} = [-3, 1, -2]$, verify Theorem 2.10.

3. Use the scalar product to determine the magnitude of $\vec{a}$ where $\vec{a} = [5, 1, -\sqrt{10}]$. Find the unit vector with the same direction as $\vec{a}$.

In Exercises 4–7 determine the measure of the angle between the vectors $\vec{a}$ and $\vec{b}$.

4. $\vec{a} = [2, 0]$ and $\vec{b} = [1, \sqrt{3}]$.

5. $\vec{a} = [-1, 1, 0]$ and $\vec{b} = [0, 1, 0]$.

6. $\vec{a} = [2, 3, -6]$ and $\vec{b} = [4, 6, -12]$.

7. $\vec{a} = [3, 6, -2]$ and $\vec{b} = [-3, -6, 2]$.

8. If two nonzero vectors are perpendicular, the vectors are called *orthogonal vectors*. Determine which pairs of vectors are orthogonal vectors.
    (a) $[2, 3]$ and $[6, -4]$; (c) $[3, 4, 0]$ and $[-4, 3, 1]$;
    (b) $[1, 4, 3]$ and $[4, 2, -4]$; (d) $[6, 3, 4]$ and $[3, 6, 9]$.

9. Prove Theorem 2.8.

10. Prove Theorem 2.11.

11. Prove Theorem 2.14.

12. Prove that $|\vec{a} \cdot \vec{b}| \le |\vec{a}|\,|\vec{b}|$. When is $|\vec{a} \cdot \vec{b}| = |\vec{a}|\,|\vec{b}|$?

13. Find the magnitude of the projection of $\vec{b}$ on $\vec{a}$ where $\vec{a} = [0, 3]$ and $\vec{b} = [\sqrt{3}, 1]$.

14. Find the magnitude of the projection of $\vec{a}$ on $\vec{b}$ where $\vec{a} = [2, -6, -3]$ and $\vec{b} = [5, -8, 3]$.

15. Find (a) $\vec{i} \cdot \vec{i}$; (b) $\vec{i} \cdot \vec{j}$; (c) $\vec{j} \cdot \vec{k}$; (d) $\vec{k} \cdot \vec{k}$.

16. Find $(3\vec{i} + 2\vec{j} - \vec{k}) \cdot (2\vec{i} + \vec{j} + 6\vec{k})$.

17. Find the direction cosines of $\vec{a}$, where $\vec{a} = [a_1, a_2, a_3]$, by taking the scalar product of $\vec{a}$ with $\vec{i}, \vec{j}$, and $\vec{k}$ respectively.

18. Use the scalar product to prove that the triangle whose vertices are $A:(1, 1, 0)$, $B:(2, 2, 0)$, and $C:(1, 1, \sqrt{2})$ is a right isosceles triangle.

19. Let $\vec{a} = [1, 1, 1]$, $\vec{b} = [2, 1, 2]$, and $\vec{c} = [1, 2, 2]$. Show that $\vec{a} \cdot \vec{b} = \vec{a} \cdot \vec{c}$ does not imply that $\vec{b} = \vec{c}$.

20. Let $|\vec{a}| = 1$. If $\vec{c} = (\vec{a} \cdot \vec{b})\vec{a}$ and $\vec{d} = \vec{b} - \vec{c}$, prove that $\vec{d} \cdot \vec{a} = 0$.

21. Let $\vec{a} = [a_1, a_2, a_3]$ be a unit vector perpendicular to the plane determined by the vectors $\vec{b} = [3, 0, 1]$ and $\vec{c} = [3, -4, 0]$. Find $\vec{a}$. (Hint: Three conditions that must be satisfied are $\vec{a} \cdot \vec{b} = 0$, $\vec{a} \cdot \vec{c} = 0$, and $|\vec{a}| = 1$.)

22. Use the scalar product to prove the Pythagorean theorem.

23. Prove that if the diagonals of a parallelogram are perpendicular, then the parallelogram is a rhombus.

24. Prove that the altitudes of a triangle are concurrent.

2.8 ORTHOGONAL AND ORTHONORMAL BASE VECTORS

In Examples 2 and 3 of §2.5, we represented three-dimensional position vectors as linear functions of different base vectors. In Example 2, we used the most convenient set of base vectors, the unit vectors $\vec{i}$, $\vec{j}$, and $\vec{k}$ along the positive halves of the x axis, y axis, and z axis respectively. In general, if $P:(x, y, z)$ is any point in space, then

$$\overrightarrow{OP} = x\vec{i} + y\vec{j} + z\vec{k},$$

as illustrated in Figure 2.33.

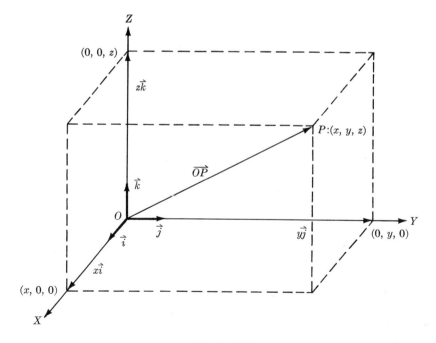

Figure 2.33

In other words,

$$[x, y, z] = x[1, 0, 0] + y[0, 1, 0] + z[0, 0, 1]$$
$$= x\vec{i} + y\vec{j} + z\vec{k}.$$

The set of base vectors $\vec{i}$, $\vec{j}$, and $\vec{k}$ constitutes an *orthogonal basis* for the geometric vectors in space since the reference vectors are pairwise mutually perpendicular:

$$\vec{i} \cdot \vec{j} = \vec{j} \cdot \vec{k} = \vec{k} \cdot \vec{i} = 0.$$

In general, any set of base vectors for two-dimensional or three-dimensional space constitutes an *orthogonal basis* if and only if the vectors are pairwise mutually perpendicular. Furthermore, if each vector of an orthogonal basis is a unit vector, the set is called a *normal orthogonal*, or *orthonormal, basis*.

Example. Let $\vec{a}$, $\vec{b}$, and $\vec{c}$ denote position vectors such that $\vec{a} = [1, 4, 2]$, $\vec{b} = [2, 1, -3]$, and $\vec{c} = [-2, 1, -1]$. Verify that the set of vectors $\vec{a}$, $\vec{b}$, and $\vec{c}$ constitutes an orthogonal basis for three-dimensional space.

$$\vec{a} \cdot \vec{b} = [1, 4, 2] \cdot [2, 1, -3]$$
$$= (1)(2) + (4)(1) + (2)(-3) = 0;$$
$$\vec{a} \cdot \vec{c} = [1, 4, 2] \cdot [-2, 1, -1]$$
$$= (1)(-2) + (4)(1) + (2)(-1) = 0;$$
$$\vec{b} \cdot \vec{c} = [2, 1, -3] \cdot [-2, 1, -1]$$
$$= (2)(-2) + (1)(1) + (-3)(-1) = 0.$$

Since the vectors are pairwise mutually perpendicular, they must also be noncoplanar. Hence the set of vectors $\vec{a}$, $\vec{b}$, and $\vec{c}$ constitutes an orthogonal basis for three-dimensional space.

Hereafter, unless otherwise stated, we shall use the unit vectors $\vec{i}$, $\vec{j}$, and $\vec{k}$ as an orthogonal basis for the set of geometric vectors in space.

Exercises

1. Determine the values of x such that the vectors $(x - 1)\vec{i} + x\vec{j}$ and $x\vec{i} + (x^2 - 1)\vec{j}$ are orthogonal.

Determine whether or not each set of vectors $\vec{a}$ and $\vec{b}$ is an orthogonal basis for the plane.

2. $\vec{a} = [1, 0]$ and $\vec{b} = [0, 1]$.

3. $\vec{a} = [3, 2]$ and $\vec{b} = [-2, 3]$.

4. $\vec{a} = [6, 1]$ and $\vec{b} = [1, 6]$.

5. $\vec{a} = [5, -2]$ and $\vec{b} = [-5, 2]$.

Determine whether or not each set of vectors $\vec{a}$, $\vec{b}$, and $\vec{c}$ is an orthogonal basis for three-dimensional space.

6. $\vec{a} = [1, 2, 3]$, $\vec{b} = [-3, 0, 1]$, and $\vec{c} = [0, 1, 0]$.

7. $\vec{a} = [2, 0, 0]$, $\vec{b} = [0, -1, 0]$, and $\vec{c} = [0, 0, 4]$.

8. $\vec{a} = [2, 1, 0]$, $\vec{b} = [0, 0, 3]$, and $\vec{c} = [3, -6, 0]$.

9. $\vec{a} = [4, -1, 2]$, $\vec{b} = [1, -2, -3]$, and $\vec{c} = [1, 2, 1]$.

Find an orthonormal basis for the plane such that one base vector has the same direction as $\vec{a}$.

10. $\vec{a} = [1, -1]$. **12.** $\vec{a} = [-1, 0]$.

11. $\vec{a} = [-1, 2]$. **13.** $\vec{a} = [3, 4]$.

In Exercises 14 and 15 find an orthonormal basis for three-dimensional space such that two of the base vectors have the same directions as $\vec{a}$ and $\vec{b}$ respectively.

14. $\vec{a} = [1, -1, 0]$ and $\vec{b} = [3, 3, 0]$.

15. $\vec{a} = [2, 1, 2]$ and $\vec{b} = [1, -4, 1]$.

16. Prove that the vectors $\vec{a}$ and $\vec{a} - \dfrac{\vec{a} \cdot \vec{a}}{\vec{a} \cdot \vec{b}} \vec{b}$ constitute an orthogonal basis for the two-dimensional space determined by the nonzero, nonparallel vectors $\vec{a}$ and $\vec{b}$.

17. Use the results of Exercise 16 to find an orthogonal basis for the two-dimensional space determined by $[1, 0, 1]$ and $[1, 1, 3]$.

2.9 DETERMINANTS

Throughout our study of analytic geometry we shall make considerable use of the concept of a determinant. The presentation in this section is not meant to be a complete, rigorous development of the theory of determinants. Only those basic concepts of the theory of determinants which are necessary for the reader to understand the use of determinants in this book are presented.

A *determinant of order 2* is a rule which associates with the square array of elements a_{ij} of the form

$$\begin{vmatrix} a_{11} & a_{12} \\ a_{21} & a_{22} \end{vmatrix}$$

the element $a_{11}a_{22} - a_{12}a_{21}$, called the *value of the determinant*.

A *determinant of order 3* is a rule which associates with the square array of elements a_{ij} of the form

$$\begin{vmatrix} a_{11} & a_{12} & a_{13} \\ a_{21} & a_{22} & a_{23} \\ a_{31} & a_{32} & a_{33} \end{vmatrix}$$

the value

$$a_{11}a_{22}a_{33} + a_{12}a_{23}a_{31} + a_{13}a_{21}a_{32} - a_{13}a_{22}a_{31} - a_{11}a_{23}a_{32} - a_{12}a_{21}a_{33}.$$

Example 1. Find the value of the determinant

$$\begin{vmatrix} 3 & 5 & 4 \\ 0 & 1 & -3 \\ -1 & 7 & 2 \end{vmatrix}.$$

By definition,

$$\begin{vmatrix} 3 & 5 & 4 \\ 0 & 1 & -3 \\ -1 & 7 & 2 \end{vmatrix} = (3)(1)(2) + (5)(-3)(-1)$$
$$+ (4)(0)(7) - (4)(1)(-1)$$
$$- (3)(-3)(7) - (5)(0)(2)$$
$$= 6 + 15 + 0 + 4 + 63 - 0 = 88.$$

In general, a *determinant of order n* is a rule which associates a value with the square array of n^2 elements a_{ij} of the form

$$\begin{vmatrix} a_{11} & a_{12} & \cdots & a_{1n} \\ a_{21} & a_{22} & \cdots & a_{2n} \\ \cdots & \cdots & \cdots & \cdots \\ a_{n1} & a_{n2} & \cdots & a_{nn} \end{vmatrix}. \tag{2.17}$$

This determinant is often denoted briefly by $\|a_{ij}\|$. The value of the determinant (2.17) is defined as the sum of $n!$ distinct terms of the form

$$(-1)^k a_{1i_1} a_{2i_2} a_{3i_3} \cdots a_{ni_n},$$

where the second subscripts $i_1, i_2, i_3, \ldots, i_n$ are equal to $1, 2, 3, \ldots, n$ taken in some order; each term contains one and only one element from each row and one and only one element from each column; and the exponent k represents the number of interchanges of two elements necessary for the second subscripts to be placed in the order $1, 2, 3, \ldots, n$. For example, consider the term containing $a_{13}a_{22}a_{35}a_{41}a_{54}$ in the evaluation of a determinant of order 5. The term has associated with it the factor $(-1)^3$ since three interchanges of two elements are necessary for the second subscripts to be placed in the order $1, 2, 3, 4, 5$:

$$\begin{aligned}
a_{13}a_{22}a_{35}a_{41}a_{54} &= a_{41}a_{22}a_{35}a_{13}a_{54} \\
&= a_{41}a_{22}a_{13}a_{35}a_{54} \\
&= a_{41}a_{22}a_{13}a_{54}a_{35}.
\end{aligned}$$

The value of determinants of order $n \geq 4$ are seldom obtained by the use of the definition since the labor of computation is almost prohibitive. A number of theorems exist which enable us to compute the value of a determinant with less labor. The theorems in this section will be stated and proved for determinants of order 3. However, each theorem can be extended to determinants of order n.

Theorem 2.15. *The value of a determinant remains unchanged if corresponding rows and columns are interchanged; that is,*

$$\begin{vmatrix} a_{11} & a_{12} & a_{13} \\ a_{21} & a_{22} & a_{23} \\ a_{31} & a_{32} & a_{33} \end{vmatrix} = \begin{vmatrix} a_{11} & a_{21} & a_{31} \\ a_{12} & a_{22} & a_{32} \\ a_{13} & a_{23} & a_{33} \end{vmatrix}.$$

Proof: By the definition of the value of a determinant of order 3,

$$\begin{vmatrix} a_{11} & a_{12} & a_{13} \\ a_{21} & a_{22} & a_{23} \\ a_{31} & a_{32} & a_{33} \end{vmatrix} = a_{11}a_{22}a_{33} + a_{12}a_{23}a_{31} + a_{13}a_{21}a_{32} \\ - a_{13}a_{22}a_{31} - a_{11}a_{23}a_{32} - a_{12}a_{21}a_{33};$$

$$\begin{vmatrix} a_{11} & a_{21} & a_{31} \\ a_{12} & a_{22} & a_{32} \\ a_{13} & a_{23} & a_{33} \end{vmatrix} = a_{11}a_{22}a_{33} + a_{21}a_{32}a_{13} + a_{31}a_{12}a_{23} \\ - a_{31}a_{22}a_{13} - a_{11}a_{32}a_{23} - a_{21}a_{12}a_{33}.$$

Hence by a simple rearrangement of factors and terms, we have

$$\begin{vmatrix} a_{11} & a_{12} & a_{13} \\ a_{21} & a_{22} & a_{23} \\ a_{31} & a_{32} & a_{33} \end{vmatrix} = \begin{vmatrix} a_{11} & a_{21} & a_{31} \\ a_{12} & a_{22} & a_{32} \\ a_{13} & a_{23} & a_{33} \end{vmatrix}.$$

As a result of Theorem 2.15, for every theorem concerning the rows of a determinant there exists an associated corollary concerning the columns of the determinant. The associated corollary will not be stated in each instance with respect to the theorems presented in this section.

Theorem 2.16. *If any two rows of a determinant are interchanged, then the value of the determinant is changed by a factor* (-1).

For example,

$$\begin{vmatrix} a_{21} & a_{22} & a_{23} \\ a_{11} & a_{12} & a_{13} \\ a_{31} & a_{32} & a_{33} \end{vmatrix} = - \begin{vmatrix} a_{11} & a_{12} & a_{13} \\ a_{21} & a_{22} & a_{23} \\ a_{31} & a_{32} & a_{33} \end{vmatrix}.$$

The proof of Theorem 2.16 is left to the reader as Exercise 7.

Theorem 2.17. *If every element of a row of a determinant is multiplied by a factor t, then the value of the determinant is multiplied by t.*

Proof: Let every element of the ith row of a determinant be multiplied by a factor t. By the definition of the value of a determinant of order 3, every term contains one and only one element from each row as a factor. Therefore, every term will contain the additional factor t. Hence the value of the determinant will be multiplied by t.
  For example,

$$\begin{vmatrix} a_{11} & a_{12} & a_{13} \\ ta_{21} & ta_{22} & ta_{23} \\ a_{31} & a_{32} & a_{33} \end{vmatrix} = t \begin{vmatrix} a_{11} & a_{12} & a_{13} \\ a_{21} & a_{22} & a_{23} \\ a_{31} & a_{32} & a_{33} \end{vmatrix}.$$

Theorem 2.18. *The value of a determinant remains unchanged if a constant multiple of each of the elements of a row is added to the corresponding element of another row.*

For example,

$$\begin{vmatrix} a_{11} & a_{12} & a_{13} \\ a_{21} & a_{22} & a_{23} \\ a_{31} & a_{32} & a_{33} \end{vmatrix} = \begin{vmatrix} a_{11} + ta_{31} & a_{12} + ta_{32} & a_{13} + ta_{33} \\ a_{21} & a_{22} & a_{23} \\ a_{31} & a_{32} & a_{33} \end{vmatrix}.$$

The proof of Theorem 2.18 is left to the reader as Exercise 8.

Consider the definition of the value of a determinant of order 3. By a rearrangement of terms, we have

$$\begin{vmatrix} a_{11} & a_{12} & a_{13} \\ a_{21} & a_{22} & a_{23} \\ a_{31} & a_{32} & a_{33} \end{vmatrix} = a_{11}(a_{22}a_{33} - a_{23}a_{32}) - a_{12}(a_{21}a_{33} - a_{23}a_{31}) + a_{13}(a_{21}a_{32} - a_{22}a_{31}).$$

Using the definition of the value of a determinant of order 2, we have

$$\begin{vmatrix} a_{11} & a_{12} & a_{13} \\ a_{21} & a_{22} & a_{23} \\ a_{31} & a_{32} & a_{33} \end{vmatrix} = a_{11}\begin{vmatrix} a_{22} & a_{23} \\ a_{32} & a_{33} \end{vmatrix} - a_{12}\begin{vmatrix} a_{21} & a_{23} \\ a_{31} & a_{33} \end{vmatrix} + a_{13}\begin{vmatrix} a_{21} & a_{22} \\ a_{31} & a_{32} \end{vmatrix}. \quad (2.18)$$

Note that each of the three determinants of order 2 may be obtained from the determinant of order 3 by deleting certain rows and columns. The determinant $\begin{vmatrix} a_{22} & a_{23} \\ a_{32} & a_{33} \end{vmatrix}$ may be obtained by deleting the row and column containing the element a_{11}; the determinant $\begin{vmatrix} a_{21} & a_{23} \\ a_{31} & a_{33} \end{vmatrix}$ may be obtained by deleting the row and column containing the element a_{12}; the determinant $\begin{vmatrix} a_{21} & a_{22} \\ a_{31} & a_{32} \end{vmatrix}$ may be obtained by deleting the row and column containing the element a_{13}.

The *cofactor* of any element a_{ij} of a determinant $\|a_{ij}\|$ is defined as the product of $(-1)^{i+j}$ and the determinant obtained by deleting the elements of the ith row and the jth column of $\|a_{ij}\|$. Equation (2.18) represents a special case of the following theorem.

Theorem 2.19. *The value of a determinant is equal to the sum of the products of the elements of any row and their cofactors.*

The proof of Theorem 2.19 is left to the reader as Exercise 9.

Example 2. Use Theorem 2.19 to find the value of the determinant

$$\begin{vmatrix} 2 & 3 & -1 & 1 \\ -1 & 1 & -2 & 2 \\ 2 & 0 & 5 & 4 \\ 0 & 2 & 6 & 8 \end{vmatrix}.$$

By Theorem 2.19, using the elements of row 3 and their cofactors, we have

$$\begin{vmatrix} 2 & 3 & -1 & 1 \\ -1 & 1 & -2 & 2 \\ 2 & 0 & 5 & 4 \\ 0 & 2 & 6 & 8 \end{vmatrix} = 2 \begin{vmatrix} 3 & -1 & 1 \\ 1 & -2 & 2 \\ 2 & 6 & 8 \end{vmatrix} - 0 \begin{vmatrix} 2 & -1 & 1 \\ -1 & -2 & 2 \\ 0 & 6 & 8 \end{vmatrix}$$

$$+ 5 \begin{vmatrix} 2 & 3 & 1 \\ -1 & 1 & 2 \\ 0 & 2 & 8 \end{vmatrix} - 4 \begin{vmatrix} 2 & 3 & -1 \\ -1 & 1 & -2 \\ 0 & 2 & 6 \end{vmatrix}$$

$$= (2)(-70) + (5)(30) + (-4)(40)$$
$$= -150.$$

Exercises

Find the value of each determinant.

1. $\begin{vmatrix} 2 & 1 \\ 5 & 7 \end{vmatrix}.$

2. $\begin{vmatrix} 6 & -3 \\ 8 & 0 \end{vmatrix}.$

3. $\begin{vmatrix} 4 & 5 & 3 \\ 1 & 5 & 4 \\ 2 & 1 & 2 \end{vmatrix}.$

4. $\begin{vmatrix} 2 & 1 & 1 \\ 1 & 2 & 1 \\ 1 & 1 & 2 \end{vmatrix}.$

5. $\begin{vmatrix} 3 & -1 & 0 \\ 1 & 2 & -1 \\ 0 & 1 & 1 \end{vmatrix}.$

6. $\begin{vmatrix} 1 & 1 & 7 \\ 2 & 3 & 3 \\ 3 & -4 & 10 \end{vmatrix}.$

7. Prove Theorem 2.16.

8. Prove Theorem 2.18.

9. Prove Theorem 2.19.

10. Prove that the value of a determinant is zero if two rows are identical.

11. Prove that

$$\begin{vmatrix} a+b & a & a \\ a & a+b & a \\ a & a & a+b \end{vmatrix} = b^2(3a+b).$$

12. Prove that

$$\begin{vmatrix} a & b & m & n \\ c & d & r & s \\ 0 & 0 & e & f \\ 0 & 0 & g & h \end{vmatrix} = \begin{vmatrix} a & b \\ c & d \end{vmatrix} \cdot \begin{vmatrix} e & f \\ g & h \end{vmatrix}.$$

2.10 THE VECTOR PRODUCT

In §2.7, the scalar product of two vectors is defined. A second type of multiplication of two vectors can be defined whereby the product is a vector. This product is meaningful only for three-dimensional vectors.

Definition 2.12. *If $\vec{a} = [a_1, a_2, a_3]$ and $\vec{b} = [b_1, b_2, b_3]$, then the vector product of $\vec{a}$ and $\vec{b}$, denoted by $\vec{a} \times \vec{b}$, is the vector*

$$[a_2b_3 - a_3b_2, a_3b_1 - a_1b_3, a_1b_2 - a_2b_1].$$

A convenient way of representing the vector product of the two vectors $\vec{a}$ and $\vec{b}$ is by the use of determinants. If the vector

$$[a_2b_3 - a_3b_2, a_3b_1 - a_1b_3, a_1b_2 - a_2b_1]$$

is written as a linear function of $\vec{i}, \vec{j}$, and $\vec{k}$, then

$$\vec{a} \times \vec{b} = (a_2b_3 - a_3b_2)\vec{i} + (a_3b_1 - a_1b_3)\vec{j} + (a_1b_2 - a_2b_1)\vec{k},$$

whereby

$$\vec{a} \times \vec{b} = \begin{vmatrix} \vec{i} & \vec{j} & \vec{k} \\ a_1 & a_2 & a_3 \\ b_1 & b_2 & b_3 \end{vmatrix}. \tag{2.19}$$

A most useful property of the vector product $\vec{a} \times \vec{b}$ is its direction, as stated in the following theorem.

Theorem 2.20. *If $\vec{a} \times \vec{b}$ is a nonzero vector, then it is perpendicular to both $\vec{a}$ and $\vec{b}$.*

Proof: Let $\vec{a} = [a_1, a_2, a_3]$ and $\vec{b} = [b_1, b_2, b_3]$. Then by definition $\vec{a} \times \vec{b} = [a_2b_3 - a_3b_2, a_3b_1 - a_1b_3, a_1b_2 - a_2b_1]$. If $\vec{a} \times \vec{b} \neq \vec{0}$, then $\vec{a} \neq \vec{0}$ and $\vec{b} \neq \vec{0}$, since $\vec{a} = \vec{0}$ or $\vec{b} = \vec{0}$ implies that $\vec{a} \times \vec{b} = \vec{0}$. Now,

$$\vec{a} \cdot (\vec{a} \times \vec{b})$$
$$= [a_1, a_2, a_3] \cdot [a_2b_3 - a_3b_2, a_3b_1 - a_1b_3, a_1b_2 - a_2b_1]$$
$$= a_1(a_2b_3 - a_3b_2) + a_2(a_3b_1 - a_1b_3) + a_3(a_1b_2 - a_2b_1)$$
$$= a_1a_2b_3 - a_1a_3b_2 + a_2a_3b_1 - a_1a_2b_3 + a_1a_3b_2 - a_2a_3b_1$$
$$= 0$$

and

$$\vec{b} \cdot (\vec{a} \times \vec{b})$$
$$= [b_1, b_2, b_3] \cdot [a_2b_3 - a_3b_2, a_3b_1 - a_1b_3, a_1b_2 - a_2b_1]$$
$$= b_1(a_2b_3 - a_3b_2) + b_2(a_3b_1 - a_1b_3) + b_3(a_1b_2 - a_2b_1)$$
$$= a_2b_1b_3 - a_3b_1b_2 + a_3b_1b_2 - a_1b_2b_3 + a_1b_2b_3 - a_2b_1b_3$$
$$= 0.$$

Hence, since $\vec{a} \neq \vec{0}$, $\vec{b} \neq \vec{0}$, and $\vec{a} \times \vec{b} \neq \vec{0}$, it follows that $\vec{a} \times \vec{b}$ is perpendicular to both $\vec{a}$ and $\vec{b}$.

Example 1. Verify that $\vec{a} \times \vec{b}$ is perpendicular to both $\vec{a}$ and $\vec{b}$ where $\vec{a} = [1, 1, -1]$ and $\vec{b} = [1, 3, 0]$.

By definition,

$$\vec{a} \times \vec{b} = \begin{vmatrix} \vec{i} & \vec{j} & \vec{k} \\ 1 & 1 & -1 \\ 1 & 3 & 0 \end{vmatrix} = 3\vec{i} - \vec{j} + 2\vec{k} = [3, -1, 2].$$

Thus

$$\vec{a} \cdot (\vec{a} \times \vec{b}) = [1, 1, -1] \cdot [3, -1, 2]$$
$$= (1)(3) + (1)(-1) + (-1)(2) = 0;$$

$$\vec{b} \cdot (\vec{a} \times \vec{b}) = [1, 3, 0] \cdot [3, -1, 2]$$
$$= (1)(3) + (3)(-1) + (0)(2) = 0.$$

Since $\vec{a} \neq \vec{0}$, $\vec{b} \neq \vec{0}$, and $\vec{a} \times \vec{b} \neq \vec{0}$, then $\vec{a} \times \vec{b}$ is perpendicular to both $\vec{a}$ and $\vec{b}$.

The following two theorems are concerned with some of the basic properties of the vector product of two three-dimensional vectors. The proofs are left to the reader as Exercises 5 and 6.

Theorem 2.21. *The vector product of two vectors is anti-commutative; that is,*

$$\vec{a} \times \vec{b} = -(\vec{b} \times \vec{a}). \tag{2.20}$$

Theorem 2.22. *The vector product is distributive with respect to the addition of vectors; that is,*

$$\vec{a} \times (\vec{b} + \vec{c}) = \vec{a} \times \vec{b} + \vec{a} \times \vec{c}. \tag{2.21}$$

Example 2. Verify equation (2.21) using $\vec{a} = [1, 6, 3]$, $\vec{b} = [2, 0, -1]$, and $\vec{c} = [3, 4, 2]$.

$$\vec{a} \times (\vec{b} + \vec{c}) = [1, 6, 3] \times ([2, 0, -1] + [3, 4, 2])$$
$$= [1, 6, 3] \times [5, 4, 1]$$
$$= \begin{vmatrix} \vec{i} & \vec{j} & \vec{k} \\ 1 & 6 & 3 \\ 5 & 4 & 1 \end{vmatrix}$$
$$= -6\vec{i} + 14\vec{j} - 26\vec{k} = [-6, 14, -26];$$

$$\vec{a} \times \vec{b} + \vec{a} \times \vec{c} = [1, 6, 3] \times [2, 0, -1] + [1, 6, 3] \times [3, 4, 2]$$
$$= \begin{vmatrix} \vec{i} & \vec{j} & \vec{k} \\ 1 & 6 & 3 \\ 2 & 0 & -1 \end{vmatrix} + \begin{vmatrix} \vec{i} & \vec{j} & \vec{k} \\ 1 & 6 & 3 \\ 3 & 4 & 2 \end{vmatrix}$$
$$= (-6\vec{i} + 7\vec{j} - 12\vec{k}) + (7\vec{j} - 14\vec{k})$$
$$= -6\vec{i} + 14\vec{j} - 26\vec{k} = [-6, 14, -26].$$

Hence $\vec{a} \times (\vec{b} + \vec{c}) = \vec{a} \times \vec{b} + \vec{a} \times \vec{c}$.

Exercises

1. Find $\vec{a} \times \vec{b}$ where:
   (a) $\vec{a} = [1, 1, 2]$ and $\vec{b} = [-3, -1, 1]$;
   (b) $\vec{a} = [4, 3, -2]$ and $\vec{b} = [-8, -6, 4]$;
   (c) $\vec{a} = [2, 1, 0]$ and $\vec{b} = [-3, 1, 0]$;
   (d) $\vec{a} = [2, 0, 1]$ and $\vec{b} = [1, 4, 0]$.

2. Verify that $\vec{a} \times \vec{b}$ is perpendicular to both $\vec{a}$ and $\vec{b}$ where $\vec{a} = [3, 1, -3]$ and $\vec{b} = [1, 1, 1]$.

3. Find a unit vector perpendicular to $\vec{a} = [0, 1, -2]$ and $\vec{b} = [1, -2, -1]$.

4. Using $\vec{a} = [2, 5, 1]$, $\vec{b} = [3, 0, 4]$, and $\vec{c} = [1, 1, -2]$, verify equation (2.21).

5. Use the properties of determinants to prove Theorem 2.21.

6. Prove Theorem 2.22.

7. Prove that if $\vec{a}$ and $\vec{b}$ are parallel, then $\vec{a} \times \vec{b} = \vec{0}$.

8. Use the results of Exercise 7 to prove that $\vec{a} \times \vec{a} = \vec{0}$.

9. Prove that if t is any real number, then
$$t(\vec{a} \times \vec{b}) = (t\vec{a}) \times \vec{b} = \vec{a} \times (t\vec{b}).$$

10. Prove that if the vector product of two nonzero vectors is the zero vector, then the two vectors are parallel.

11. Let $\vec{a} = [2, 4, 1]$, $\vec{b} = [3, -1, 2]$, and $\vec{c} = [9, 11, 5]$. Show that $\vec{a} \times \vec{b} = \vec{a} \times \vec{c}$ does not imply that $\vec{b} = \vec{c}$.

12. Find the nine possible vector products using the unit position vectors $\vec{i}$, $\vec{j}$, and $\vec{k}$.

13. Use the results of Exercise 12 to find
    (a) $(3\vec{i} + 2\vec{j} - \vec{k}) \times (4\vec{i} - \vec{j} + 5\vec{k})$;
    (b) $(x_1\vec{i} + y_1\vec{j} + z_1\vec{k}) \times (x_2\vec{i} + y_2\vec{j} + z_2\vec{k})$.

14. Find   (a) $\vec{j} \cdot (\vec{k} \times \vec{i})$;   (b) $\vec{i} \cdot (\vec{j} \times \vec{i})$.

15. Find   (a) $\vec{j} \times (\vec{k} \times \vec{i})$;   (b) $\vec{i} \times (\vec{j} \times \vec{i})$.

16. Cite a counterexample to show that the vector product is not associative.

17. Describe geometrically the position in space of the vector $\vec{a} \times (\vec{b} \times \vec{c})$ relative to the vectors $\vec{a}$, $\vec{b}$, and $\vec{c}$.

18. Using $\vec{a} = [1, 1, 3]$, $\vec{b} = [2, -1, 2]$, and $\vec{c} = [4, 5, 0]$, verify that
$$\vec{a} \times (\vec{b} \times \vec{c}) = (\vec{a} \cdot \vec{c})\vec{b} - (\vec{a} \cdot \vec{b})\vec{c}.$$

19. The real number $\vec{a} \cdot (\vec{b} \times \vec{c})$ is called the *scalar triple product* of $\vec{a}$, $\vec{b}$, and $\vec{c}$. Let $\vec{a} = [a_1, a_2, a_3]$, $\vec{b} = [b_1, b_2, b_3]$, and $\vec{c} = [c_1, c_2, c_3]$. Show that
$$\vec{a} \cdot (\vec{b} \times \vec{c}) = \begin{vmatrix} a_1 & a_2 & a_3 \\ b_1 & b_2 & b_3 \\ c_1 & c_2 & c_3 \end{vmatrix}.$$

20. Use the results of Exercise 19 to find $\vec{a} \cdot (\vec{b} \times \vec{c})$ where $\vec{a} = [1, -6, 3]$, $\vec{b} = [-1, -1, 2]$, and $\vec{c} = [3, 1, 0]$.

21. Prove that $\vec{a} \cdot (\vec{b} \times \vec{c}) = \vec{b} \cdot (\vec{c} \times \vec{a}) = \vec{c} \cdot (\vec{a} \times \vec{b})$.

22. Describe the geometric situation if the nonzero vectors $\vec{a}$, $\vec{b}$, and $\vec{c}$ are such that $\vec{a} \cdot (\vec{b} \times \vec{c}) = 0$.

23. Determine whether or not each set of vectors $\vec{a}$, $\vec{b}$, and $\vec{c}$ is a set of coplanar vectors.

(**a**) $\vec{a} = [1, 1, 0]$, $\vec{b} = [2, 0, 3]$, and $\vec{c} = [0, 2, -3]$;

(**b**) $\vec{a} = [5, 6, 3]$, $\vec{b} = [4, 2, 7]$, and $\vec{c} = [-2, 6, 5]$.

24. Show that if $\vec{a} \cdot \vec{b} = 0$, then $|\vec{a} \times \vec{b}|^2 = |\vec{a}|^2 |\vec{b}|^2$.

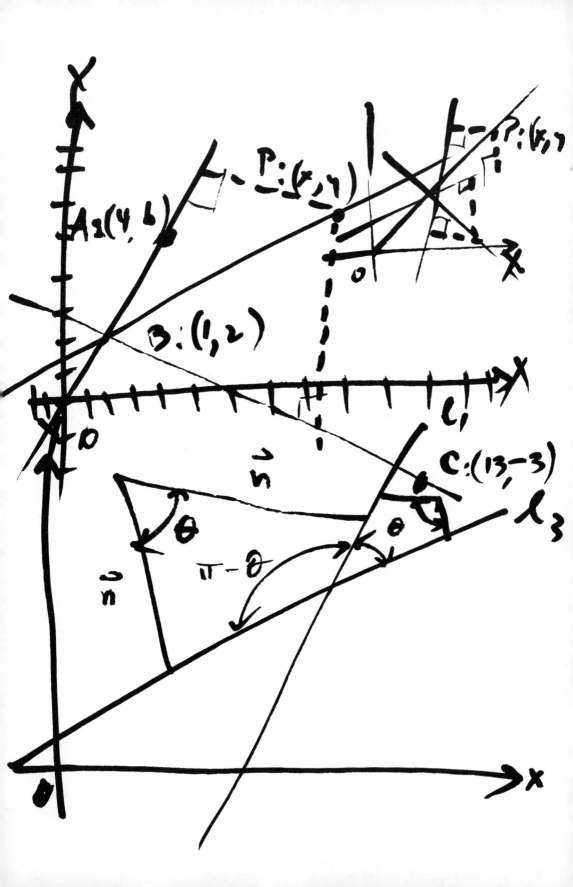

LINES IN A PLANE

3.1 EQUATION AND LOCUS

We shall be concerned throughout our study with two fundamental problems of analytic geometry:

(i) To determine a mathematical statement (equation, inequality, or system of equations or inequalities) representing a given set of points on a line, in a plane, or in space described by sufficient geometric conditions.

(ii) To determine a set of points on a line, in a plane, or in space whose coordinates satisfy a given mathematical statement, that is, whose coordinates make the mathematical statement true. The set of points is often called a *locus* (plural: *loci*), or *graph*, of the mathematical statement.

Generally, the graph of a mathematical statement in two variables consists of the set of all points in the plane, and only those points, whose coordinates satisfy the mathematical statement. The graph of a mathematical statement in three variables consists of the set of all points in space, and only those points, whose coordinates satisfy the mathematical statement. In some cases we may wish to consider a mathematical statement which appears to be in two variables as a statement in three variables with the coefficients of the terms containing the third variable equal to zero. In such cases, the graph of the statement is a set of points in space.

The following examples illustrate the two types of fundamental problems of analytic geometry. In subsequent chapters we shall study various techniques of graphing and certain properties of graphs in general which will enable us to graph equations and inequalities more easily.

Example 1. Sketch the graph (locus) of the equation

$$x^2 + y^2 = 4.$$

If we solve for y in terms of x, we obtain

$$y = \pm\sqrt{4 - x^2}.$$

Several points on the graph of this equation can be obtained from the following table of values for x and y.

x	-2	$-\frac{3}{2}$	-1	$-\frac{1}{2}$	0	$\frac{1}{2}$	1	$\frac{3}{2}$	2
y	0	$\pm\frac{\sqrt{7}}{2}$	$\pm\sqrt{3}$	$\pm\frac{\sqrt{15}}{2}$	± 2	$\pm\frac{\sqrt{15}}{2}$	$\pm\sqrt{3}$	$\pm\frac{\sqrt{7}}{2}$	0

If we assume that the graph of the given equation is a smooth continuous curve, then the table furnishes us enough points to sketch the graph. The graph of $x^2 + y^2 = 4$ is a circle with center at the origin and radius equal to 2, as shown in Figure 3.1.

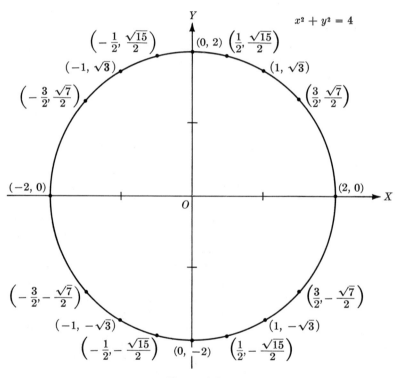

Figure 3.1

Example 2. Find an equation of the set of points which are equidistant from the origin and the point $A:(-1, 1)$.

Let $P:(x, y)$ represent a general point in the set of points (locus). The geometric condition to be satisfied can be expressed by the equation

$$|OP| = |AP|.$$

By the distance formula,

$$|OP| = \sqrt{(x-0)^2 + (y-0)^2} = \sqrt{x^2 + y^2},$$
$$|AP| = \sqrt{(x-(-1))^2 + (y-1)^2}$$
$$= \sqrt{(x+1)^2 + (y-1)^2};$$

hence

$$\sqrt{x^2 + y^2} = \sqrt{(x+1)^2 + (y-1)^2},$$
$$x^2 + y^2 = (x+1)^2 + (y-1)^2$$
$$= x^2 + 2x + 1 + y^2 - 2y + 1,$$

whereby

$$x - y + 1 = 0.$$

The graph (locus) of this equation is a straight line, as shown in Figure 3.2.

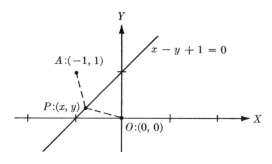

Figure 3.2

Equations of special loci described by various geometric conditions will be studied in detail throughout the book whenever appropriate.

Exercises

In Exercises 1–18 sketch the graph of each equation.

1. $y = x$.
2. $y = 3x + 1$.
3. $3x - 2y = 6$.
4. $y = 3$.
5. $x = -2$.
6. $y = x^2$.
7. $y = x^2 + 2$.
8. $x^2 + y^2 = 9$.
9. $x^2 - y^2 = 9$.

10. $4x^2 + 9y^2 = 36$.
11. $y = x^3$.
12. $y = \sqrt{x}$.
13. $x^2 - y^2 = 0$.
14. $y = |x|$.
15. $y = |x + 3|$.
16. $y = |x| + 3$.
17. $y = 3|x|$.
18. $|x| + |y| = 1$.

19. Find an equation of the set of points $P:(x, y)$ equidistant from the following points: **(a)** $A:(1, 1)$ and $B:(-1, -1)$; **(b)** $A:(0, 0)$ and $B:(2, 0)$; **(c)** $A:(0, 2)$ and $B:(0, 0)$.

20. Find an equation of the set of points $P:(x, y)$ equidistant from the origin.

21. Find an equation of the set of points $P:(x, y)$ equidistant from the point $A:(6, 0)$ and the line $x = 0$.

3.2 LINES PARALLEL TO A GIVEN VECTOR

In this section and in subsequent sections of this chapter we shall examine the problem of determining the equation of a line in the plane subject to certain sets of conditions.

Infinitely many lines exist that are parallel to a given vector. However, only one line exists that is parallel to the given vector and contains a given point. For example, in Figure 3.3, lines ℓ_1, ℓ_2, ℓ_3, and ℓ_4 are parallel to the vector $\vec{n}$, but only the line ℓ_2 contains the point P_0.

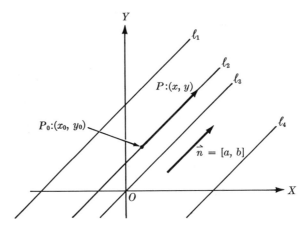

Figure 3.3

To determine the equation of the line ℓ_2 in Figure 3.3, let $P:(x, y)$ be a general point on the line. Since $\overrightarrow{P_0P}$ lies along line ℓ_2 and ℓ_2 is parallel to $\vec{n}$, it follows that

$$\overrightarrow{P_0P} = t\vec{n} \qquad (3.1)$$

where t is an arbitrary real number. Equation (3.1) represents a *vector form* of the equation of the line ℓ_2. A *coordinate form* of the equation of the line ℓ_2 can be obtained from the vector form by using the fact that $\overrightarrow{P_0P} = [x - x_0, y - y_0]$ and $\overrightarrow{n} = [a, b]$. Thus

$$[x - x_0, y - y_0] = t[a, b],$$
$$[x - x_0, y - y_0] = [ta, tb].$$

Since the corresponding components of the vectors in this equation are equal,

$$\begin{cases} x - x_0 = at \\ y - y_0 = bt; \end{cases}$$

that is,

$$\begin{cases} x = x_0 + at \\ y = y_0 + bt. \end{cases} \tag{3.2}$$

The equations of (3.2) represent a set of *parametric equations* of a line, with parameter t. Each value of t yields the coordinates of a point on the line ℓ_2. Since $\dfrac{x - x_0}{a} = t$ and $\dfrac{y - y_0}{b} = t$, then

$$\frac{x - x_0}{a} = \frac{y - y_0}{b}, \tag{3.3}$$

provided that $ab \neq 0$. Equation (3.3), as well as the set of equations (3.2), represents a line which is parallel to the vector $[a, b]$ and which contains the point $P_0:(x_0, y_0)$.

Note that equation (3.3) cannot be used if the vector is parallel to either of the coordinate axes. Furthermore, the components a and b of the vector parallel to the line whose equation is given by (3.3) constitute a set of direction numbers of the line.

Equation (3.3) is called the *point-direction number form* of the equation of a line.

> **Example 1.** Determine a set of parametric equations of the line that contains the point $P_0:(3, 5)$ and is parallel to the vector $\overrightarrow{n}$ where $\overrightarrow{n} = [2, 1]$.
>
> Let $P:(x, y)$ be a general point on the line. Then
>
> $$\overrightarrow{P_0P} = t\overrightarrow{n},$$
> $$[x - 3, y - 5] = t[2, 1],$$
>
> and
>
> $$\begin{cases} x - 3 = 2t \\ y - 5 = t; \end{cases}$$

that is,

$$\begin{cases} x = 3 + 2t \\ y = 5 + t \end{cases}$$

represents a set of parametric equations of the line that contains the point P_0 and is parallel to the vector $\vec{n}$.

Example 2. Determine an equation of the line ℓ that contains the point P_0:$(1, -3)$ and is parallel to the line that contains the points A:$(5, 1)$ and B:$(-2, 4)$.

The two distinct points A and B determine a unique line AB. Since the line ℓ is parallel to the line AB, then vectors along the two lines are parallel. Let P:(x, y) be a general point on line ℓ. Then $\overrightarrow{P_0P}$ lies along line ℓ, $\overrightarrow{AB}$ lies along line AB, and

$$\overrightarrow{P_0P} = t\overrightarrow{AB}.$$

Thus

$$\begin{aligned}[x - 1, y + 3] &= t[-2 - 5, 4 - 1] \\ &= [-7t, 3t],\end{aligned}$$

and

$$\begin{cases} x - 1 = -7t \\ y + 3 = 3t \end{cases}$$

represents a set of parametric equations of line ℓ. Eliminating the parameter t, we obtain

$$\frac{x - 1}{-7} = \frac{y + 3}{3},$$

which represents the point-direction number form of the equation of line ℓ shown in Figure 3.4.

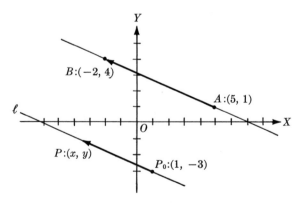

Figure 3.4

Exercises

Determine a set of parametric equations of the line that contains the point P_0 and is parallel to the vector $\vec{n}$.

1. P_0:(3, 1); $\vec{n} = [2, -1]$.   **3.** P_0:(−3, 0); $\vec{n} = [3, 1]$.

2. P_0:(2, 4); $\vec{n} = [5, 0]$.   **4.** P_0:(0, 0); $\vec{n} = [1, 2]$.

If possible, write the equation of the line that contains the point P_0 and is parallel to the vector $\vec{n}$ in point-direction number form.

5. P_0:(5, 2); $\vec{n} = [3, 2]$.   **7.** P_0:(2, 1); $\vec{n} = [0, 3]$.

6. P_0:(−3, 0); $\vec{n} = [1, -5]$.   **8.** P_0:(4, −1); $\vec{n} = [1, 0]$.

In Exercises 9–12 determine a set of parametric equations of the line that contains the point P_0 and is parallel to the line that contains the points A and B.

9. P_0:(5, 3); A:(2, −1) and B:(1, 2).

10. P_0:(2, 0); A:(0, 1) and B:(1, 6).

11. P_0:(−6, 6); A:(7, 3) and B:(5, 9).

12. P_0:(3, 2); A:(3, 2) and B:(1, 1).

13. Determine a set of parametric equations of the line through the point P_0:(3, −2) and which is parallel to the y axis.

14. Given the line whose parametric equations are

$$\begin{cases} x = 1 + 2t \\ y = 1, \end{cases}$$

find   **(a)** a set of direction numbers of the line;   **(b)** three points on the line.

15. Find a set of direction cosines of the line whose parametric equations are

$$\begin{cases} x = 2 + 3t \\ y = -1 + 4t. \end{cases}$$

16. Determine the point-direction number form of the equation of the line through the point P_0:(6, −2) and parallel to the line $(x - 1)/2 = (y + 3)/5$.

17. Determine a set of direction cosines of the line whose equation is $(x + 3)/5 = (y - 1)/12$.

3.3   LINES PERPENDICULAR TO A GIVEN VECTOR

Consider the problem of determining the equation of a line that contains the point P_0:(4, 3) and is perpendicular to the vector $\vec{n}$ where $\vec{n} = [1, 2]$, as shown in Figure 3.5. Let P:(x, y) be a general point on the line. Since $\vec{P_0P}$ is perpendicular to $\vec{n}$, then

$$\vec{P_0P} \cdot \vec{n} = 0. \tag{3.4}$$

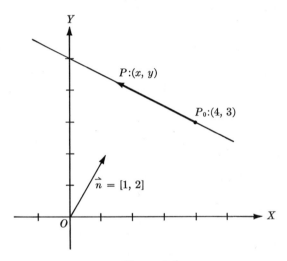

Figure 3.5

Equation (3.4) represents a vector form of the equation of the line ℓ through P_0 and perpendicular to the vector $\vec{n}$. A coordinate form of the equation of the line ℓ can be obtained from the vector form:

$$\vec{P_0P} = [x - 4,\ y - 3],$$
$$\vec{n} = [1, 2],$$
$$\vec{P_0P} \cdot \vec{n} = (x - 4) + 2(y - 3);$$

hence

$$(x - 4) + 2(y - 3) = 0,$$
$$x + 2y - 10 = 0.$$

This equation represents a coordinate form of the equation of the line ℓ.
   The general coordinate form of the equation of a line ℓ that contains

the point P_0:(x_0, y_0) and is perpendicular to the vector $\vec{n}$, where $\vec{n} = [a, b]$, can be obtained from equation (3.4):

$$\vec{P_0P} = [x - x_0, y - y_0],$$

$$\vec{P_0P} \cdot \vec{n} = a(x - x_0) + b(y - y_0);$$

hence

$$a(x - x_0) + b(y - y_0) = 0 \tag{3.5}$$

represents a coordinate form of the equation of the line ℓ. Note that the coefficients of x and y are the first and second components respectively of the vector $\vec{n}$ perpendicular to the line.

Example 1. Determine an equation of the line that contains the point P_0:$(5, 2)$ and is perpendicular to the vector $\vec{n}$ where $\vec{n} = [-2, 3]$.

Using equation (3.5) with $(x_0, y_0) = (5, 2)$ and $[a, b] = [-2, 3]$, we obtain

$$-2(x - 5) + 3(y - 2) = 0;$$

that is,

$$2x - 3y - 4 = 0$$

represents a coordinate form of the equation of the line.

Example 2. Find an equation of the line ℓ passing through $(1, 2)$ and perpendicular to the line $2x - y - 3 = 0$.

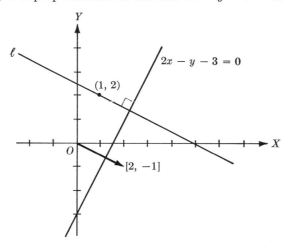

Figure 3.6

It has been noted that the coefficients of x and y in an equation of a line represent the first and second components respectively of a vector perpendicular to the line. Hence if a line ℓ is perpendicular to the line $2x - y - 3 = 0$, then the line is parallel to the vector $[2, -1]$. By the method of the previous section, a vector form of the equation of the line ℓ is given by

$$[x - 1, y - 2] = t[2, -1],$$

whereby

$$\begin{cases} x - 1 = 2t \\ y - 2 = -t, \end{cases}$$

$$\frac{x - 1}{2} = \frac{y - 2}{-1},$$

$$x + 2y - 5 = 0.$$

Exercises

Determine an equation of the line that contains the point P_0 and is perpendicular to the vector $\vec{n}$.

1. $P_0:(8, 5); \vec{n} = [4, 2]$.

2. $P_0:(3, -1); \vec{n} = [2, 0]$.

3. $P_0:(4, 0); \vec{n} = [5, -1]$.

4. $P_0:(0, 3); \vec{n} = [-1, 1]$.

5. $P_0:(-2, 2); \vec{n} = [3, 2]$.

6. $P_0:(0, 0); \vec{n} = [-2, 5]$.

Determine a unit vector perpendicular to each line.

7. $6x + 8y - 3 = 0$.

8. $x - y + 2 = 0$.

Find an equation of the line ℓ passing through the point P_0 and perpendicular to the line whose equation is given.

9. $P_0:(-4, 1); 5x + 3y + 2 = 0$.

10. $P_0:(5, 2); x - y + 5 = 0$.

11. $P_0:(3, 4); 2x + y - 10 = 0$.

12. $P_0:(7, 0); (x - 2)/3 = (y + 6)/2$.

In Exercises 13–16 find an equation of the line passing through the point P_0 and perpendicular to the line that contains the points A and B.

13. $P_0:(-2,\ -1)$; $A:(5,\ 6)$ and $B:(3,\ -2)$.

14. $P_0:(3,\ 0)$; $A:(2,\ 1)$ and $B:(0,\ 4)$.

15. $P_0:(0,\ 0)$; $A:(-4,\ 6)$ and $B:(5,\ -1)$.

16. $P_0:(2,\ 6)$; $A:(3,\ 8)$ and $B:(5,\ 12)$.

17. Determine the equation of the line that contains the point $P_0:(2,\ -3)$ and is parallel to the line $5x + 2y - 10 = 0$.

18. Prove that the lines $3x + 2y + 3 = 0$ and $6x + 4y - 10 = 0$ are parallel.

3.4 EQUATION OF A LINE THROUGH TWO POINTS

Two distinct points in a plane determine one and only one line. Consider two distinct points $A:(x_0,\ y_0)$ and $B:(x_1,\ y_1)$ which determine the line ℓ, as shown in Figure 3.7. If $P:(x,\ y)$ is a general point on the line ℓ, then a definite relationship exists among the three position vectors $\overrightarrow{OA}$, $\overrightarrow{OB}$, and $\overrightarrow{OP}$. By Theorem 2.7,

$$\overrightarrow{OP} = t\overrightarrow{OA} + (1 - t)\overrightarrow{OB} \tag{3.6}$$

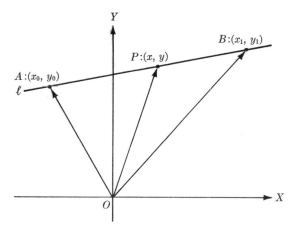

Figure 3.7

where t is a real number. Equation (3.6) represents a vector form of the equation of line ℓ through points A and B. Since

$$\overrightarrow{OA} = [x_0, y_0], \qquad \overrightarrow{OB} = [x_1, y_1], \qquad \text{and} \qquad \overrightarrow{OP} = [x, y],$$

then

$$[x, y] = t[x_0, y_0] + (1 - t)[x_1, y_1]$$
$$= [tx_0 + (1 - t)x_1, ty_0 + (1 - t)y_1].$$

Hence we equate corresponding components and obtain a set of *parametric equations of a line through two points*:

$$\begin{cases} x = tx_0 + (1 - t)x_1 \\ y = ty_0 + (1 - t)y_1. \end{cases} \tag{3.7}$$

Each point on the line corresponds to a particular value of the parameter t. For example, note that if $t = 0$, the coordinates of point B are obtained; if $t = 1$, the coordinates of point A are obtained; if $t = \frac{1}{2}$, the coordinates of the midpoint of line segment AB are obtained.

In certain cases, the parameter t in (3.7) can be eliminated to obtain another coordinate form of the equation of the line. Using the equations of (3.7), we obtain

$$\frac{x - x_1}{x_0 - x_1} = t \qquad \text{and} \qquad \frac{y - y_1}{y_0 - y_1} = t,$$

provided that $x_0 \neq x_1$ and $y_0 \neq y_1$, that is, provided that the line is not parallel to a coordinate axis. It follows that

$$\frac{x - x_1}{x_0 - x_1} = \frac{y - y_1}{y_0 - y_1}. \tag{3.8}$$

Equation (3.8) is often referred to as the *two-point form* of the equation of a line in a plane.

Example 1. Use the two-point form to find the equation of a line that contains the points $(7, 3)$ and $(5, 8)$.

Let $(x_0, y_0) = (7, 3)$ and $(x_1, y_1) = (5, 8)$. Then, by equation (3.8),

$$\frac{x - 5}{7 - 5} = \frac{y - 8}{3 - 8},$$
$$-5(x - 5) = 2(y - 8),$$
$$5x + 2y + 9 = 0.$$

Example 2. Determine a set of parametric equations of the line in Example 1.

Given the equations of (3.7), we can express a set of parametric equations of the line by

$$\begin{cases} x = 7t + 5(1 - t) \\ y = 3t + 8(1 - t); \end{cases}$$

that is,

$$\begin{cases} x = 5 + 2t \\ y = 8 - 5t. \end{cases}$$

Exercises

Use the two-point form, if possible, to find the equation of a line that contains the points A and B.

1. $A:(3, 1)$; $B:(6, 3)$.

3. $A:(-5, -1)$; $B:(-1, -5)$.

2. $A:(0, 2)$; $B:(1, 4)$.

4. $A:(2, 1)$; $B:(6, 5)$.

In Exercises 5–8 determine a set of parametric equations of the line that contains the points A and B.

5. $A:(-1, 0)$; $B:(-6, 5)$.

7. $A:(5, 1)$; $B:(10, 1)$.

6. $A:(7, 3)$; $B:(12, -1)$.

8. $A:(2, 0)$; $B:(2, 5)$.

9. Find the point $P:(x, y)$ on the line segment AB, where $A:(9, 4)$ and $B:(3, 0)$, such that P is one-fourth of the way from A to B.

10. Determine the coordinates of the point B if $P:(1, 5)$ divides the line segment AB, where $A:(-3, 8)$, in the ratio 2 to 3.

11. Let $A:(x_0, y_0)$ and $B:(x_1, y_1)$ be any two points on a plane. Show that the coordinates of the midpoint of the line segment AB are

$$\left(\frac{x_0 + x_1}{2}, \frac{y_0 + y_1}{2} \right).$$

12. Find the coordinates of the midpoint of the line segment AB where $A:(5, -3)$ and $B:(1, 7)$.

13. Find the equation of the set of points equidistant from the points $A:(-1, 4)$ and $B:(3, 6)$. Graph the equation, and locate the points A and B.

14. Determine the equations of the medians of the triangle ABC where $A:(2, 3)$, $B:(7, 4)$, and $C:(5, 0)$.

15. Find the coordinates of the two points of trisection of the line segment AB where $A:(-10, 3)$ and $B:(2, 9)$.

16. Show that the equation of the line that contains the points (x_1, y_1) and (x_2, y_2) may be written in the form

$$\begin{vmatrix} x & y & 1 \\ x_1 & y_1 & 1 \\ x_2 & y_2 & 1 \end{vmatrix} = 0.$$

17. Use the results of Exercise 16 to find the equation of the line determined by the points $(4, -1)$ and $(6, 5)$.

3.5   THE SLOPE OF A LINE

Unless a line is parallel to the x axis, it must intersect that axis. When a line ℓ intersects the x axis in a unique point, the line makes an angle ϕ with the positive half of the x axis such that $0 < \phi < \pi$, as shown in Figure 3.8. The angle ϕ is called the *angle of inclination* of the line. If the line ℓ is

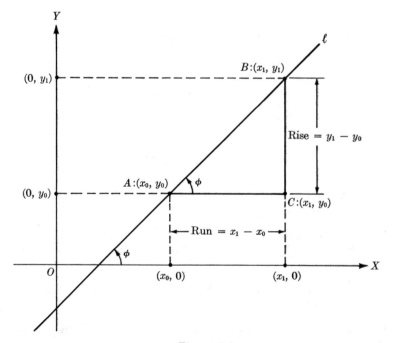

Figure 3.8

parallel to or coincident with the x axis, the angle of inclination is defined to be 0. Hence the angle of inclination is always less than π.

Let $A:(x_0, y_0)$ and $B:(x_1, y_1)$ be any two distinct points in the plane such that $x_1 \neq x_0$ and $y_1 \neq y_0$. The two-point form of the equation of line AB can be expressed as

$$\frac{y - y_0}{y_1 - y_0} = \frac{x - x_0}{x_1 - x_0}.$$

Then

$$y - y_0 = \frac{y_1 - y_0}{x_1 - x_0}(x - x_0). \tag{3.9}$$

In (3.9), the expression $y_1 - y_0$ is often referred to as the *rise* and the expression $x_1 - x_0$ is referred to as the *run*, as indicated in Figure 3.8. The *rise* and the *run* are the second and first components of $\overrightarrow{AB}$ respectively. The ratio of the *rise* to the *run*, that is, $\frac{y_1 - y_0}{x_1 - x_0}$, is called the *slope* of the line AB and will be denoted by m:

$$m = \frac{\text{rise}}{\text{run}} = \frac{y_1 - y_0}{x_1 - x_0}. \tag{3.10}$$

The slope of a line parallel to or coincident with the x axis is defined to be zero; the slope of a line parallel to or coincident with the y axis is undefined.

It should be mentioned that the rise and the run of the line AB could also be considered as the second and first components of $\overrightarrow{BA}$ respectively instead of $\overrightarrow{AB}$. In each case the slope is given by the same real number since

$$m = \frac{y_1 - y_0}{x_1 - x_0} = \frac{y_0 - y_1}{x_0 - x_1}.$$

Note that the slope m of the line AB in Figure 3.8 is equal to the tangent of the angle of inclination; that is,

$$m = \tan \phi. \tag{3.11}$$

Since the angle of inclination of a given line is constant, the slope of a line, if it exists, is constant. Furthermore, if $0 < \phi < \pi/2$, then $\tan \phi$ is a positive real number; hence the slope m of a line ℓ whose angle of inclination is acute is positive (Figure 3.9). If $\pi/2 < \phi < \pi$, then $\tan \phi$ is a negative real number; hence the slope m of a line ℓ whose angle of inclination is obtuse is negative (Figure 3.10).

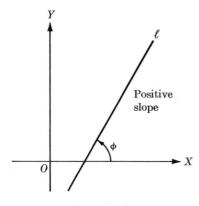

Figure 3.9

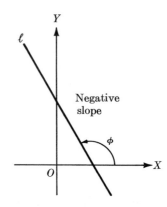

Figure 3.10

Example 1. Determine an equation of the line that contains the points $A:(3, 1)$ and $B:(5, 7)$.

Let $A:(3, 1) = A:(x_0, y_0)$ and $B:(5, 7) = B:(x_1, y_1)$. Substituting the coordinates of the points A and B in equation (3.9), we obtain

$$y - 1 = \frac{7 - 1}{5 - 3}(x - 3).$$

Simplifying, we obtain $3x - y - 8 = 0$, which is an equation of the line that contains points A and B.

Example 2. Find the angle of inclination of the line in Example 1.

Using equations (3.10) and (3.11), we have

$$\tan \phi = m = \frac{y_1 - y_0}{x_1 - x_0} = \frac{7 - 1}{5 - 3} = 3.$$

Hence $\phi = \arctan 3$.

If the statements of equations (3.9) and (3.10) are combined, the resulting equation

$$y - y_0 = m(x - x_0) \tag{3.12}$$

is called the *point-slope form* of the equation of a line in a plane since the line passes through the point $P_0:(x_0, y_0)$ and its slope is m.

Example 3. Determine an equation of the line that passes through $P_0:(-2, 4)$ and whose angle of inclination is $\pi/3$.

Now, $m = \tan (\pi/3) = \sqrt{3}$. Using the point-slope form of the equation of a line, where $P_0:(x_0, y_0) = P_0:(-2, 4)$, we have

$$y - 4 = \sqrt{3}(x + 2).$$

Simplifying, we have

$$\sqrt{3}x - y + 4 + 2\sqrt{3} = 0.$$

Exercises

Find the slope, if it exists, of the line passing through the points A and B.

1. $A:(3, 2); B:(4, 1)$.   3. $A:(-6, 2); B:(-3, 8)$.

2. $A:(3, 3); B:(-5, 3)$.   4. $A:(2, 5); B:(2, 10)$.

Use the point-slope form to determine the equation of the line that contains the points A and B.

5. $A:(2, 1); B:(6, 5)$.   7. $A:(2, 3); B:(-4, -7)$.

6. $A:(-1, 0); B:(-6, 5)$.   8. $A:(3, 1); B:(6, 1)$.

Find the angle of inclination of each line.

9. $x + y + 3 = 0$.   10. $x - \sqrt{3}y - 10 = 0$.

Find the slope, if it exists, of any line parallel to the position vector $\vec{n}$.

11. $\vec{n} = [3, 1]$.   12. $\vec{n} = [-5, 8]$.

Find the slope, if it exists, of any line perpendicular to the position vector $\vec{n}$.

13. $\vec{n} = [5, -10]$.   14. $\vec{n} = [2, 3]$.

Determine an equation of the line that passes through P_0 and whose slope is m. Graph the equation.

15. $P_0:(0, 6); m = -3$.   16. $P_0:(-3, 7); m = \frac{5}{8}$.

Determine an equation of the line that passes through P_0 and whose angle of inclination is ϕ. Graph the equation.

17. $P_0:(0, 0); \phi = 5\pi/6$.   18. $P_0:(2, 1); \phi = \pi/4$.

Find the slope, if it exists, of the line containing the origin and the point P_0.

19. $P_0:(2, 6)$.   20. $P_0:(3, -2)$.

In Exercises 21 and 22 determine k if the line containing each pair of points has the slope m.

21. $(0, k)$ and $(1, 3k)$; $m = 4$.   **22.** $(k, 6)$ and $(3, -2k)$; $m = -1$.

23. Show that the equation of a line that contains the origin and whose slope is m is of the form $y = mx$.

24. Find the equation of each line whose slope is $-\frac{2}{5}$ and which forms with the coordinate axes a triangle 20 square units in area.

3.6   OTHER FORMS OF THE EQUATION OF A LINE

The x coordinate of the point where a line intersects the x axis is called the *x intercept* of the line; the y coordinate of the point where a line intersects the y axis is called the *y intercept* of the line. For example, the x intercept of the line $2x - 3y + 12 = 0$ is -6 since $x = -6$ when $y = 0$; the y intercept is 4 since $y = 4$ when $x = 0$.

If the point P_0 has coordinates $(0, b)$, then the point-slope form of the equation of a line can be written as

$$y = mx + b. \tag{3.13}$$

This form of the equation of a line is called the *slope-intercept form* since m is the slope of the line and b is the y intercept. Note that the slope-intercept form cannot be used to represent a line parallel to the y axis. (Why?) Furthermore, it is important to note that the slope of a line whose equation is given in slope-intercept form is the coefficient of x.

Example 1. Find an equation of the line with slope 4 and y intercept -1.

Since $m = 4$ and $b = -1$, then, by equation (3.13),

$$y = 4x - 1.$$

Example 2. On a single coordinate plane, graph the equations $y = mx - 1$ where $m = \pm\frac{1}{3}, \pm\frac{1}{2}, \pm1, \pm2, \pm3$.

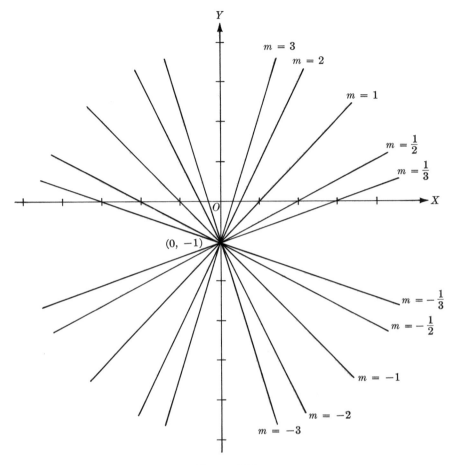

Figure 3.11

Since the graphs of the ten equations have the same y intercept, each line passes through a common point $(0, -1)$ on
the y axis. Note that the lines whose slopes are positive
slant upward to the right; the lines whose slopes are nega-
tive slant downward to the right. Furthermore, as $|m|$ in-
creases in value, the steepness of the line increases.

In Figure 3.12, the line ℓ contains the points $A:(a, 0)$ and $B:(0, b)$.
Hence the x intercept of line ℓ is a and the y intercept is b. Using the two-
point form of the equation of a line, equation (3.8), we can write the equation of line ℓ as

$$\frac{x - 0}{a - 0} = \frac{y - b}{0 - b}.$$

Simplifying, we obtain

$$\frac{x}{a} + \frac{y}{b} = 1. \tag{3.14}$$

This form of the equation of a line is called the *intercept form* since a and b are the x and y intercepts respectively. The intercept form of the equation of a line does not exist if the line is parallel to either coordinate axis. (Why?)

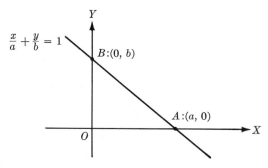

Figure 3.12

Example 3. Find the intercept form of the equation of the line passing through the points $A:(-2, -2)$ and $B:(1, -8)$.

The equation of the line, $2x + y + 6 = 0$, can be obtained by using the two-point form or the point-slope form once the slope is determined. If $2x + y + 6 = 0$, then

$$2x + y = -6,$$

so that

$$\frac{x}{-3} + \frac{y}{-6} = 1$$

represents the intercept form of the equation of the line. Note that the x intercept is -3 and the y intercept is -6.

Exercises

Find **(a)** the x intercept; **(b)** the y intercept of the line whose equation is given.

1. $3x + 4y - 24 = 0.$ 3. $x = 3.$

2. $5x - 2y + 10 = 0.$ 4. $2y + 5 = 0.$

Find an equation of the line with slope m and whose y intercept is given.

5. $m = \frac{3}{4}$; y intercept is 2. **7.** $m = 0$; y intercept is -3.

6. $m = -2$; y intercept is 7. **8.** $m = 3$; y intercept is 0.

Determine, if possible, the intercept form of the equation of the line passing through the points A and B.

9. $A:(0, 3)$; $B:(-3, 0)$. **11.** $A:(0, -2)$; $B:(1, 1)$.

10. $A:(2, 0)$; $B:(5, 0)$. **12.** $A:(5, 3)$; $B:(7, 2)$.

In Exercises 13–16 write the equation of the line in **(a)** slope-intercept form; **(b)** intercept form.

13. $2y - 4x = 6$. **15.** $\frac{1}{2}x + \frac{1}{3}y = 2$.

14. $3y + 7x + 4 = 0$. **16.** $5x - 3y = 15$.

17. Prove that the points $A:(0, 1)$, $B:(1, 4)$, and $C:(-1, -2)$ are collinear.

18. Show that the points $A:(6, -2)$, $B:(3, 5)$, and $C:(12, -10)$ are noncollinear.

19. On a single coordinate plane, graph the equations $y = mx + 2$ where $m = \pm\frac{1}{2}, \pm 2$.

20. On a single coordinate plane, graph the equations $3x + 2y - 6 = 0$ and $2x - 3y + 12 = 0$. Find the slope of each line. Make a conjecture about the graphs of the equations $ax + by + c = 0$ and $bx - ay + d = 0$ where $ab \neq 0$.

3.7 THE GENERAL LINEAR EQUATION IN TWO VARIABLES

Each of the forms of the equation of a line is useful in determining the equation of a line subject to certain specific geometric conditions. It was noted that certain of these forms cannot be used to obtain the equation of a line if the line is parallel to one of the coordinate axes. However, each form of the equation of a line can be expressed in the equivalent form

$$ax + by + c = 0 \tag{3.15}$$

where a, b, and c are real numbers such that $a^2 + b^2 \neq 0$. Equation (3.15) is called a *linear equation in x and y;* the equation is sometimes also referred to as the *general linear form* of the equation of a line. The graph of every linear equation in two variables is a line in a plane.

Theorem 3.1. *In a plane, the graph of the linear equation* $ax + by + c = 0$, *where a, b, and c are real numbers such that* $a^2 + b^2 \neq 0$, *is a line.*

Proof: If $a = 0$, then $b \neq 0$ and

$$y = -\frac{c}{b}.$$

The graph of this equation is a line parallel to the x axis. If $c = 0$, the line is the x axis.
　　If $b = 0$, then $a \neq 0$ and

$$x = -\frac{c}{a}.$$

The graph of this equation is a line parallel to the y axis. If $c = 0$, the line is the y axis.
　　If $a \neq 0$ and $b \neq 0$, then

$$y = -\frac{a}{b}x - \frac{c}{b}.$$

This equation is the slope-intercept form of the equation of a line; the slope is $-a/b$ and the y intercept is $-c/b$. Hence the graph is a line.

Hereafter, it will sometimes be convenient to refer to "the line $ax + by + c = 0$" to mean the graph of the linear equation $ax + by + c = 0$.

Example 1. Determine that value of c for which the line $5x - 2y + c = 0$ passes through the point $(4, 2)$.

Letting $x = 4$ and $y = 2$ in the equation of the line, we obtain
$$5(4) - 2(2) + c = 0,$$
$$16 + c = 0,$$
$$c = -16.$$

Example 2. Determine that value of b for which the line $3x + by - 18 = 0$ has a y intercept of -3.

The equation of the line can be expressed in intercept form:

$$3x + by - 18 = 0,$$
$$3x + by = 18,$$
$$\frac{3x}{18} + \frac{by}{18} = 1,$$
$$\frac{x}{6} + \frac{y}{18/b} = 1.$$

If $18/b = -3$, then $b = -6$.

Example 3. Find the value of b if the slope of the line $6x - by + c = 0$ is 2.

The equation of the line can be expressed in slope-intercept form:

$$6x - by + c = 0,$$
$$by = 6x + c,$$
$$y = \frac{6}{b}x + \frac{c}{b}.$$

If $6/b = 2$, then $b = 3$.

Exercises

1. Determine that value of b for which the line $2x + by + 3 = 0$ passes through the point $(4, -1)$.

2. Determine that value of c for which the line $2x + 3y - c = 0$ has an x intercept of 4.

3. Find the value of a if the slope of the line $ax + 9y - 1 = 0$ is -3.

4. Write the equation of the line whose x and y intercepts are 5 and 3 respectively.

5. State the conditions placed upon the coefficients of the equation of a line $ax + by + c = 0$ if
   (a) the line has an x intercept equal to 3;
   (b) the line has equal intercepts on both axes.

6. Find the equation of the line that contains the point $P_0:(2, 1)$ and whose x intercept is three times the value of its y intercept.

7. Show that the equation of a line that contains the origin is of the form $ax + by = 0$.

8. Find the general coordinate form of the equation of a line parallel to the   (a) x axis;   (b) y axis.

9. The graphs of two linear equations have the point $(3, -1)$ in common. The y intercepts of the two lines are 2 and -4 respectively. Find each linear equation.

3.8   LINEAR INEQUALITIES IN TWO VARIABLES

Every straight line in a plane separates the plane into three sets of points:

(i)   The set of points "above" or "to the left" of the line.

(ii)   The set of points on the line.

(iii)   The set of points "below" or "to the right" of the line.

The sets of points described in (i) and (iii) are called *half-planes* determined by the line; the line is the *boundary*, or *edge*, of each half-plane. The points on the line do not belong to either half-plane determined by the line.

In this section we shall concern ourselves with the problem of obtaining a mathematical statement whose graph is a half-plane. The following example is instructive.

> **Example 1.** Graph the set of points whose coordinates satisfy the *linear inequality* $x + 2y - 6 > 0$.

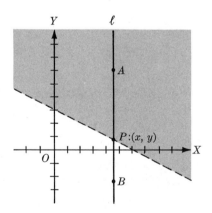

Figure 3.13

The graph of the related linear equation $x + 2y - 6 = 0$ is shown as a dashed line in Figure 3.13. The coordinates of every point on the line make the linear expression $x + 2y - 6$ identically equal to 0. Let $P:(x, y)$ be any point on that line. Consider a vertical line ℓ that contains the point P. Every point on line ℓ has the same x coordinate as P. However, each point A on line ℓ "above" point P has a y coordinate greater than the y coordinate of P. The coordinates of the points on ℓ "above" P make the linear expression $x + 2y - 6$ greater than 0. In a similar manner, the coordinates of each point B on ℓ "below" P make the linear expression $x + 2y - 6$ less than 0. Hence the graph of the set of points whose coordinates satisfy the linear inequality $x + 2y - 6 > 0$ is the shaded half-plane to which A belongs. The line $x + 2y - 6 = 0$ is shown as a dashed line in Figure 3.13 since the points on the line do not satisfy the linear inequality; that is, the boundary $x + 2y - 6 = 0$ does not belong to the graph of the linear inequality $x + 2y - 6 > 0$.

In general, the graph of a linear inequality $ax + by + c > 0$ (or $ax + by + c < 0$) is a half-plane determined by the line $ax + by + c = 0$. Recall that the set of points whose coordinates satisfy the inequality $ax + by + c \geq 0$ is equal to the set of points whose coordinates satisfy the linear inequality $ax + by + c > 0$ or the linear equation $ax + by + c = 0$. The graph of a linear inequality $ax + by + c \geq 0$ (or $ax + by + c \leq 0$) consists of the set of points of a half-plane determined by the line $ax + by + c = 0$ and the points on the line.

Theorem 3.2. *If $b > 0$, the graph of the linear inequality $ax + by + c > 0$ is the half-plane above the line $ax + by + c = 0$; the graph of the linear inequality $ax + by + c < 0$ is the half-plane below the line.*

Proof: Let $P_0:(x_0, y_0)$ be any point on the line $ax + by + c = 0$. Then

$$ax_0 + by_0 + c = 0.$$

Let $P:(x_0, y)$ be any point on a vertical line ℓ that contains $P_0:(x_0, y_0)$. If

$$ax_0 + by + c > 0,$$

then by subtraction

$$(ax_0 + by + c) - (ax_0 + by_0 + c) > 0,$$
$$by - by_0 > 0,$$
$$b(y - y_0) > 0.$$

If $b > 0$, then $y - y_0 > 0$; that is, $y > y_0$. Hence the point $P:(x_0, y)$ is above the line $ax + by + c = 0$.

Conversely, if $P:(x_0, y)$ is a point on ℓ above the line $ax + by + c = 0$, then $y > y_0$. Since $b > 0$, then $by > by_0$ and

$$ax_0 + by + c > ax_0 + by_0 + c,$$
$$ax_0 + by + c > 0.$$

Therefore, the points above the line $ax + by + c = 0$ satisfy the linear inequality $ax + by + c > 0$.

Now, only those points whose coordinates satisfy the linear equation $ax + by + c = 0$ lie on the line. If $b > 0$, those points and only those points whose coordinates satisfy the linear inequality $ax + by + c > 0$ lie in the half-plane above the line. Every point in the plane lies on the line $ax + by + c = 0$, in the half-plane above the line, or in the half-plane below the line. Furthermore, every point in the plane has coordinates which satisfy the linear equation $ax + by + c = 0$, the linear inequality $ax + by + c > 0$, or the linear inequality $ax + by + c < 0$. Hence it follows that those points and only those points whose coordinates satisfy the linear inequality $ax + by + c < 0$ lie in the half-plane below the line.

Example 2. Graph the linear inequality $3x + 4y + 12 \leq 0$.

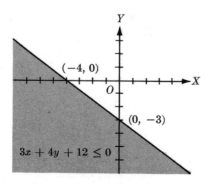

Figure 3.14

Since $b > 0$, the graph of the linear inequality $3x + 4y + 12 < 0$ is the half-plane in Figure 3.14 below the line $3x + 4y + 12 = 0$. The line $3x + 4y + 12 = 0$ is shown in the figure as a solid line since its points belong to the graph of $3x + 4y + 12 \leq 0$.

Exercises

In Exercises 1–10 graph each linear inequality.

1. $x \geq 1$.

2. $y < 2$.

3. $y - x > 0$.

4. $x - 2y - 4 > 0$.

5. $3x + 4y \leq 12$.

6. $x + y + 2 < 0$.

7. $2x + y \geq 4$.

8. $3x + y - 6 < 0$.

9. $3x + y - 6 > 0$.

10. $3x + y - 6 \geq 0$.

In Exercises 11–20 graph each statement.

11. $|x| = 2$.

12. $|x| \leq 3$.

13. $|y| > 1$.

14. $|x + 3| \geq 1$.

15. $y < |x|$.

16. $y \leq |x + 1|$.

17. $x > |y + 1|$.

18. $|x| + |y| < 3$.

19. $|x| + |y| \leq 3$.

20. $|x + y| < 2$.

21. Prove that if $b = 0$ and $a > 0$, then the graph of the linear inequality $ax + by + c > 0$ is the half-plane "to the right" of the line $ax + by + c = 0$; the graph of the linear inequality $ax + by + c < 0$ is the half-plane "to the left" of the line.

3.9 PARALLEL LINES

It has already been mentioned that two nonzero vectors are parallel if and only if one of the vectors is a real multiple of the other. Let $\vec{r}$ and $\vec{s}$ be two nonzero parallel vectors. Then

$$\vec{r} = t\vec{s}$$

where t is a nonzero real number. If $A:(x_0, y_0)$ and $B:(x_1, y_1)$ are the initial and terminal points of $\vec{r}$ respectively, and if $C:(x_2, y_2)$ and $D:(x_3, y_3)$ are the initial and terminal points of $\vec{s}$ respectively, then

$$[x_1 - x_0, y_1 - y_0] = t[x_3 - x_2, y_3 - y_2]$$
$$= [t(x_3 - x_2), t(y_3 - y_2)].$$

Since corresponding components are equal, then

$$\begin{cases} x_1 - x_0 = t(x_3 - x_2) \\ y_1 - y_0 = t(y_3 - y_2), \end{cases}$$

whereby

$$\frac{x_1 - x_0}{x_3 - x_2} = t \quad \text{and} \quad \frac{y_1 - y_0}{y_3 - y_2} = t,$$

provided that $x_3 \neq x_2$ and $y_3 \neq y_2$. Hence

$$\frac{x_1 - x_0}{x_3 - x_2} = \frac{y_1 - y_0}{y_3 - y_2},$$

and by the properties of proportions

$$\frac{y_1 - y_0}{x_1 - x_0} = \frac{y_3 - y_2}{x_3 - x_2}. \tag{3.16}$$

If vectors $\vec{r}$ and $\vec{s}$ lie along nonvertical lines ℓ_1 and ℓ_2 respectively, as shown in Figure 3.15, then equation (3.16) states that the slopes of ℓ_1 and ℓ_2 are equal. Hence *if two lines are parallel, then the lines have the same slope.*

The converse, *if two lines have the same slope, then the lines are parallel,* can be proved by reversing the steps of the preceding argument. The proof

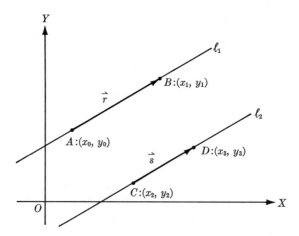

Figure 3.15

of the converse is left to the reader as Exercise 6. Thus the following theorem is valid.

Theorem 3.3. *Two lines in a plane are parallel if and only if they have the same slope, provided that the slope is defined.*

It follows from Theorem 3.3 that the equations of two distinct parallel lines can be expressed in forms that differ only by the constant term:

$$\begin{cases} ax + by + c_1 = 0 \\ ax + by + c_2 = 0, \qquad c_1 \neq c_2. \end{cases}$$

Example 1. Show that the lines $3x + 4y - 5 = 0$ and $6x + 8y - 3 = 0$ are distinct parallel lines.

The equations of the lines can be expressed in slope-intercept form as $y = -\frac{3}{4}x + \frac{5}{4}$ and $y = -\frac{3}{4}x + \frac{3}{8}$ respectively. Since the lines have the same slope, $-\frac{3}{4}$, then by Theorem 3.3 they are parallel. Note that the graphs of the equations are distinct parallel lines since they have different y intercepts, $\frac{5}{4}$ and $\frac{3}{8}$ respectively.

Example 2. Determine the form of the equations of lines parallel to the line $4x + 6y + 3 = 0$ and whose x intercepts are positive.

The equation of every line parallel to the line $4x + 6y + 3 = 0$ is of the form $4x + 6y + c = 0$. The x intercept of the line $4x + 6y + c = 0$ is expressed by $-(c/4)$. If $-(c/4) > 0$, then $c < 0$. Hence every line whose equation is of the form

$$4x + 6y + c = 0,$$

where $c < 0$, is parallel to the given line and has a positive x intercept.

Exercises

In Exercises 1–4 determine the equation of the line passing through the point P_0 and parallel to the line whose equation is given.

1. $P_0:(2, 6)$; $5x + 2y - 12 = 0$.

2. $P_0:(5, -1)$; $x = 2$.

3. $P_0:(3, -2)$; $3x - 7y + 4 = 0$.

4. $P_0:(4, 2); y - 1 = 0.$

5. The points $A:(2, -2)$, $B:(4, 2)$, and $C:(-2, 4)$ are the vertices of a triangle. Show that the line containing the midpoints of sides AB and BC is parallel to side AC.

6. Prove that if two lines have the same slope, then the lines are parallel.

3.10 PERPENDICULAR LINES

Two nonzero vectors are perpendicular if and only if the scalar product of the vectors is zero. Let $\vec{r}$ and $\vec{s}$ be two nonzero orthogonal vectors. Then

$$\vec{r} \cdot \vec{s} = 0.$$

If $A:(x_0, y_0)$ and $B:(x_1, y_1)$ are the initial and terminal points of $\vec{r}$ respectively, and if $C:(x_2, y_2)$ and $D:(x_3, y_3)$ are the initial and terminal points of $\vec{s}$ respectively, then

$$[x_1 - x_0, y_1 - y_0] \cdot [x_3 - x_2, y_3 - y_2] = 0.$$

Thus

$$(x_1 - x_0)(x_3 - x_2) + (y_1 - y_0)(y_3 - y_2) = 0,$$

$$(y_1 - y_0)(y_3 - y_2) = -(x_1 - x_0)(x_3 - x_2),$$

$$\left(\frac{y_1 - y_0}{x_1 - x_0}\right)\left(\frac{y_3 - y_2}{x_3 - x_2}\right) = -1, \tag{3.17}$$

provided that $x_1 \neq x_0$ and $x_3 \neq x_2$; that is,

$$\frac{y_1 - y_0}{x_1 - x_0} = -\frac{1}{\dfrac{y_3 - y_2}{x_3 - x_2}}. \tag{3.18}$$

If vectors $\vec{r}$ and $\vec{s}$ lie along the lines ℓ_1 and ℓ_2 respectively, as shown in Figure 3.16, and neither ℓ_1 nor ℓ_2 is parallel to either coordinate axis, then equation (3.17) states that the product of the slopes of ℓ_1 and ℓ_2 is equal to -1. Hence *if two nonvertical lines are perpendicular, then the product of the slopes of the two lines is equal to* -1.

The converse, *if two nonvertical lines have slopes whose product is equal to* -1, *then the two lines are perpendicular*, can be proved by reversing the steps of the preceding argument. The proof of the converse is left to the reader as Exercise 17. Therefore, the following theorem is valid.

Theorem 3.4. *Two nonvertical lines in a plane with slopes m_1 and m_2 respectively are perpendicular if and only if $m_1m_2 = -1$.*

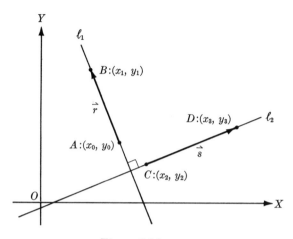

Figure 3.16

Example 1. Find the equation of a line ℓ through the origin and perpendicular to the line $3x + 4y + 6 = 0$.

Since the slope of the line $3x + 4y + 6 = 0$ is $-\dfrac{3}{4}$, the slope m of the line ℓ is $\dfrac{4}{3}$. Hence, by a substitution in the point-slope form, the equation of the line ℓ is

$$y - 0 = \frac{4}{3}(x - 0);$$

that is,

$$4x - 3y = 0.$$

Example 2. Find the equation of the perpendicular bisector of the line segment AB where $A:(1, 1)$ and $B:(-3, 2)$.

Since line segment AB lies along line AB and the slope of line AB is $\dfrac{2 - 1}{-3 - 1}$, that is, $-\dfrac{1}{4}$, the slope of the perpendicular bisector is 4. The midpoint of line segment AB is

$$\left(\frac{1 - 3}{2}, \frac{1 + 2}{2}\right), \quad \text{that is,} \quad \left(-1, \frac{3}{2}\right).$$

By a substitution in the point-slope form, the equation of the perpendicular bisector is $y - \dfrac{3}{2} = 4(x + 1)$. Simplifying, we obtain

$$8x - 2y + 11 = 0.$$

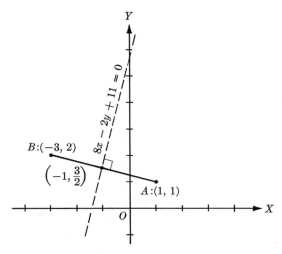

Figure 3.17

Exercises

Determine if the line through the points A and B is parallel or perpendicular to the line through the points C and D.

1. $A:(3, 5)$, $B:(4, 1)$; $C:(-1, 2)$, $D:(-5, 1)$.

2. $A:(4, 2)$, $B:(6, 4)$; $C:(1, 0)$, $D:(5, 4)$.

3. $A:(1, 0)$, $B:(1, 5)$; $C:(2, 0)$, $D:(2, 5)$.

4. $A:(1, 0)$, $B:(1, 5)$; $C:(0, 0)$, $D:(5, 0)$.

5. $A:(-3, -1)$, $B:(1, 1)$; $C:(-3, 1)$, $D:(-5, 5)$.

6. $A:(1, 4)$, $B:(-1, -4)$; $C:(0, 0)$, $D:(0, 4)$.

Determine whether the lines whose equations are given are parallel or perpendicular.

7. $3x - y + 4 = 0$ and $-3x + y + 4 = 0$.

8. $4x + 5y - 1 = 0$ and $5x - 4y - 1 = 0$.

9. $y = 1$ and $x = 3$.

10. $2x + 3y - 7 = 0$ and $6x - 4y + 2 = 0$.

In Exercises 11–14 determine the equation of the line passing through the point P_0 and perpendicular to the line whose equation is given.

11. $P_0:(10, 7)$; $2x - 3y + 1 = 0$. **13.** $P_0:(1, 5)$; $y = 3$.

12. $P_0:(3, -1)$; $2x + 3y - 1 = 0$. **14.** $P_0:(1, 5)$; $x = 3$.

15. Is the triangle whose vertices are $A:(1, 5)$, $B:(5, 3)$, and $C:(2, -3)$ a right triangle? Explain your answer.

16. Determine the equations of the altitudes of triangle ABC where $A:(3, -1)$, $B:(4, 3)$, and $C:(7, -1)$.

17. Prove that if two nonvertical lines have slopes whose product is equal to -1, then the two lines are perpendicular.

In Exercises 18–21 find the equation of the perpendicular bisector of the line segment AB where:

18. $A:(5, 7)$ and $B:(-1, 0)$.   **20.** $A:(3, 4)$ and $B:(10, -\frac{3}{2})$.

19. $A:(3, 2)$ and $B:(7, 2)$.   **21.** $A:(6, -1)$ and $B:(6, 3)$.

3.11 THE ANGLE BETWEEN TWO LINES

When two lines ℓ_1 and ℓ_2 intersect, two pairs of supplementary angles are formed. As shown in Figure 3.18, the measures of these angles are equal to the measures of the angles between vectors perpendicular to the lines. It is our purpose in this section to determine a formula for the measures of the angles between two intersecting lines.

It was noted in §3.3 that the coefficients of x and y in any linear equa- tion are the first and second components of a vector perpendicular to the line which is the graph of the equation. If the equations of two intersecting lines are

$$a_1x + b_1y + c_1 = 0 \quad \text{and} \quad a_2x + b_2y + c_2 = 0,$$

then two vectors $\vec{n}_1$ and $\vec{n}_2$ perpendicular to the two lines respectively are given by

$$\vec{n} = [a_1, b_1] \quad \text{and} \quad \vec{n}_2 = [a_2, b_2].$$

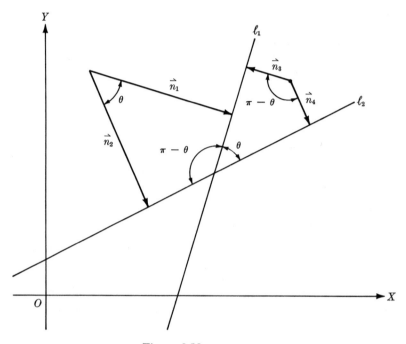

Figure 3.18

The angle between these two vectors, θ, may be found by using the scalar product relationship

$$\vec{n_1} \cdot \vec{n_2} = |\vec{n_1}| \, |\vec{n_2}| \cos \theta.$$

It follows that

$$\cos \theta = \pm \frac{\vec{n_1} \cdot \vec{n_2}}{|\vec{n_1}| \, |\vec{n_2}|}, \tag{3.19}$$

where the $+$ and $-$ signs are considered in order to obtain the measures of the two supplementary angles formed by the lines. In coordinate form, equation (3.19) may be written as

$$\cos \theta = \pm \frac{a_1 a_2 + b_1 b_2}{\sqrt{a_1^2 + b_1^2} \sqrt{a_2^2 + b_2^2}}. \tag{3.20}$$

Note that the lines are perpendicular if and only if $\cos \theta = 0$; that is, if and only if

$$a_1 a_2 + b_1 b_2 = 0.$$

The results of Theorem 3.4 are included in this statement.

Example 1. Find the measure of the acute angle formed by the two intersecting lines $4x - 2y - 1 = 0$ and $3x + y - 1 = 0$.

Since the acute angle of intersection is desired, we may use equation (3.20) with an appropriate choice of sign:

$$\cos \theta = \frac{|a_1a_2 + b_1b_2|}{\sqrt{a_1{}^2 + b_1{}^2}\sqrt{a_2{}^2 + b_2{}^2}}$$

$$= \frac{|(4)(3) + (-2)(1)|}{\sqrt{4^2 + (-2)^2}\sqrt{3^2 + 1^2}}$$

$$= \frac{10}{\sqrt{20}\sqrt{10}} = \frac{1}{\sqrt{2}}.$$

Hence $\theta = \pi/4$.

Example 2. Show that

$$\tan \theta = \left| \frac{m_2 - m_1}{1 + m_1m_2} \right|,$$

where θ is the measure of the acute angle of intersection of the nonvertical lines ℓ_1 and ℓ_2 with slopes m_1 and m_2 respectively.

Let the equations of the nonvertical lines ℓ_1 and ℓ_2 be $y = m_1x + b_1$ and $y = m_2x + b_2$ respectively. Then vectors $\vec{n}_1$ and $\vec{n}_2$ are perpendicular to the lines ℓ_1 and ℓ_2 respectively where

$$\vec{n}_1 = [m_1, -1] \quad \text{and} \quad \vec{n}_2 = [m_2, -1].$$

If θ is the measure of the acute angle of intersection of ℓ_1 and ℓ_2, then, using the scalar product, we have

$$\cos \theta = \frac{|\vec{n}_1 \cdot \vec{n}_2|}{|\vec{n}_1| |\vec{n}_2|} = \frac{|m_1m_2 + 1|}{\sqrt{m_1{}^2 + 1}\sqrt{m_2{}^2 + 1}}.$$

Since $\sin^2 \theta = 1 - \cos^2 \theta$, then

$$\sin^2 \theta = 1 - \frac{(m_1m_2 + 1)^2}{(m_1{}^2 + 1)(m_2{}^2 + 1)} = \frac{m_2{}^2 - 2m_1m_2 + m_1{}^2}{(m_1{}^2 + 1)(m_2{}^2 + 1)}$$

$$= \frac{(m_2 - m_1)^2}{(m_1{}^2 + 1)(m_2{}^2 + 1)};$$

$$\sin \theta = \frac{|m_2 - m_1|}{\sqrt{m_1{}^2 + 1}\sqrt{m_2{}^2 + 1}}.$$

Hence

$$\tan \theta = \frac{\sin \theta}{\cos \theta} = \left| \frac{m_2 - m_1}{1 + m_1 m_2} \right|.$$

If two lines in a plane do not intersect, they are parallel. If the lines $a_1 x + b_1 y + c_1 = 0$ and $a_2 x + b_2 y + c_2 = 0$ are parallel, then the vectors $[a_1, b_1]$ and $[a_2, b_2]$ perpendicular to the lines respectively are parallel, and

$$[a_1, b_1] = t[a_2, b_2]$$

where t is a nonzero real number. Thus

$$\frac{a_1}{a_2} = \frac{b_1}{b_2}$$

represents a necessary condition for two nonvertical and nonhorizontal lines to be parallel. It is also a sufficient condition.

Exercises

1. Find the cosine of the acute angle between the lines whose equations are $x + y + 1 = 0$ and $x - 3y + 1 = 0$.

2. Find the sine of the acute angle between the lines whose equations are $x + y - 1 = 0$ and $x - 2y + 1 = 0$.

Find the measure of the angles formed by the two intersecting lines.

3. $\sqrt{3}x + y = 0$ and $x - 1 = 0$.

4. $2x + 3y + 2 = 0$ and $6x + 4y + 1 = 0$.

5. $x + y - 1 = 0$ and $x = 3$.

6. $x + y - 3 = 0$ and $3x - 3y + 7 = 0$.

In Exercises 7–10 find the equations of the two lines that contain the point A and form the angle α with the line whose equation is given.

7. $A:(0, 1)$, $\alpha = \pi/4$, and $x + y = 0$.

8. $A:(1, 1)$, $\alpha = 3\pi/4$, and $x - y = 1$.

9. $A:(1, 0)$, $\tan \alpha = 3/4$, and $3x - y - 2 = 0$.

10. $A:(4, 2)$, $\cos \alpha = 0$, and $7x + 2y + 3 = 0$.

11. Determine whether or not the line AB, where $A:(6, 3)$ and $B:(-1, 4)$, is perpendicular to the line $2x + 14y - 7 = 0$.

12. Determine whether or not the line AB, where $A:(2, 0)$ and $B:(5, 3)$, is parallel to the line $3x + 3y + 10 = 0$.

3.12   NORMAL FORM OF THE EQUATION OF A LINE

The perpendicular distance from the origin to a line is called the *normal intercept* of the line and is denoted by p. Let the unit position vector $\vec{n}$ perpendicular to the line, as shown in Figure 3.19, form an angle whose measure is ϕ with the positive half of the x axis. Then $\vec{n} = [\cos\phi, \sin\phi]$. If $P:(x, y)$ is a general point on the line ℓ, then the length of the projection of vector $\overrightarrow{OP}$ on vector $\vec{n}$ is equal to p; that is,

$$\frac{|\overrightarrow{OP} \cdot \vec{n}|}{|\vec{n}|} = p.$$

Thus

$$x \cos\phi + y \sin\phi = p,$$
$$x \cos\phi + y \sin\phi - p = 0. \qquad (3.21)$$

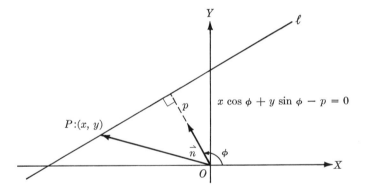

Figure 3.19

Equation (3.21) is called the *normal form* of the equation of a line. The normal form of the equation of a line can be determined immediately if the length p of the shortest line segment from the origin to the line and the angle of inclination ϕ of this segment are known.

Example. Find the equation of the line where $p = 4$ and $\phi = \pi/6$.

$$x \cos(\pi/6) + y \sin(\pi/6) - 4 = 0,$$

$$\frac{\sqrt{3}}{2} x + \frac{1}{2} y - 4 = 0,$$

$$\sqrt{3}x + y - 8 = 0.$$

Exercises

Find the equation of the line given p and ϕ. Graph each equation.

1. $p = 2$; $\phi = \pi/4$.

2. $p = 1$; $\phi = \pi$.

3. $p = 0$; $\phi = \pi/6$.

4. $p = 6$; $\phi = \pi/3$.

In Exercises 5–10 write the normal form of the equation of each line, and find the distance from the origin to the line.

5. $5x + 12y - 13 = 0$.

6. $8x + 6y + 5 = 0$.

7. $x + y = 0$.

8. $x - 5 = 0$.

9. $7x - 24y + 50 = 0$.

10. $y + 7 = 0$.

11. Prove that the distance of the origin from the line $ax + by + c = 0$ is given by $|c|/\sqrt{a^2 + b^2}$.

12. Find the equations of the lines perpendicular to the line $4x - 3y + 8 = 0$ and whose distances from the origin are 3.

3.13 DISTANCE OF A POINT FROM A LINE

Let $ax + by + c = 0$ be the equation of any line in a plane; let $P_1:(x_1, y_1)$ be any point in the plane. In order to determine the shortest distance of the point P_1 from the line, choose any point $P_0:(x_0, y_0)$ on the line. The shortest distance r, as shown in Figure 3.20, is the length of the projection of $\overrightarrow{P_0P_1}$ on $\vec{n}$ where $\vec{n}$ is a unit vector perpendicular to the line. Since

$$\vec{n} = \left[\frac{a}{\sqrt{a^2 + b^2}}, \frac{b}{\sqrt{a^2 + b^2}} \right] \text{ is a unit vector perpendicular to the line,}$$

then

$$r = |\overrightarrow{P_0P_1} \cdot \vec{n}|$$

$$= \left| [x_1 - x_0, y_1 - y_0] \cdot \left[\frac{a}{\sqrt{a^2 + b^2}}, \frac{b}{\sqrt{a^2 + b^2}} \right] \right|$$

$$= \frac{|a(x_1 - x_0) + b(y_1 - y_0)|}{\sqrt{a^2 + b^2}} = \frac{|ax_1 + by_1 - ax_0 - by_0|}{\sqrt{a^2 + b^2}}.$$

Since P_0 lies on the line $ax + by + c = 0$, then $ax_0 + by_0 + c = 0$, and

$$r = \frac{|ax_1 + by_1 + c|}{\sqrt{a^2 + b^2}}. \qquad (3.22)$$

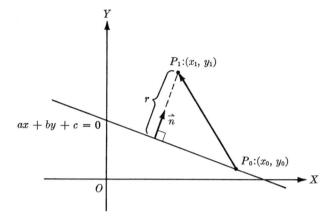

Figure 3.20

Example 1. Find the distance of the point $P_1:(2, 1)$ from the line $3x + 4y - 5 = 0$.

By equation (3.22),

$$r = \frac{|3(2) + 4(1) - 5|}{\sqrt{3^2 + 4^2}} = 1.$$

Example 2. Derive a formula for the distance of the origin from the line $ax + by + c = 0$.

Let r be the distance of the origin from the line. Then by equation (3.22),

$$r = \frac{|a(0) + b(0) + c|}{\sqrt{a^2 + b^2}} = \frac{|c|}{\sqrt{a^2 + b^2}}.$$

The formula for the distance of a point from a line can be used to determine the equations of the pair of lines that bisect the angles formed when two lines ℓ_1 and ℓ_2 intersect. Let $a_1x + b_1y + c_1 = 0$ and $a_2x + b_2y + c_2 = 0$ be the equations of the intersecting lines ℓ_1 and ℓ_2 respectively. If $P:(x, y)$ is a general point on a line bisecting any of the angles formed by lines ℓ_1 and ℓ_2, then the point P must be equidistant from ℓ_1 and ℓ_2, as shown in Figure 3.21. By equation (3.22), the equation

$$\frac{|a_1x + b_1y + c_1|}{\sqrt{a_1^2 + b_1^2}} = \frac{|a_2x + b_2y + c_2|}{\sqrt{a_2^2 + b_2^2}} \qquad (3.23)$$

represents the conditions placed upon $P:(x, y)$. Equation (3.23) is equivalent to the pair of equations

$$\frac{a_1x + b_1y + c_1}{\sqrt{a_1{}^2 + b_1{}^2}} = \pm\frac{a_2x + b_2y + c_2}{\sqrt{a_2{}^2 + b_2{}^2}}. \qquad (3.24)$$

Equation (3.23) or (3.24) represents the equations of the two lines that bisect the angles formed by ℓ_1 and ℓ_2.

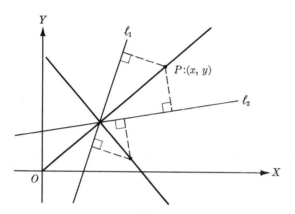

Figure 3.21

Recall from §3.8 that if $b > 0$, then the points whose coordinates satisfy the expression $ax + by + c > 0$ lie in the half-plane above the line $ax + by + c = 0$ and the points whose coordinates satisfy the expression $ax + by + c < 0$ lie in the half-plane below the line. If $ax + by + c > 0$, then $\dfrac{ax + by + c}{\sqrt{a^2 + b^2}} > 0$; if $ax + by + c < 0$, then $\dfrac{ax + by + c}{\sqrt{a^2 + b^2}} < 0$. This information enables us to determine whether the $+$ or the $-$ sign in equation (3.24) is needed to obtain a particular angle bisector. The next example illustrates the procedure.

Example 3. Find the equation of the line that bisects the angle ABC where $A:(4, 6)$, $B:(1, 2)$, and $C:(13, -3)$.

The equations of lines BA and BC are $-4x + 3y - 2 = 0$ and $5x + 12y - 29 = 0$ respectively. Let $P:(x, y)$ be any point on the line that bisects the angle ABC. In general, any point on this angle bisector has coordinates that simultaneously make the expression $-4x + 3y - 2$ negative and the expression $5x + 12y - 29$ positive *or* simultaneously make the expression $-4x + 3y - 2$ positive and the expression $5x + 12y - 29$ negative. Hence the equation of the line that bisects the angle ABC is

$$\frac{-4x + 3y - 2}{\sqrt{(-4)^2 + 3^2}} = -\frac{5x + 12y - 29}{\sqrt{5^2 + 12^2}}.$$

Simplifying, we obtain

$$3x - 11y + 19 = 0.$$

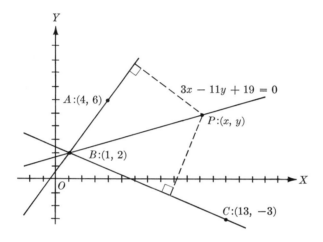

Figure 3.22

Exercises

In Exercises 1–4 find the distance of the point P_1 from the given line.

1. $P_1:(3, -1)$; $5x + 12y - 29 = 0$.

2. $P_1:(5, 4)$; $4x + 3y + 13 = 0$.

3. $P_1:(4, 6)$; $x - 5 = 0$.

4. $P_1:(4, 6)$; $y + 5 = 0$.

5. Determine the values of y if the distance of the point $P_1:(2, y)$ from the line $3x - 4y + 5 = 0$ is 3.

6. Determine the value of x if the distance of the point $P_1:(x, 3)$ from the line $7x + 24y - 36 = 0$ is 2 and the point P_1 is in the same half-plane determined by the line as is the origin.

7. The point $P_1:(3, 1)$ is 2 units from the line $4x + 3y + c = 0$. Find c if the point P_1 and the origin are in the same half-plane determined by the line.

8. A line has parametric equations

$$\begin{cases} x = 3 + 4t \\ y = -1 + 2t. \end{cases}$$

What is the distance of the origin from the line?

9. Derive a formula for the distance between the parallel lines $ax + by + c_1 = 0$ and $ax + by + c_2 = 0$.

In Exercises 10 and 11 use the results of Exercise 9 to determine the distance between the parallel lines.

10. $5x + 12y - 3 = 0$ and $5x + 12y + 10 = 0$.

11. $3x + 4y - 7 = 0$ and $6x + 8y + 26 = 0$.

12. Find the equations of the parallel lines 2 units from the line whose equation is $8x + 6y - 1 = 0$.

In Exercises 13–16 find the equations of the lines that bisect the angles formed by each pair of given lines. Graph each pair of lines and the angle bisectors.

13. $3x - 4y + 5 = 0$ and $5x + 12y - 1 = 0$.

14. $x + 3y - 5 = 0$ and $3x + y - 9 = 0$.

15. $2x + 2y - 1 = 0$ and $2x - 2y + 1 = 0$.

16. $3x + 4y - 12 = 0$ and $4x - 3y + 12 = 0$.

17. Prove that the angle bisectors of the angles formed by any two intersecting lines $a_1 x + b_1 y + c_1 = 0$ and $a_2 x + b_2 y + c_2 = 0$ are perpendicular.

18. Verify the results of Exercise 17 for the angle bisectors of the angles formed by the lines $24x - 7y + 25 = 0$ and $3x + 4y + 12 = 0$.

19. Find the area of the triangle whose vertices are $A:(5, 7)$, $B:(2, 0)$, and $C:(-2, 4)$.

3.14 SYSTEMS OF LINEAR EQUATIONS

The solution of a system of two linear equations in two variables consists of the ordered pairs of values of the variables which satisfy both equations.

Any system of two linear equations in two variables can be expressed in the form

$$\begin{cases} a_1x + b_1y = c_1 \\ a_2x + b_2y = c_2. \end{cases} \tag{3.25}$$

If both members of the first equation are multiplied by b_2, and if both members of the second equation are multiplied by b_1, we obtain

$$\begin{cases} a_1b_2x + b_1b_2y = c_1b_2 \\ b_1a_2x + b_1b_2y = b_1c_2. \end{cases}$$

Subtracting equals from equals, we obtain

$$(a_1b_2 - b_1a_2)x = c_1b_2 - b_1c_2,$$

and, if $a_1b_2 - b_1a_2 \neq 0$,

$$x = \frac{c_1b_2 - b_1c_2}{a_1b_2 - b_1a_2}. \tag{3.26}$$

In a similar manner, the system of linear equations (3.25) is equivalent to

$$\begin{cases} a_1a_2x + b_1a_2y = c_1a_2 \\ a_1a_2x + a_1b_2y = a_1c_2, \end{cases}$$

and, if $a_1b_2 - b_1a_2 \neq 0$,

$$y = \frac{a_1c_2 - c_1a_2}{a_1b_2 - b_1a_2}. \tag{3.27}$$

Each of the expressions in (3.26) and (3.27) for the variables x and y respectively can be written as a quotient of determinants:

$$x = \frac{\begin{vmatrix} c_1 & b_1 \\ c_2 & b_2 \end{vmatrix}}{\begin{vmatrix} a_1 & b_1 \\ a_2 & b_2 \end{vmatrix}}; \tag{3.28}$$

$$y = \frac{\begin{vmatrix} a_1 & c_1 \\ a_2 & c_2 \end{vmatrix}}{\begin{vmatrix} a_1 & b_1 \\ a_2 & b_2 \end{vmatrix}}. \tag{3.29}$$

These quotients of determinants can be used as formulas for the solution of a system of two linear equations in two variables. A unique solution can be found provided that $a_1b_2 - b_1a_2 \neq 0$.

The formulas for x and y can be remembered by comparing the determinants with the coefficients and with the constant terms of the equations.

Note the following:

(i) The denominator is the determinant of the coefficients of x and y arranged as they appear in (3.25). Call this determinant D.

(ii) The numerator for x may be obtained by replacing the column of coefficients of x in the determinant D by the column of constant terms.

(iii) The numerator for y may be obtained by replacing the column of coefficients of y in the determinant D by the column of constant terms.

Example 1. Use determinants to solve the system of equations

$$\begin{cases} x + y = 1 \\ 3x + 2y = 5. \end{cases}$$

$$x = \frac{\begin{vmatrix} 1 & 1 \\ 5 & 2 \end{vmatrix}}{\begin{vmatrix} 1 & 1 \\ 3 & 2 \end{vmatrix}} = \frac{-3}{-1} = 3; \qquad y = \frac{\begin{vmatrix} 1 & 1 \\ 3 & 5 \end{vmatrix}}{\begin{vmatrix} 1 & 1 \\ 3 & 2 \end{vmatrix}} = \frac{2}{-1} = -2.$$

The set of formulas (3.28) and (3.29) for the solution of a system of two linear equations in two variables is a special case of a rule known as *Cramer's rule*, which is applicable to the solution of certain systems of n linear equations in n variables. Each variable is equal to a quotient of determinants such that: (i) the denominator is the determinant of coefficients; (ii) the numerator is the determinant of the coefficients with the column of coefficients of the unknown which is being found replaced by the column of constant terms.

Example 2. Solve the following system of equations by Cramer's rule:

$$\begin{cases} x + 2y - z = 4 \\ 2x - y + 3z = 3 \\ 7x - 2y + 4z = 7. \end{cases}$$

The denominator for x, y, and z is

$$\begin{vmatrix} 1 & 2 & -1 \\ 2 & -1 & 3 \\ 7 & -2 & 4 \end{vmatrix} = -4 + 42 + 4 - 7 - (-6) - 16 = 25.$$

Then

$$x = \frac{\begin{vmatrix} 4 & 2 & -1 \\ 3 & -1 & 3 \\ 7 & -2 & 4 \end{vmatrix}}{25} = 1;$$

$$y = \frac{\begin{vmatrix} 1 & 4 & -1 \\ 2 & 3 & 3 \\ 7 & 7 & 4 \end{vmatrix}}{25} = 2;$$

$$z = \frac{\begin{vmatrix} 1 & 2 & 4 \\ 2 & -1 & 3 \\ 7 & -2 & 7 \end{vmatrix}}{25} = 1.$$

If a system of linear equations is such that the equations are satisfied by at least one set of values of the variables, then the system of equations is said to be *consistent*. If the equations are not satisfied simultaneously by any set of values of the variables, then the system of equations is said to be *inconsistent*.

Consider again the general set of linear equations in two variables:

$$\begin{cases} a_1 x + b_1 y = c_1 \\ a_2 x + b_2 y = c_2. \end{cases} \tag{3.30}$$

According to Cramer's rule, if $D \neq 0$, a unique solution exists, and the system of equations is consistent. Furthermore, the equations of the system are linearly independent. For if k_1 and k_2 exist such that

$$k_1(a_1 x + b_1 y - c_1) + k_2(a_2 x + b_2 y - c_2) = 0$$

and $k_1 k_2 \neq 0$, then

$$a_1 = -\frac{k_2}{k_1} a_2, \qquad b_1 = -\frac{k_2}{k_1} b_2,$$

and

$$D = \begin{vmatrix} a_1 & b_1 \\ a_2 & b_2 \end{vmatrix} = \begin{vmatrix} -\dfrac{k_2}{k_1} a_2 & -\dfrac{k_2}{k_1} b_2 \\ a_2 & b_2 \end{vmatrix} = 0.$$

Therefore, $D = 0$ is a necessary condition for two linear equations in two variables to be linearly dependent. It is not, however, a sufficient condition.

If $D = 0$, it follows that a unique solution does not exist. (Why?) Furthermore,

$$\frac{a_1}{a_2} = \frac{b_1}{b_2} = k$$

where k is a nonzero real number. Now, if either

$$\begin{vmatrix} c_1 & b_1 \\ c_2 & b_2 \end{vmatrix} \quad \text{or} \quad \begin{vmatrix} a_1 & c_1 \\ a_2 & c_2 \end{vmatrix}$$

vanishes, then so does the other determinant, and

$$\frac{a_1}{a_2} = \frac{b_1}{b_2} = \frac{c_1}{c_2} = k.$$

Therefore, some k exists such that

$$(a_1x + b_1y - c_1) + k(a_2x + b_2y - c_2) = 0;$$

that is, the equations are linearly dependent. However, the system is consistent since infinitely many solutions satisfy both equations simultaneously.

If $D = 0$, but neither

$$\begin{vmatrix} c_1 & b_1 \\ c_2 & b_2 \end{vmatrix} \quad \text{nor} \quad \begin{vmatrix} a_1 & c_1 \\ a_2 & c_2 \end{vmatrix}$$

vanishes, then the system is inconsistent. While $a_1/a_2 = b_1/b_2 = k$, $c_1/c_2 \neq k$; that is,

$$\frac{a_1}{a_2} = \frac{b_1}{b_2} \neq \frac{c_1}{c_2},$$

and the equations are linearly independent.

In summary, the system of equations (3.30) may be characterized in one of three ways:

(i)   If $\dfrac{a_1}{a_2} \neq \dfrac{b_1}{b_2}$, the system is consistent and has one and only one solution; the equations are linearly independent.

(ii)   If $\dfrac{a_1}{a_2} = \dfrac{b_1}{b_2} \neq \dfrac{c_1}{c_2}$, the system is inconsistent, that is, no solution exists; the equations are linearly independent.

(iii)   If $\dfrac{a_1}{a_2} = \dfrac{b_1}{b_2} = \dfrac{c_1}{c_2}$, the system is consistent and has infinitely many solutions; the equations are linearly dependent.

Geometrically, the system of equations in (3.30) may be represented by two lines in the plane. Case (i) occurs when the two lines intersect in a unique point whose coordinates are the solution of the system of equations (Figure 3.23). Case (ii) is represented by two distinct parallel lines (Figure 3.24). Finally, if the two lines are coincident, the coordinates of the infinitely many points the lines have in common represent the unlimited number of solutions of the system of equations noted in case (iii) (Figure 3.25).

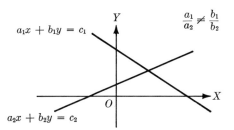

Figure 3.23

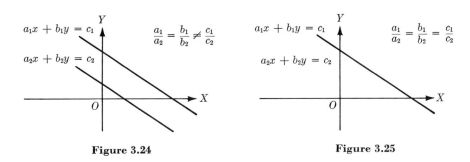

Figure 3.24   **Figure 3.25**

In order to discuss the questions of consistency of systems of linear equations in three or more variables and linear independence of the equations, it is best to consider the concept of the rank of a matrix first. (See §7.7.)

Example 3. Show that the system of equations

$$\begin{cases} 3x - 2y = 5 \\ 6x - 4y = 8 \end{cases}$$

is inconsistent.

The system is inconsistent since the determinant of coefficients

$$\begin{vmatrix} 3 & -2 \\ 6 & -4 \end{vmatrix}$$

vanishes, while neither

$$\begin{vmatrix} 5 & -2 \\ 8 & -4 \end{vmatrix} \quad \text{nor} \quad \begin{vmatrix} 3 & 5 \\ 6 & 8 \end{vmatrix}$$

vanishes. The equations represent a pair of parallel lines. This can also be seen by writing these equations in slope-intercept form:

$$\begin{cases} y = \frac{3}{2}x - \frac{5}{2} \\ y = \frac{3}{2}x - 2. \end{cases}$$

While the slopes of both lines equal $\frac{3}{2}$, the lines have different y intercepts.

Exercises

Solve each system of linear equations by Cramer's rule.

1. $\begin{cases} 3x - y + 2z = 3 \\ x + y - 3z = 3 \\ 2x + 2y + 3z = -12. \end{cases}$ **2.** $\begin{cases} x + y + z = 2 \\ x + y - z = 0 \\ x - y + z = \; 2. \end{cases}$

In Exercises 3–6 state whether each system of equations is **(a)** consistent or inconsistent; **(b)** dependent or independent. Interpret each system geometrically.

3. $\begin{cases} x - 2y - 5 = 0 \\ 2x + y + 1 = 0. \end{cases}$ **5.** $\begin{cases} x + 2y \quad\;\; = 0 \\ 2x + 4y - 3 = 0. \end{cases}$

4. $\begin{cases} 3x - y + 1 = 0 \\ 9x - 3y + 3 = 0. \end{cases}$ **6.** $\begin{cases} x + 2by = a^2 + b^2 \\ x - by = a^2 - b^2. \end{cases}$

7. Determine the equation of the line passing through the point of intersection of the lines $x + y - 2 = 0$ and $2x + 3y - 9 = 0$ and the point $(1, 4)$.

8. Determine the equation of the line that is perpendicular to the line $5x - 3y + 10 = 0$ and contains the point of intersection of the lines $2x - 5y - 4 = 0$ and $3x + y - 6 = 0$.

9. Find the coordinates of the point on the line $7x + 2y + 4 = 0$ that is equidistant from $A:(0, 1)$ and $B:(-6, 3)$.

10. Find the coordinates of the two points on the line $3x + 2y + 3 = 0$ that are 6 units from the line $7x - 24y - 15 = 0$.

11. Verify that the medians of the triangle ABC, where $A:(3, -5)$, $B:(1, 7)$, and $C:(8, 4)$, are concurrent.

12. Find the coordinates of the point of intersection of the medians of the triangle whose vertices are $A:(x_1, y_1)$, $B:(x_2, y_2)$, and $C:(x_3, y_3)$.

13. Verify that the perpendicular bisectors of the sides of the triangle ABC, where $A:(3, 0)$, $B:(1, -2)$, and $C:(7, 6)$, are concurrent.

14. Verify that the altitudes of the triangle ABC, where $A:(5, 4)$, $B:(3, -2)$, and $C:(0, -6)$, are concurrent.

15. Verify that the angle bisectors of the interior angles of the triangle ABC, where $A:(2, 7)$, $B:(-4, 3)$, and $C:(5, 1)$, are concurrent.

Graph each system of inequalities.

16. $\begin{cases} x > 2 \\ x + y - 3 > 0. \end{cases}$

18. $\begin{cases} |x| \leq 1 \\ 2x - 5y - 10 > 0. \end{cases}$

17. $\begin{cases} 3x + y < 2 \\ 6x + 2y \geq 7. \end{cases}$

19. $\begin{cases} x + 3y \geq 3 \\ x - 3y \leq 3 \\ 3x - y \leq 3. \end{cases}$

3.15   FAMILIES OF LINES

A set of lines with a common property is called a *family of lines*. The set of lines in Example 2 of §3.6 is an example of a family of lines; the property which the lines have in common is that they have the same y intercept.

> **Example 1.** On a single coordinate plane, graph the family of lines $2x + y + k = 0$ where $k = -3, -2, -1, 0, 1, 2, 3$.
>
> The property which the seven lines have in common is that they have the same slope, namely -2. The set of lines represent a family of parallel lines (Figure 3.26).

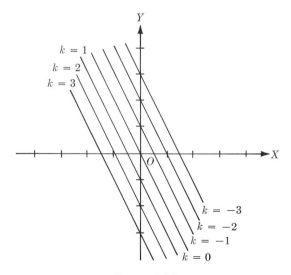

Figure 3.26

The system of linear equations

$$\begin{cases} 2x + y - 8 = 0 \\ 3x - 2y - 5 = 0 \end{cases}$$

is a consistent system of independent equations. The unique point of intersection of the lines is $(3, 2)$, as in Figure 3.27. Since $k_1(2x + y - 8) = 0$,
where k_1 is any nonzero real number, is equivalent to the equation $2x + y - 8 = 0$, and since $k_2(3x - 2y - 5) = 0$, where k_2 is any
nonzero real number, is equivalent to the equation $3x - 2y - 5 = 0$, then
the given system of linear equations is equivalent to

$$\begin{cases} k_1(2x + y - 8) = 0 \\ k_2(3x - 2y - 5) = 0. \end{cases}$$

Furthermore, any point common to the graphs of both equations has
coordinates which satisfy the equation

$$k_1(2x + y - 8) + k_2(3x - 2y - 5) = 0,$$

where k_1 and k_2 are real numbers such that k_1 and k_2 are not both zero.
Therefore, the set of lines of the form just given is a family of lines. The
property which these lines have in common is that they all pass through
the point $(3, 2)$. In Figure 3.27, several members of this family of lines are
illustrated for particular values of k_1 and k_2.

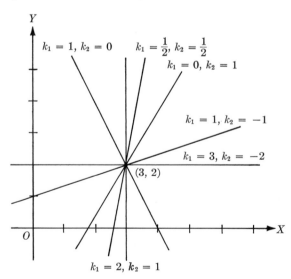

Figure 3.27

In general, the set of lines of the form

$$k_1(a_1x + b_1y + c_1) + k_2(a_2x + b_2y + c_2) = 0, \qquad (3.31)$$

where k_1 and k_2 are real numbers such that k_1 and k_2 are not both zero, represents a family of lines with one point in common if and only if the set of linear equations

$$\begin{cases} a_1x + b_1y + c_1 = 0 \\ a_2x + b_2y + c_2 = 0 \end{cases}$$

is a consistent system of independent equations. The set of lines of the form (3.31) represents a family of parallel lines if and only if the set of linear equations is an inconsistent system and provided that $k_1a_1 \neq -k_2a_2$.

Example 2. On a single coordinate plane, graph the family of lines $k_1(2x - y + 2) + k_2(4x - 2y + 11) = 0$ where

(**a**) $k_1 = 1, k_2 = 0$; (**b**) $k_1 = 0, k_2 = 1$; (**c**) $k_1 = \frac{1}{2}, k_2 = \frac{1}{2}$;
(**d**) $k_1 = 4, k_2 = -1$; (**e**) $k_1 = 10, k_2 = -3$.

Since the system of linear equations

$$\begin{cases} 2x - y + 2 = 0 \\ 4x - 2y + 11 = 0 \end{cases}$$

is an inconsistent system, the family of lines is a family of parallel lines, as shown in Figure 3.28.

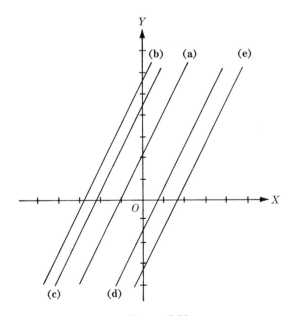

Figure 3.28

Exercises

1. Describe the family of lines $5x - 4y + k = 0$ where k is any real number.

2. On a single coordinate plane, graph the family of lines in Exercise 1 with $k = -4, -2, 0, 2, 4$.

3. Describe the family of lines

$$k_1(2x + 7y + 5) + k_2(x - y - 2) = 0$$

where k_1 and k_2 are real numbers such that k_1 and k_2 are not both zero.

4. On a single coordinate plane, graph the family of lines in Exercise 3 with
   (a) $k_1 = 1, k_2 = 0$;
   (b) $k_1 = 0, k_2 = 1$;
   (c) $k_1 = 3, k_2 = -2$;
   (d) $k_1 = 2, k_2 = -4$;
   (e) $k_1 = 1, k_2 = 7$;
   (f) $k_1 = \frac{1}{2}, k_2 = \frac{1}{3}$.

5. Describe the family of lines

$$k_1(x + 3y + 9) + k_2(2x + 6y) = 0$$

where k_1 and k_2 are real numbers and $k_1 \neq -2k_2$.

6. On a single coordinate plane, graph the family of lines in Exercise 5 with
   (a) $k_1 = 1, k_2 = 0$;
   (b) $k_1 = 0, k_2 = 1$;
   (c) $k_1 = \frac{1}{2}, k_2 = \frac{1}{2}$;
   (d) $k_1 = 2, k_2 = 3$;
   (e) $k_1 = 5, k_2 = -2$;
   (f) $k_1 = 2, k_2 = 1$.

In Exercises 7–10 write a form of the equation of the family of lines subject to the given condition.

7. Having slope equal to -2.

8. Passing through the point $(6, -1)$.

9. Parallel to the line $8x + 3y + 2 = 0$.

10. Perpendicular to the line $11x - 7y - 3 = 0$.

11. On a single coordinate plane, graph the family of equations

$$y = |x + k| \quad \text{where } k = -3, -2, -1, 0, 1, 2, 3.$$

12. On a single coordinate plane, graph the family of equations

$$y = |x| + k \quad \text{where } k = -3, -2, -1, 0, 1, 2, 3.$$

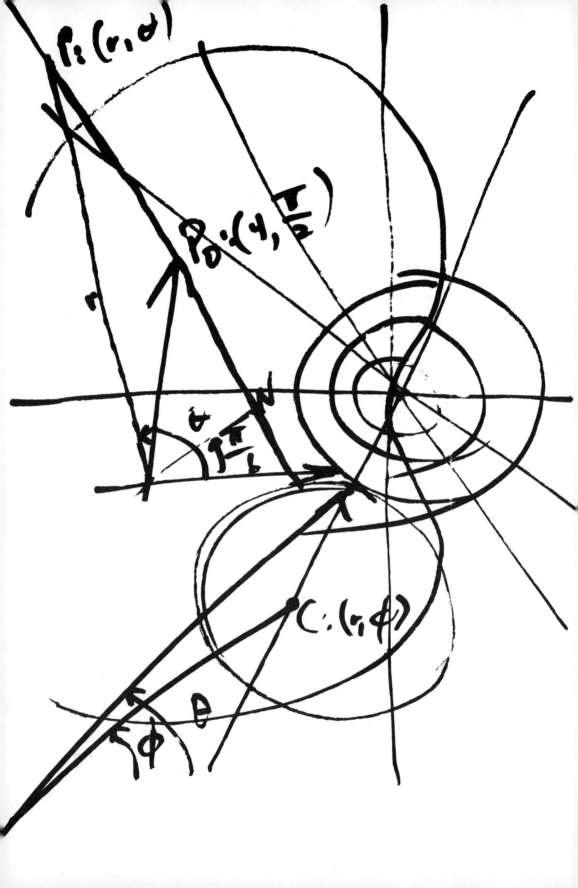

POLAR COORDINATES

4.1 POLAR COORDINATES

In Chapter 1, linear coordinate systems for the plane were studied in detail, and it was suggested that other types of coordinate systems exist for the line, for the plane, and for space. The choice of a particular coordinate system depends upon the relative advantages of that system compared to another coordinate system. The most frequently used alternatives to the linear coordinate systems for the plane, in general, and for the rectangular Cartesian coordinate systems, in particular, are the *polar coordinate systems*.

In a rectangular Cartesian coordinate system, the coordinates of a point P:(a, b) represent the directed distances of the point from two perpendicular reference lines, the x axis and the y axis respectively. The location of point P can be specified by another pair of numbers in the following manner. Choose a fixed point O called the *pole*. Select a ray, called the *polar axis*, with O as the endpoint, as shown in Figure 4.1. Then the *polar coordinates* of the point P are (r, θ), where r represents the distance between the point P and the pole O, and θ represents the measure of the directed angle from the polar axis to the ray OP.

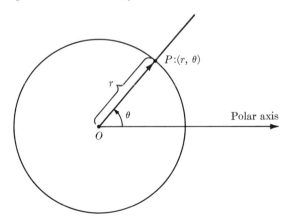

Figure 4.1

This association of ordered pairs of real numbers (r, θ) with the points in the plane is called a *polar coordinate system*. Recall that the association of the ordered pairs of real numbers (x, y) with the points in the plane by means of any linear coordinate system was a one-to-one correspondence. This is not the case with a polar coordinate system. For example, other polar coordinates of $P:(r, \theta)$ are $P:(r, \theta + 2\pi)$ and $P:(r, \theta - 2\pi)$. Indeed, any integral multiple of 2π may be added to θ so that, in general, the polar coordinates of point P in Figure 4.1 are all of the form $(r, \theta + 2\pi t)$ where t is an integer. Furthermore, it is sometimes convenient to consider the first component of the polar coordinates of a point as a negative number. We shall adopt the convention that if r is negative, distance from the pole is measured in a direction opposite to the ray which is the terminal side of the angle θ; that is, the point (r, θ) where r is positive is the same as the point $(-r, \theta + \pi)$.

Example 1. Locate the points A, B, and C whose polar coordinates are $(2, \pi/6)$, $(3, 9\pi/2)$, and $(-2, \pi/3)$ respectively.

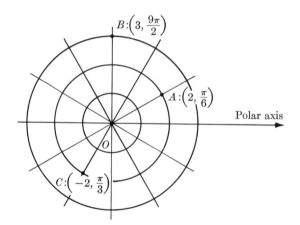

Figure 4.2

Note that the polar coordinates of points B and C can also be expressed in the form $(3, \pi/2)$ and $(2, 4\pi/3)$ respectively.

It is possible to establish a relationship between the rectangular Cartesian coordinates of any point P in the plane and the polar coordinates of P. Consider the origin of the rectangular Cartesian coordinate system as coinciding with the pole of the polar coordinate system, and let the positive half of the x axis coincide with the polar axis, as shown in Figure 4.3.

The rectangular Cartesian coordinates and the polar coordinates of P are (x, y) and (r, θ) respectively. Since triangle OQP is a right triangle, the relationship between (x, y) and (r, θ) is expressed by the pair of equations

$$\begin{cases} x = r \cos \theta \\ y = r \sin \theta, \end{cases} \tag{4.1}$$

or

$$\begin{cases} r = \sqrt{x^2 + y^2} \\ \theta = \arctan{(y/x)}. \end{cases} \tag{4.2}$$

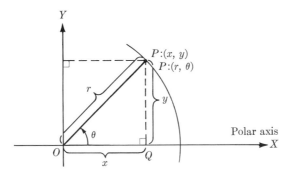

Figure 4.3

Example 2. Find the rectangular Cartesian coordinates (x, y) of the point P whose polar coordinates are $(-2, 7\pi/3)$.

Using equations (4.1), we have

$$\begin{cases} x = -2 \cos{(7\pi/3)} = -1 \\ y = -2 \sin{(7\pi/3)} = -\sqrt{3}. \end{cases}$$

Therefore, the rectangular Cartesian coordinates of P are $(-1, -\sqrt{3})$.

Example 3. Determine a formula for the distance between the points $P_1:(r_1, \theta_1)$ and $P_2:(r_2, \theta_2)$.

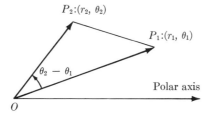

Figure 4.4

The distance $|P_1P_2|$ in Figure 4.4 can be determined by the law of cosines:

$$|P_1P_2|^2 = |OP_1|^2 + |OP_2|^2 - 2|OP_1|\,|OP_2|\cos(\theta_2 - \theta_1)$$
$$= r_1^2 + r_2^2 - 2r_1r_2\cos(\theta_2 - \theta_1);$$
$$|P_1P_2| = \sqrt{r_1^2 + r_2^2 - 2r_1r_2\cos(\theta_2 - \theta_1)}.$$

Example 4. Prove that

$$\cos(\theta - \phi) = \cos\theta\cos\phi + \sin\theta\sin\phi.$$

Let $A:(x_1, y_1)$ and $B:(x_2, y_2)$ be any two points in the plane, as shown in Figure 4.5. Then, by the distance formula,

$$|AB|^2 = (x_2 - x_1)^2 + (y_2 - y_1)^2.$$

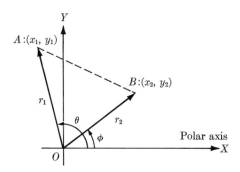

Figure 4.5

Let the polar coordinates of points A and B be (r_1, θ) and (r_2, ϕ) respectively. Then

$$|AB|^2 = (r_2\cos\phi - r_1\cos\theta)^2 + (r_2\sin\phi - r_1\sin\theta)^2$$
$$= r_2^2\cos^2\phi - 2r_1r_2\cos\theta\cos\phi + r_1^2\cos^2\theta$$
$$\quad + r_2^2\sin^2\phi - 2r_1r_2\sin\theta\sin\phi + r_1^2\sin^2\theta$$
$$= r_1^2(\cos^2\theta + \sin^2\theta) + r_2^2(\cos^2\phi + \sin^2\phi)$$
$$\quad - 2r_1r_2(\cos\theta\cos\phi + \sin\theta\sin\phi)$$
$$= r_1^2 + r_2^2 - 2r_1r_2(\cos\theta\cos\phi + \sin\theta\sin\phi).$$

However, by the law of cosines,

$$|AB|^2 = |OA|^2 + |OB|^2 - 2|OA|\,|OB|\cos(\theta - \phi)$$
$$= r_1^2 + r_2^2 - 2r_1r_2\cos(\theta - \phi).$$

Hence, by comparing the expressions for $|AB|^2$, we have

$$\cos(\theta - \phi) = \cos\theta\cos\phi + \sin\theta\sin\phi.$$

If $f(x, y) = 0$ is the equation of a geometric figure with reference to a rectangular Cartesian coordinate system, then $f(r \cos \theta, r \sin \theta) = 0$ is the *polar coordinate form* of the equation, or *polar equation*, of that figure since $x = r \cos \theta$ and $y = r \sin \theta$.

Example 5. Sketch the graph of the polar equation

$$r = 2 - 2 \cos \theta.$$

Several points on the graph of this equation can be obtained from the following table of values for r and θ.

θ	0	$\dfrac{\pi}{6}$	$\dfrac{\pi}{4}$	$\dfrac{\pi}{3}$	$\dfrac{\pi}{2}$	$\dfrac{2\pi}{3}$	$\dfrac{3\pi}{4}$	$\dfrac{5\pi}{6}$	π
r	0	0.27	0.59	1	2	3	3.41	3.73	4

Since $\cos \theta = \cos(-\theta)$, the graph of the equation is *symmetric* with respect to the polar axis. Once again, if we assume that the graph of the given equation is a smooth continuous curve, then the table furnishes us enough points to sketch the graph (Figure 4.6).

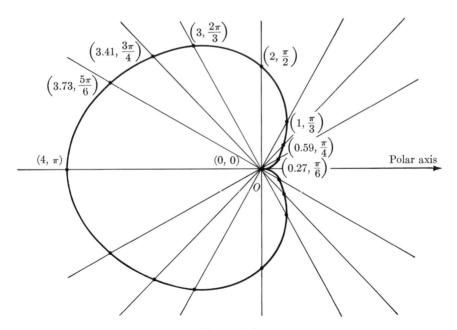

Figure 4.6

Exercises

1. Locate the points with polar coordinates
   (a) $A:(3, \pi/3)$;
   (b) $B:(-2, 3\pi/2)$;
   (c) $C:(1, 33\pi/6)$;
   (d) $D:(-5, -\pi/2)$;
   (e) $E:(-1, 0)$;
   (f) $F:(0, \pi)$;
   (g) $G:(-4, -3\pi/4)$;
   (h) $H:(2, 2\pi)$.

2. Find the rectangular Cartesian coordinates (x, y) of the point whose polar coordinates are
   (a) $(2, \pi/3)$;
   (b) $(-1, 9\pi/4)$;
   (c) $(3, 11\pi)$;
   (d) $(-5, -\pi/2)$;
   (e) $(-1, 0)$;
   (f) $(1, \pi)$;
   (g) $(0, 2\pi)$;
   (h) $(\sqrt{3}, -7\pi/3)$.

3. Find the polar coordinates (r, θ) of the point whose rectangular Cartesian coordinates are
   (a) $(-\sqrt{2}, \sqrt{2})$;
   (b) $(3, 3)$;
   (c) $(2, -2)$;
   (d) $(0, 4)$;
   (e) $(1, 0)$;
   (f) $(\sqrt{3}, 1)$;
   (g) $(-\sqrt{3}, 1)$;
   (h) $(1, \sqrt{3})$.

4. Determine the distance between the points A and B with polar coordinates
   (a) $A:(3, \pi/4)$ and $B:(3, 3\pi/4)$;
   (b) $A:(1, \pi/2)$ and $B:(2, \pi/4)$;
   (c) $A:(0, \pi)$ and $B:(5, 2\pi)$;
   (d) $A:(3, 5\pi/6)$ and $B:(-2, \pi/3)$.

5. Graph each polar equation.
   (a) $r = a \sin 2\theta$;
   (b) $r = a \cos 2\theta$;
   (c) $r = a \sin 3\theta$;
   (d) $r = a \cos 3\theta$;
   (e) $r = a \sin 4\theta$;
   (f) $r = a \cos 4\theta$;
   (g) $r = a \sin 5\theta$;
   (h) $r = a \cos 5\theta$.
   Describe the graph of each *rose curve* $r = a \sin n\theta$ and $r = a \cos n\theta$, where n is a positive integer.

In Exercises 6–9 graph each polar equation.

6. $r^2 = 4 \cos 2\theta$ (*lemniscate*).

7. $r = 3\theta$ (*spiral of Archimedes*).

8. $r = 2 + 2 \cos \theta$ (*cardioid*).

9. $r = 1 + 3 \cos \theta$ (*limaçon*).

10. Show that the area of the triangle whose vertices are $(0, 0)$, (r_1, θ_1), and (r_2, θ_2) is equal to $|\frac{1}{2}r_1r_2 \sin(\theta_2 - \theta_1)|$.

11. Use the results of Exercise 10 to find the area of the triangle whose vertices are $(0, 0)$, $(4, 7\pi/6)$, and $(-5, -\pi/3)$.

4.2   POLAR COORDINATE FORM OF THE EQUATION OF A LINE

Consider the line ℓ and the ray ON from the pole perpendicular to ℓ, as shown in Figure 4.7. The ray ON intersects line ℓ at the point $N:(p, \phi)$. Note that p is the fixed distance of the pole from the line ℓ, and ϕ is the angle that the ray ON makes with the polar axis. Let $P:(r, \theta)$ be a general point on the line. Since triangle ONP is a right triangle, then

$$r \cos (\theta - \phi) = p. \tag{4.3}$$

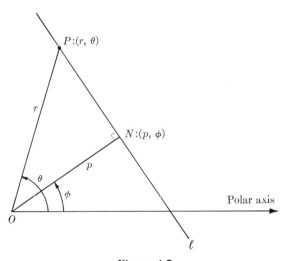

Figure 4.7

Equation (4.3) is a *polar coordinate form of the equation of line* ℓ. If $p = 0$, then the line ℓ contains the pole, and its equation is

$$\cos (\theta - \phi) = 0.$$

This equation is equivalent to the statement that θ is a constant. Thus the polar coordinate form of the equation of every line through the pole is $\theta = k$ where k is a real number.

Example 1. Determine a polar coordinate form of the equation of the line ℓ which intersects the ray from the pole perpendicular to ℓ at the point $N:(3, \pi/4)$.

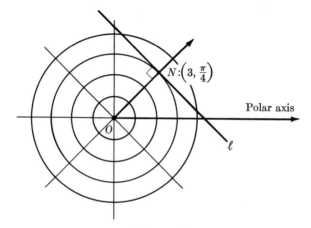

Figure 4.8

Since $p = 3$ and $\phi = \pi/4$, a polar coordinate form of the equation of line ℓ is $r \cos (\theta - \pi/4) = 3$.

Example 2. Determine a polar coordinate form of the equation of the line ℓ that contains the point $P_0:(2\sqrt{3}, \pi/3)$ and is perpendicular to the polar axis (Figure 4.9).

Let $P:(r, \theta)$ be any point on the line ℓ. Then

$$r \cos \theta = 2\sqrt{3} \cos (\pi/3)$$
$$= (2\sqrt{3})(\tfrac{1}{2}) = \sqrt{3}.$$

Hence $r \cos \theta = \sqrt{3}$ is a polar coordinate form of the equation of line ℓ.

In general, it can be shown that the polar coordinate form of the equation of every line perpendicular to the polar axis is

$$r \cos \theta = k,$$

where k is a real number (Exercise 7). The polar coordinate form of the equation of every line parallel to the polar axis is

$$r \sin \theta = k$$

where k is a real number (Exercise 10).

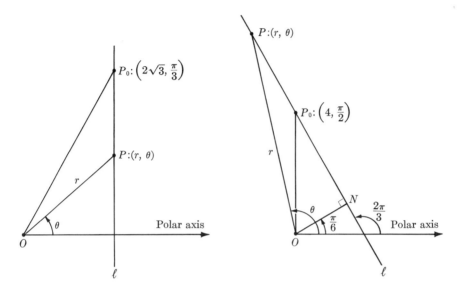

Figure 4.9   Figure 4.10

Example 3. Determine a polar coordinate form of the equation of the line ℓ that contains the point P_0:$(4, \pi/2)$ and makes an angle whose measure is $2\pi/3$ with the polar axis (Figure 4.10).

Let P:(r, θ) be any point on the line. Then

$$r \cos (\theta - \pi/6) = |ON| = 4 \sin (\pi/6) = 2.$$

Hence $r \cos (\theta - \pi/6) = 2$ is a polar coordinate form of the equation of line ℓ.

It is interesting to note that since

$$\cos (\theta - \phi) = \cos \theta \cos \phi + \sin \theta \sin \phi,$$

equation (4.3) may be expressed in the form

$$r(\cos \theta \cos \phi + \sin \theta \sin \phi) = p,$$
$$(r \cos \theta) \cos \phi + (r \sin \theta) \sin \phi = p,$$
$$x \cos \phi + y \sin \phi - p = 0.$$

This equation represents the normal form of the equation of a line, which was derived in §3.12.

Exercises

In Exercises 1–4 determine a polar coordinate form of the equation of the line ℓ which intersects the perpendicular from the pole at the given point N.

1. $N:(2, \pi/3)$.

2. $N:(1, 5\pi)$.

3. $N:(1, -9\pi/2)$.

4. $N:(2, 0)$.

5. Determine a polar coordinate form of the equation of the line ℓ that contains the point $P_0:(6, \pi/3)$ and is perpendicular to the polar axis.

6. Determine a polar coordinate form of the equation of the line ℓ that contains the point $P_0:(\sqrt{2}, 3\pi/4)$ and is perpendicular to the polar axis.

7. Prove that the polar coordinate form of the equation of every line perpendicular to the polar axis is $r \cos \theta = k$ where k is a real number.

8. Determine a polar coordinate form of the equation of the line ℓ that contains the point $P_0:(4, \pi/6)$ and is parallel to the polar axis.

9. Determine a polar coordinate form of the equation of the line ℓ that contains the point $P_0:(-3, \pi/2)$ and is parallel to the polar axis.

10. Prove that the polar coordinate form of the equation of every line parallel to the polar axis is $r \sin \theta = k$ where k is a real number.

11. Find a polar coordinate form of the equation of the line determined by the pole and the point $P_0:(6, \pi/4)$.

12. Derive the polar coordinate form of the equation of every line that contains the pole.

13. Determine a polar coordinate form of the equation of the line that contains $P_0:(3, \pi/4)$ and makes an angle whose measure is $5\pi/6$ with the polar axis.

14. Derive a formula for the distance d of the point $P_1:(r_1, \theta_1)$ from the line whose equation in polar coordinate form is $r \cos (\theta - \phi) = p$.

15. Use the results of Exercise 14 to find the distance of the point $P_1:(4\sqrt{3}, \pi/2)$ from the line $r \cos (\theta - \pi/6) = 1$.

4.3   THE EQUATION OF A CIRCLE

The equation of a circle, in terms of a rectangular Cartesian coordinate system, and some of the properties of a circle will be derived in this section by vector methods. In Chapter 6 the circle will be studied again as a special case of the ellipse.

Let $P:(x, y)$ be any point on the circle with center at the point $C:(x_0, y_0)$ and radius r, as shown in Figure 4.11. Then a vector form of the equation of a circle is

$$\overrightarrow{CP} \cdot \overrightarrow{CP} = r^2. \tag{4.4}$$

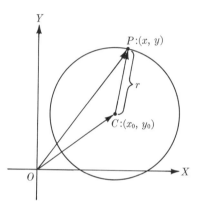

Figure 4.11

Since $\overrightarrow{CP} = [x - x_0, y - y_0]$, equation (4.4) may be written as

$$[x - x_0, y - y_0] \cdot [x - x_0, y - y_0] = r^2,$$
$$(x - x_0)^2 + (y - y_0)^2 = r^2. \tag{4.5}$$

This equation represents a rectangular Cartesian coordinate form of the equation of a circle with center at $C:(x_0, y_0)$ and radius r.

> **Example 1.** Determine the equation of the circle with center at $C:(2, -1)$ and radius 5.
>
> By equation (4.5), where $x_0 = 2$, $y_0 = -1$, and $r = 5$,
>
> $$(x - 2)^2 + (y + 1)^2 = 5^2;$$
> hence
> $$x^2 + y^2 - 4x + 2y - 20 = 0$$
>
> is the equation of the circle.

Example 2. Determine the center and the radius of the circle whose equation is $x^2 + y^2 + 6x - 2y - 26 = 0$.

Rearranging the terms of the equation, we obtain

$$x^2 + 6x + y^2 - 2y = 26.$$

Completing the square in x and in y respectively, we obtain

$$(x^2 + 6x + 9) + (y^2 - 2y + 1) = 36,$$
$$(x + 3)^2 + (y - 1)^2 = 6^2,$$
$$(x - (-3))^2 + (y - 1)^2 = 6^2.$$

Thus the center of the circle is at the point $C:(-3, 1)$, and the radius is equal to 6.

The equation of each circle in Examples 1 and 2 is of the form

$$x^2 + y^2 + Dx + Ey + F = 0. \tag{4.6}$$

The equation of every circle is of this form; however, not every equation of this form has a circle as its graph. Note that, by completing the square in x and in y respectively, we obtain

$$\left(x^2 + Dx + \frac{D^2}{4}\right) + \left(y^2 + Ey + \frac{E^2}{4}\right) = \frac{D^2}{4} + \frac{E^2}{4} - F,$$
$$\left(x + \frac{D}{2}\right)^2 + \left(y + \frac{E}{2}\right)^2 = \frac{D^2 + E^2 - 4F}{4}.$$

The graph of this equation is a circle provided that $D^2 + E^2 - 4F > 0$. (Why?) Furthermore, the center of the circle is $\left(-\frac{D}{2}, -\frac{E}{2}\right)$, and the radius is $\frac{\sqrt{D^2 + E^2 - 4F}}{2}$. If $D^2 + E^2 - 4F = 0$, the graph of the equation is the point $\left(-\frac{D}{2}, -\frac{E}{2}\right)$. If $D^2 + E^2 - 4F < 0$, the graph of the equation in the real plane is the null set; that is, no real points exist on the graph.

From elementary geometry, we know that three distinct noncollinear points determine a circle. Equation (4.6) can be used to determine the equation of a circle that contains three distinct noncollinear points, as illustrated in the following example.

Example 3. Determine an equation of the circle that contains the points $M:(0, 1)$, $N:(1, 0)$, and $R:(2, 1)$.

Since M, N, and R lie on the circle, the coordinates of each point must satisfy an equation of the form $x^2 + y^2 + Dx + Ey + F = 0$. If the coordinates of each point are substituted for x and y, a system of three linear equations in D, E, and F is obtained:

$$\begin{cases} (0)^2 + (1)^2 + D(0) + E(1) + F = 0 \\ (1)^2 + (0)^2 + D(1) + E(0) + F = 0 \\ (2)^2 + (1)^2 + D(2) + E(1) + F = 0; \end{cases}$$

that is,

$$\begin{cases} E + F = -1 \\ D \quad\quad + F = -1 \\ 2D + E + F = -5. \end{cases}$$

The solution of this system of equations is given by $D = -2$, $E = -2$, and $F = 1$. Hence an equation of the circle that contains M, N, and R is

$$x^2 + y^2 - 2x - 2y + 1 = 0;$$

that is,

$$(x - 1)^2 + (y - 1)^2 = 1.$$

The circle has its center at the point $C:(1, 1)$, and the radius is equal to 1, as shown in Figure 4.12.

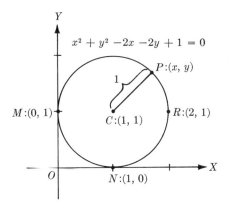

Figure 4.12

Exercises

Determine the equation of the circle with center at C and radius equal to r.

1. $C:(2, 4)$; $r = 6$.

2. $C:(-3, -1)$; $r = \frac{1}{3}$.

3. $C:(\frac{1}{2}, \frac{1}{3})$; $r = 4$.

4. $C:(0, 0)$; $r = 2$.

Determine the equation of the circle with center at C and passing through the point P_0.

5. $C:(2, 4); P_0:(0, 0)$.   7. $C:(4, -3); P_0:(0, 5)$.

6. $C:(-1, 1); P_0:(1, 1)$.   8. $C:(\pi, \pi); P_0:(\pi, 2\pi)$.

Find the center and the radius of the circle whose equation is given.

9. $x^2 + y^2 - 8x + 2y - 8 = 0$.

10. $x^2 + y^2 + 4y = 0$.

11. $2x^2 + 2y^2 + x + y = 0$.

12. $x^2 + y^2 - 2x - 2y - 10 = 0$.

In Exercises 13 and 14 find an equation of the circle that contains the non-collinear points M, N, and R:

13. $M:(2, 3)$, $N:(1, 4)$, and $R:(5, 2)$.

14. $M:(9, -7)$, $N:(6, 2)$, and $R:(-3, -1)$.

15. For what values of k is the graph of the equation $2x^2 + 2y^2 + 4x + 6y + k = 0$ a point?

16. Find the equation of the circle with diameter AB where $A:(3, -1)$ and $B:(9, 5)$.

17. Determine the equation of the set of points $P:(x, y, z)$ such that $\overrightarrow{AP} \cdot \overrightarrow{BP} = 0$ where $A:(1, 6)$ and $B:(5, 0)$.

18. Determine the set of points whose coordinates satisfy the statement (a) $x^2 + y^2 < 1$; (b) $x^2 + y^2 + 6x - 4y - 17 \geq 0$. Graph each set of points.

19. Show that the equation of the set of points $P:(x, y)$ such that the distance of each point from $A:(3, -1)$ is three times its distance from $B:(5, 5)$ is a circle.

20. Find the shortest distance from the point $(9, 13)$ to the circle

$$x^2 + y^2 - 6x - 10y - 15 = 0.$$

21. Find the equation of the circle passing through the points $A:(6, 2)$ and $B:(-1, 1)$ and whose radius is 5.

22. Show that the equation of the circle that contains the noncollinear points (x_1, y_1), (x_2, y_2), and (x_3, y_3) may be written in the form

$$\begin{vmatrix} x^2 + y^2 & x & y & 1 \\ x_1^2 + y_1^2 & x_1 & y_1 & 1 \\ x_2^2 + y_2^2 & x_2 & y_2 & 1 \\ x_3^2 + y_3^2 & x_3 & y_3 & 1 \end{vmatrix} = 0.$$

23. Use the results of Exercise 22 to find the equation of the circle determined by the points in **(a)** Exercise 13; **(b)** Exercise 14.

24. Determine the equation of the circumscribed circle of the triangle whose vertices are $A:(3, 7)$, $B:(10, 0)$, and $C:(-7, -17)$.

25. Find the equation of the circle passing through the points $A:(1, 5)$ and $B:(5, 3)$ and whose center lies on the line $2x - 3y - 12 = 0$.

26. Show that any point common to the graphs of the nonconcentric circles $x^2 + y^2 + D_1x + E_1y + F_1 = 0$ and $x^2 + y^2 + D_2x + E_2y + F_2 = 0$ satisfies the equation

$$k_1(x^2 + y^2 + D_1x + E_1y + F_1) + k_2(x^2 + y^2 + D_2x + E_2y + F_2) = 0,$$

where k_1 and k_2 are real numbers such that k_1 and k_2 are not both zero.
(a) If $k_1 \neq -k_2$, the graph of this equation is called a *family of circles*. Describe the graph of the family of circles.
(b) If $k_1 = -k_2$, the graph of this equation is called a *radical axis*. Describe the graph of the radical axis.

27. On a single coordinate plane, graph the family of circles

$$k_1(x^2 + y^2 - 8x + 6) + k_2(x^2 + y^2 - 2x - 6y + 6) = 0$$

where **(a)** $k_1 = 1, k_2 = 0$; **(b)** $k_1 = 0, k_2 = 1$; **(c)** $k_1 = 2, k_2 = 1$; **(d)** $k_1 = -3, k_2 = -2$; **(e)** $k_1 = 3, k_2 = -1$. Describe the location of the centers of these circles.

28. Determine the equation of the radical axis of the two nonconcentric circles $x^2 + y^2 + 6x - 10y - 16 = 0$ and $x^2 + y^2 - 12x - 16y + 80 = 0$.

29. Show that the radical axis of the two nonconcentric circles in Exercise 28 is perpendicular to the line segment whose endpoints are the centers of the circle.

30. Verify that the three radical axes of the circles $x^2 + y^2 + 5x - 2y + 3 = 0$, $x^2 + y^2 + 4x + 8 = 0$, and $x^2 + y^2 + 2x - 3y + 4 = 0$ taken in pairs are concurrent.

31. Describe each family of circles.
(a) $x^2 + y^2 + Dx + F = 0$;   **(c)** $x^2 + y^2 + Dx + Ey = 0$;
(b) $x^2 + y^2 + Ey + F = 0$;   **(d)** $x^2 + y^2 + F = 0$.

4.4 TANGENT LINES TO A CIRCLE

Consider the problem of determining an equation of the line ℓ that is tangent at the point $T:(2, 3)$ to the circle with center at $C:(1, 0)$, as shown in Figure 4.13. Let $P:(x, y)$ be a general point on the *tangent line* ℓ. Line ℓ is tangent to the circle at $T:(2, 3)$ if and only if $\overrightarrow{TP}$ is perpendicular to the vector $\overrightarrow{CT}$, the *radius vector* to the point of tangency. Therefore,

$$\overrightarrow{TP} \cdot \overrightarrow{CT} = 0 \tag{4.7}$$

represents a vector form of the tangent line. Since $\overrightarrow{TP} = [x - 2, y - 3]$ and $\overrightarrow{CT} = [2 - 1, 3 - 0] = [1, 3]$,

$$[x - 2, y - 3] \cdot [1, 3] = 0,$$
$$(x - 2) + 3(y - 3) = 0;$$

that is, $x + 3y - 11 = 0$ represents a rectangular Cartesian coordinate form of the equation of the tangent line ℓ.

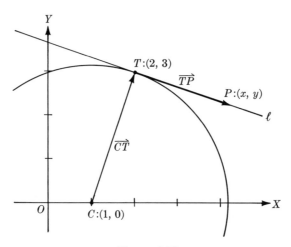

Figure 4.13

The procedure in the preceding problem can be generalized to obtain a coordinate form of the line ℓ that is tangent at $T:(x_1, y_1)$ to a circle with center at $C:(x_0, y_0)$. If $P:(x, y)$ is a general point on the tangent line, equation (4.7) represents a vector form of the tangent line. Now, $\overrightarrow{TP} = [x - x_1, y - y_1]$, $\overrightarrow{CT} = [x_1 - x_0, y_1 - y_0]$, and

$$\vec{TP} \cdot \vec{CT} = [x - x_1, y - y_1] \cdot [x_1 - x_0, y_1 - y_0] = 0,$$

whereby

$$(x - x_1)(x_1 - x_0) + (y - y_1)(y_1 - y_0) = 0 \qquad (4.8)$$

represents a rectangular Cartesian coordinate form of the equation of the tangent line ℓ.

Example 1. Determine the equation of the line tangent at T:(2, 3) to the circle whose equation is $x^2 + y^2 - 10x - 14y + 49 = 0$.

Since the equation $x^2 + y^2 - 10x - 14y + 49 = 0$ is equivalent to $(x - 5)^2 + (y - 7)^2 = 25$, the center of the circle is at the point C:(5, 7). Using equation (4.8), we find the equation of the tangent line to be

$$(x - 2)(2 - 5) + (y - 3)(3 - 7) = 0;$$

that is,

$$3x + 4y - 18 = 0.$$

Example 2. Find equations of two distinct lines ℓ_1 and ℓ_2 that are parallel to $x - y - 1 = 0$ and tangent to the circle whose equation is $x^2 + y^2 + 4y = 0$ (Figure 4.14).

Since the lines ℓ_1 and ℓ_2 are parallel to $x - y - 1 = 0$, they are of the form $x - y + k = 0$. The equation of the circle $x^2 + y^2 + 4y = 0$ is equivalent to $x^2 + (y + 2)^2 = 4$. Therefore, the center of the circle $x^2 + y^2 + 4y = 0$ is at C:(0, −2), and the radius is equal to 2. Using (3.22), the distance from the center C to each tangent line $x - y + k = 0$ is expressed by the formula

$$2 = \frac{|(0) - (-2) + k|}{\sqrt{(1)^2 + (-1)^2}}.$$

Thus

$$|k + 2| = 2\sqrt{2},$$
$$k = -2 \pm 2\sqrt{2}.$$

Hence the equations of the tangent lines ℓ_1 and ℓ_2 are

$$x - y + (-2 + 2\sqrt{2}) = 0$$

and

$$x - y + (-2 - 2\sqrt{2}) = 0.$$

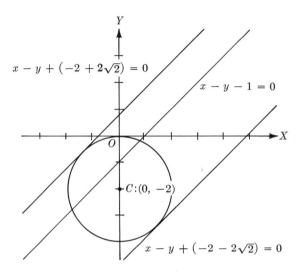

Figure 4.14

Exercises

Determine the equation of the line tangent at T to the circle whose center is the point C.

1. $T:(2, 3)$; $C:(1, 0)$.   3. $T:(-1, -1)$; $C:(2, 3)$.

2. $T:(3, -1)$; $C:(0, 1)$.   4. $T:(1, 1)$; $C:(0, 2)$.

In Exercises 5–8 determine the equation of the line tangent at T to the circle whose equation is given.

5. $T:(1, 5)$; $x^2 + y^2 - 26 = 0$.

6. $T:(3, 4)$; $x^2 + y^2 - 6x - 10y + 33 = 0$.

7. $T:(0, 0)$; $x^2 + y^2 - 2x = 0$.

8. $T:(0, -2)$; $x^2 + y^2 + 2x + 2y = 0$.

9. Find the equation of the line tangent at $T:(x_1, y_1)$ to the circle whose equation is $x^2 + y^2 = r^2$.

10. Determine the equation of the circle with center at $C:(-1, 3)$ and which is tangent to the line $5x - 12y + 2 = 0$.

11. Determine the equation of the circle with center at $C:(2, 4)$ and which is tangent to the line passing through the points $A:(0, -1)$ and $B:(6, 1)$.

12. Determine the values of c for which the line $3x + 3y + c = 0$ is tangent to the circle $x^2 + y^2 + 4x - 4y - 8 = 0$.

13. Find equations of two distinct lines ℓ_1 and ℓ_2 that are parallel to $6x - 8y + 3 = 0$ and tangent to the circle whose equation is $x^2 + y^2 + 9x - 2y - 15 = 0$.

14. Find equations of two distinct lines ℓ_1 and ℓ_2 that are perpendicular to $3x - 6y + 1 = 0$ and tangent to the circle whose equation is $x^2 + y^2 + 4x - 4y - 8 = 0$.

15. Prove that if d is the length of the tangent line segment from the point $P_1:(x_1, y_1)$ to the circle $x^2 + y^2 + Dx + Ey + F = 0$, then

$$d^2 = x_1{}^2 + y_1{}^2 + Dx_1 + Ey_1 + F.$$

16. Use the results of Exercise 15 to find the length of the tangent line segment from the point $P_1:(7, 1)$ to the circle $x^2 + y^2 - 4x - 2y - 4 = 0$. Check your results by a direct application of the Pythagorean theorem.

17. Find the equations of the tangent lines from $P_1:(6, -4)$ to the circle with center at $C:(1, -4)$ and radius equal to 3.

18. Determine the equation of the inscribed circle of the triangle whose vertices are $A:(11, -7)$, $B:(23, 9)$, and $C:(-1, 2)$.

19. Find the equation of the circle tangent to both coordinate axes and to the line $4x - 3y + 24 = 0$.

4.5 POLAR COORDINATE FORM OF THE EQUATION OF A CIRCLE

Let $P:(r, \theta)$ be a general point on a circle of radius a with center at $C:(r_1, \phi)$ in a polar coordinate system (Figure 4.15). The vectors $\overrightarrow{OP}$, $\overrightarrow{OC}$, and $\overrightarrow{CP}$ form a triangle. Hence the vector relationship among these vectors is represented by

$$\overrightarrow{OP} - \overrightarrow{OC} = \overrightarrow{CP}. \tag{4.9}$$

Taking the scalar product of each side with itself yields

$$(\overrightarrow{OP} - \overrightarrow{OC}) \cdot (\overrightarrow{OP} - \overrightarrow{OC}) = \overrightarrow{CP} \cdot \overrightarrow{CP},$$

$$\overrightarrow{OP} \cdot \overrightarrow{OP} + \overrightarrow{OC} \cdot \overrightarrow{OC} - 2\overrightarrow{OP} \cdot \overrightarrow{OC} = \overrightarrow{CP} \cdot \overrightarrow{CP},$$

$$|OP|^2 + |OC|^2 - 2|OP|\,|OC| \cos (\theta - \phi) = |CP|^2.$$

Since $|OP| = r$, $|OC| = r_1$, and $|CP| = a$, a polar coordinate form of the equation of the circle of radius a with center at $C:(r_1, \phi)$ is

$$r^2 + r_1^2 - 2rr_1 \cos (\theta - \phi) = a^2. \qquad (4.10)$$

Several special cases of this equation are of particular interest because of the simplified form of the equation which arises.

(i)   If the center of the circle is at the pole, then $r_1 = 0$ and the equation of the circle is $r^2 = a^2$; that is,

$$r = a. \qquad (4.11)$$

(ii)   If the center of the circle is at $(a, 0)$, then the equation of the circle is

$$r^2 + a^2 - 2ra \cos \theta = a^2;$$

that is,

$$r = 2a \cos \theta. \qquad (4.12)$$

(iii)   If the center of the circle is at $(a, \pi/2)$, then the equation of the circle is

$$r^2 + a^2 - 2ra \cos (\theta - \pi/2) = a^2,$$

$$r^2 - 2ra \sin \theta = 0;$$

that is,

$$r = 2a \sin \theta. \qquad (4.13)$$

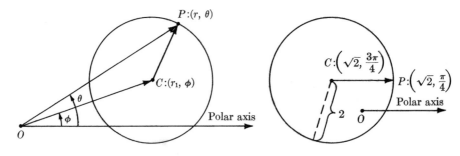

Figure 4.15   **Figure 4.16**

Example. Given a polar coordinate system, determine a polar coordinate form of the equation of the circle that contains the point $P:(\sqrt{2}, \pi/4)$ and whose center is at $C:(\sqrt{2}, 3\pi/4)$, as shown in Figure 4.16.

The magnitude of the radius vector $\overrightarrow{CP}$ may be determined by using the formula for the distance between two points in a polar coordinate system (Example 3 of §4.1):

$$|CP|^2 = r_1{}^2 + r_2{}^2 - 2r_1r_2 \cos (\theta_2 - \theta_1)$$

where $(r_1, \theta_1) = (\sqrt{2}, 3\pi/4)$ and $(r_2, \theta_2) = (\sqrt{2}, \pi/4)$. Thus

$$|CP|^2 = (\sqrt{2})^2 + (\sqrt{2})^2 - 2(\sqrt{2})(\sqrt{2}) \cos (\pi/4 - 3\pi/4)$$
$$= 2 + 2 - 4(0) = 4;$$

that is, $|CP| = 2$. Hence, using (4.10), the equation of the circle is

$$r^2 + 2 - 2\sqrt{2}\, r \cos (\theta - 3\pi/4) = 4,$$
$$r^2 - 2\sqrt{2}\, r \cos (\theta - 3\pi/4) = 2.$$

Exercises

Determine a polar coordinate form of the equation of the circle with center at C and radius equal to a.

1. $C:(2, \pi/6)$; $a = 3$.

2. $C:(1, \pi/2)$; $a = 1$.

3. $C:(-1, \pi/3)$; $a = 2$.

4. $C:(\pi, \pi)$; $a = \pi$.

5. $C:(2, 0)$; $a = 2$.

6. $C:(0, 0)$; $a = 4$.

In Exercises 7–10 determine the polar equation of the circle with center at C and passing through the point P_0.

7. $C:(1, \pi/6)$; $P_0:(3, 2\pi/3)$.

8. $C:(-1, \pi)$; $P_0:(2, \pi)$.

9. $C:(3, 5\pi/4)$; $P_0:(1, \pi/4)$.

10. $C:(3, 7\pi/4)$; $P_0:(8, \pi/4)$.

11. Find the polar coordinates of the centers of several circles whose radius is 5 and which pass through the point $P_0:(1, \pi)$. What is the equation of the locus of these points?

12. Find the center and radius of the circle
$$r^2 - 3r \cos \theta - 3\sqrt{3}\, r \sin \theta - 16 = 0.$$

13. Determine the polar coordinate form of the equation of the circle with center at $C:(4, \pi/6)$ and tangent to the polar axis.

14. Prove that a polar coordinate form of the equation of a circle determined by the pole, $A:(a, 0)$, and $B:(b, \pi/2)$ is $r = a \cos \theta + b \sin \theta$.

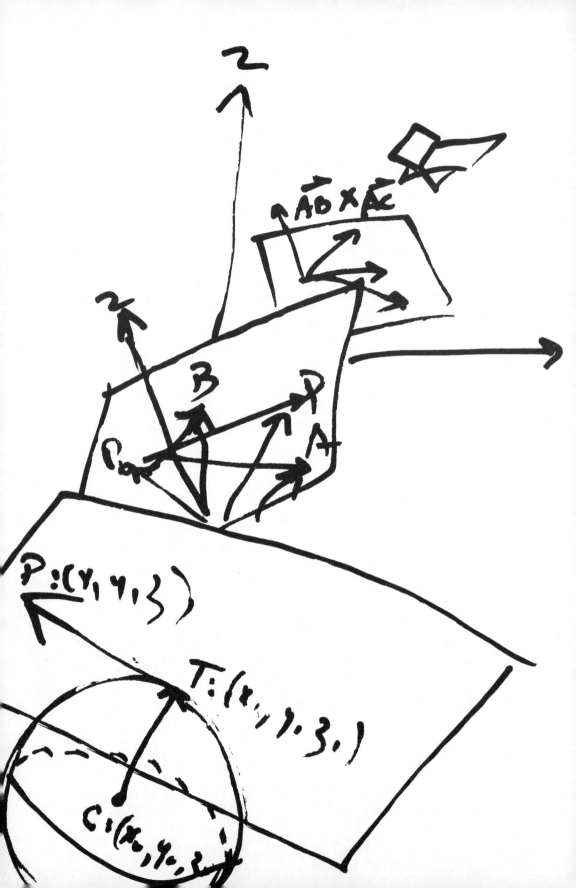

$$Z$$

$$\vec{Ab} \times \vec{Ac}$$

$$Z$$

$$B$$

$$P$$

$$P_o$$

$$A$$

$$P:(Y, Y, 3)$$

$$T:(x, Y, 3,)$$

$$C:(x_o, Y_o, 3,)$$

PLANES AND LINES IN SPACE

5.1 PARAMETRIC EQUATIONS OF A PLANE

In this section and in subsequent sections of this chapter, several vector forms of the equation of a plane will be developed. As in the case of the line in Chapter 3, the various rectangular Cartesian coordinate forms of the equation of a plane will be derived along with the vector forms.

Infinitely many planes exist that are parallel to two given nonzero, nonparallel vectors. However, only one plane exists that is parallel to these vectors and contains a given point. Let $\vec{a}$ and $\vec{b}$ be any two nonzero, nonparallel vectors. Consider a point $P_0:(x_0, y_0, z_0)$ in a plane π parallel to the plane determined by $\vec{a}$ and $\vec{b}$, as shown in Figure 5.1. If $P:(x, y, z)$ is a

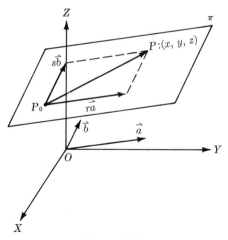

Figure 5.1

general point in the plane π, then

$$\overrightarrow{P_0P} = r\vec{a} + s\vec{b} \tag{5.1}$$

where r and s are arbitrary real numbers. Since $\overrightarrow{OP} = \overrightarrow{OP_0} + \overrightarrow{P_0P}$, then

$$\overrightarrow{OP} = \overrightarrow{OP_0} + r\vec{a} + s\vec{b}. \tag{5.2}$$

Equations (5.1) and (5.2) represent vector forms of the equation of the plane π.

Note that the vector form (5.1) of the equation of a plane through a given point and parallel to two nonzero, nonparallel vectors requires the use of two parameters, while the vector form (3.1) of the equation of a line through a given point and parallel to a nonzero vector requires the use of only one parameter.

A coordinate form of the equation of the plane, as shown in Figure 5.1, can be derived from equation (5.1) or (5.2), resulting in a set of parametric equations. The procedure is illustrated in the following example.

Example 1. Determine a set of parametric equations of the plane that contains the point P_0:(2, -4, 3) and parallels the plane determined by vectors $\vec{a}$ and $\vec{b}$ where $\vec{a} = [1, 4, 2]$ and $\vec{b} = [3, -1, 5]$.

Let P:(x, y, z) be a general point on the plane. Then, by equation (5.2),

$$\overrightarrow{OP} = \overrightarrow{OP_0} + r\vec{a} + s\vec{b},$$
$$[x, y, z] = [2, -4, 3] + r[1, 4, 2] + s[3, -1, 5]$$
$$= [2 + r + 3s, -4 + 4r - s, 3 + 2r + 5s].$$

By equating corresponding components, we obtain

$$\begin{cases} x = 2 + r + 3s \\ y = -4 + 4r - s \\ z = 3 + 2r + 5s. \end{cases}$$

This is a set of parametric equations of the plane that contains the point P_0 and is parallel to the plane determined by vectors $\vec{a}$ and $\vec{b}$.

Three noncollinear points determine a unique plane. It is thus possible to find the equation of the plane when the coordinates of the three points

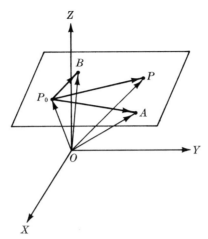

Figure 5.2

are known. Let $P_0:(x_0, y_0, z_0)$, $A:(x_1, y_1, z_1)$, and $B:(x_2, y_2, z_2)$ be three non-collinear points, and let $P:(x, y, z)$ be a general point of the plane P_0AB, as shown in Figure 5.2. Since $\overrightarrow{P_0A}$ and $\overrightarrow{P_0B}$ are vectors in the plane, they may be used in place of the vectors $\vec{a}$ and $\vec{b}$ respectively in equation (5.2). Hence

$$\overrightarrow{OP} = \overrightarrow{OP_0} + r\overrightarrow{P_0A} + s\overrightarrow{P_0B}$$
$$= \overrightarrow{OP_0} + r(\overrightarrow{OA} - \overrightarrow{OP_0}) + s(\overrightarrow{OB} - \overrightarrow{OP_0}).$$

Simplifying, we have

$$\overrightarrow{OP} = (1 - r - s)\overrightarrow{OP_0} + r\overrightarrow{OA} + s\overrightarrow{OB} \tag{5.3}$$

where r and s are arbitrary real numbers. Equation (5.3) represents a vector form of the equation of a plane through the points P_0, A, and B. Note that the sum of the real multiples of $\overrightarrow{OP_0}$, $\overrightarrow{OA}$, and $\overrightarrow{OB}$ is 1. Furthermore, note the similarity between equation (5.3) and the vector form of the equation of a line through two distinct points, equation (3.6). Since $\overrightarrow{OP_0} = [x_0, y_0, z_0]$, $\overrightarrow{OA} = [x_1, y_1, z_1]$, $\overrightarrow{OB} = [x_2, y_2, z_2]$, and $\overrightarrow{OP} = [x, y, z]$, then

$$[x, y, z] = (1 - r - s)[x_0, y_0, z_0] + r[x_1, y_1, z_1] + s[x_2, y_2, z_2].$$

Hence, equating corresponding components, we obtain a set of parametric equations of a plane through three points:

$$\begin{cases} x = (1 - r - s)x_0 + rx_1 + sx_2 \\ y = (1 - r - s)y_0 + ry_1 + sy_2 \\ z = (1 - r - s)z_0 + rz_1 + sz_2. \end{cases} \tag{5.4}$$

Each point on the plane corresponds to a particular set of values of the parameters r and s. For example, if $r = 0$ and $s = 0$, the coordinates of point P_0 are obtained; if $r = 1$ and $s = 0$, the coordinates of point A are obtained; if $r = 0$ and $s = 1$, the coordinates of point B are obtained. Furthermore, if the values of r and s are chosen such that $r + s = 1$, the coordinates of points on line AB in the plane can be obtained.

Example 2. Find a set of parametric equations of the plane that contains the points $P_0:(1, 2, 1)$, $A:(0, -2, 3)$, and $B:(-1, 2, -1)$. Find another point in the plane.

Using equations (5.4), we obtain

$$\begin{cases} x = (1 - r - s)(1) + r(0) + s(-1) \\ y = (1 - r - s)(2) + r(-2) + s(2) \\ z = (1 - r - s)(1) + r(3) + s(-1), \end{cases}$$

which can be written as

$$\begin{cases} x = 1 - r - 2s \\ y = 2 - 4r \\ z = 1 + 2r - 2s. \end{cases}$$

Let $r = 1$ and $s = 1$. Then another point in the plane is $(-2, -2, 1)$.

Exercises

Determine a set of parametric equations of the plane that contains the point P_0 and is parallel to the plane determined by vectors $\vec{a}$ and $\vec{b}$.

1. $P_0:(-5, 4, 6)$; $\vec{a} = [1, -2, -3]$ and $\vec{b} = [3, -1, -2]$.

2. $P_0:(1, 0, 7)$; $\vec{a} = [2, 4, 2]$ and $\vec{b} = [7, -1, -1]$.

3. $P_0:(1, 5, 3)$; $\vec{a} = [3, 8, 0]$ and $\vec{b} = [2, 5, 0]$.

4. $P_0:(3, 2, 4)$; $\vec{a} = [1, 1, 1]$ and $\vec{b} = [3, 0, -1]$.

In Exercises 5–8 find a set of parametric equations of the plane that contains the points P_0, A, and B.

5. P_0:(1, 1, 1), A:(0, 2, 0), and B:(1, 0, 1).

6. P_0:(2, 1, -1), A:(5, 5, 0), and B:(0, -1, -2).

7. P_0:(0, 1, 2), A:(0, -2, 4), and B:(0, 4, 2).

8. P_0:(3, 4, 2), A:(5, -1, 3), and B:(-4, 0, 1).

9. Determine a set of parametric equations of the plane through the points A:(2, 5, 1) and B:(4, 6, 0) and parallel to the z axis.

10. Write a set of parametric equations of the plane that contains the point P_0:(3, 6, 2) and is parallel to the plane determined by the origin and by the points A:(1, 2, 3) and B:(4, 2, 1).

5.2 OTHER COORDINATE FORMS OF THE EQUATION OF A PLANE

The rectangular Cartesian coordinate form of the equation of a plane π that contains the point P_0:(x_0, y_0, z_0) and is perpendicular to the vector $\vec{n}$ where $\vec{n} = [a, b, c]$ can be obtained by the use of the scalar product. Let P:(x, y, z) be a general point in the plane π, as shown in Figure 5.3. Since

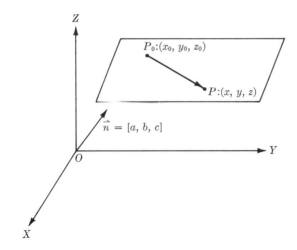

Figure 5.3

$\vec{n}$ is perpendicular to every vector in the plane π, then

$$\vec{n} \cdot \overrightarrow{P_0P} = 0. \qquad (5.5)$$

This equation is a vector form of the equation of the plane π. Now, $\overrightarrow{P_0P} = [x - x_0,\, y - y_0,\, z - z_0]$; thus, by equation (5.5),

$$a(x - x_0) + b(y - y_0) + c(z - z_0) = 0 \qquad (5.6)$$

represents a coordinate form of the equation of the plane through the point P_0 and perpendicular to the vector $\vec{n}$. Equation (5.6) is called the *point-direction number form* of the equation of a plane.

Equation (5.6) may be written in the equivalent form

$$ax + by + cz + d = 0 \qquad (5.7)$$

where $d = -ax_0 - by_0 - cz_0$. This equation is the general linear equation in three variables x, y, and z; the equation is sometimes referred to as the *general coordinate form* of the equation of a plane. Note that the coefficients of x, y, and z in equation (5.7) are the first, second, and third components respectively of a vector perpendicular to the plane.

Theorem 5.1. *In space, the graph of the linear equation $ax + by + cz + d = 0$, where a, b, c, and d are real numbers such that $a^2 + b^2 + c^2 \neq 0$, is a plane.*

Proof: Let $P_0:(x_0,\, y_0,\, z_0)$ satisfy the given linear equation. Then

$$ax_0 + by_0 + cz_0 + d = 0,$$

and

$$(ax + by + cz + d) - (ax_0 + by_0 + cz_0 + d) = 0,$$
$$a(x - x_0) + b(y - y_0) + c(z - z_0) = 0.$$

However, if a, b, and c are not all zero, this equation represents the equation of a plane through P_0 and perpendicular to the vector $[a,\, b,\, c]$.

Example 1. Find the equation of the plane π passing through $P_0:(2, 2, 1)$ and perpendicular to $\overrightarrow{OP_0}$.

Let $P:(x, y, z)$ be a general point in the plane. If the plane π is perpendicular to $\overrightarrow{OP_0}$, then

$$\overrightarrow{OP_0} \cdot \overrightarrow{P_0P} = 0.$$

Since $\overrightarrow{OP_0} = [2,\ 2,\ 1]$ and $\overrightarrow{P_0P} = [x - 2,\ y - 2,\ z - 1]$, then

$$[2,\ 2,\ 1] \cdot [x - 2,\ y - 2,\ z - 1] = 0,$$

$$2(x - 2) + 2(y - 2) + 1(z - 1) = 0,$$

$$2x + 2y + z - 9 = 0.$$

Example 2. Determine a unit vector perpendicular to the plane $3x + 6y - 2z + 10 = 0$.

A vector $\vec{n}$ perpendicular to the plane is $[3,\ 6,\ -2]$. Since $|\vec{n}| = \sqrt{3^2 + 6^2 + (-2)^2} = 7$, a unit vector perpendicular to the plane is given by the equation

$$\frac{\vec{n}}{|\vec{n}|} = \frac{1}{7}[3,\ 6,\ -2] = \left[\frac{3}{7}, \frac{6}{7}, -\frac{2}{7}\right].$$

As in the case of the line in the plane, there exists an intercept form of the equation of a plane in space. If $abcd \neq 0$, the equation of the plane $ax + by + cz + d = 0$ can be expressed in the form

$$\frac{x}{e} + \frac{y}{f} + \frac{z}{g} = 1, \tag{5.8}$$

where $e = -(d/a)$, $f = -(d/b)$, and $g = -(d/c)$. Equation (5.8) is called the *intercept form* of the equation of a plane since e, f, and g are the x, y, and z intercepts respectively. The intercept form of the equation of a plane does not exist if the plane is parallel to a coordinate axis. (Why?)

Example 3. Determine, if possible, the intercept form of the equation of the plane $3x + 4y + 6z - 12 = 0$. Sketch the plane.

If $3x + 4y + 6z - 12 = 0$, then

$$3x + 4y + 6z = 12,$$

$$\frac{3x}{12} + \frac{4y}{12} + \frac{6z}{12} = 1,$$

$$\frac{x}{4} + \frac{y}{3} + \frac{z}{2} = 1.$$

The x, y, and z intercepts are 4, 3, and 2 respectively.

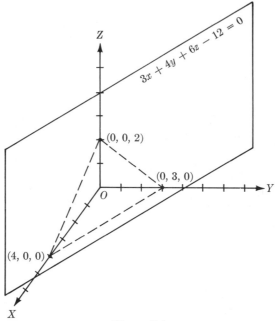

Figure 5.4

Exercises

Find the equation of the plane passing through the point P_0 and perpendicular to the vector $\vec{n}$.

1. P_0:(3, 7, 4); $\vec{n} = [8, 0, -3]$.

2. P_0:(4, 2, 5); $\vec{n} = [4, -1, 1]$.

3. P_0:(6, 3, 2); $\vec{n} = [6, 3, 2]$.

4. P_0:(0, 5, 12); $\vec{n} = [-1, 9, 4]$.

In Exercises 5 and 6 determine a unit vector perpendicular to each plane.

5. $x - 2y + 2z + 8 = 0$.

6. $5x - 12z - 10 = 0$.

7. Find a set of direction numbers of any line perpendicular to the plane $7x - 2y + 3z + 2 = 0$.

8. Find a set of direction cosines of any line perpendicular to the plane $3x - 3y + 1 = 0$.

9. Find the measure of the acute angle θ between $\overrightarrow{AB}$, where $A:(6, 4, -3)$ and $B:(3, -1, 5)$, and a vector perpendicular to the plane $3x - 2y + 6z + 2 = 0$.

10. Find the equation of the set of points equidistant from the points $A:(1, 4, 3)$ and $B:(-3, 0, 1)$.

11. Write the equation of the plane whose x, y, and z intercepts are 2, -1, and 5 respectively.

12. State the conditions placed upon the coefficients of the equation of a plane $ax + by + cz + d = 0$ if
    (a) the plane has an x intercept equal to 1;
    (b) the plane has equal intercepts on the x axis and the y axis;
    (c) the plane has equal intercepts on all three axes.

13. Show that the equation of a plane that contains the origin is of the form $ax + by + cz = 0$.

14. Find the general coordinate form of the equation of a plane that is parallel to the   (a) x axis;   (b) y axis;   (c) z axis;   (d) xy plane;   (e) yz plane;   (f) zx plane.

15. Find the equation of the plane through the points $A:(3, 2, 0)$ and $B:(-1, 1, 0)$ and parallel to the z axis.

16. Find the equation of the plane through the point $A:(1, 3, 5)$ and parallel to the xy plane.

5.3 THE EQUATION OF A PLANE THROUGH THREE POINTS

In §5.1 the equation of a plane through three points was obtained in parametric form by the use of the concept of linear dependence of vectors. The equation of a plane determined by three noncollinear points can also be obtained by the use of the scalar triple product defined in §2.10.

Let $A:(x_1, y_1, z_1)$, $B:(x_2, y_2, z_2)$, and $C:(x_3, y_3, z_3)$ by any three noncollinear points, and let $P:(x, y, z)$ be a general point in the plane determined by the points A, B, and C, as shown in Figure 5.5. The vector $\overrightarrow{AB} \times \overrightarrow{AC}$ is

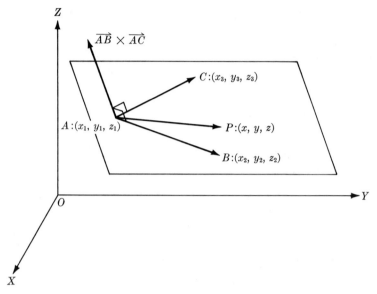

Figure 5.5

perpendicular to the plane. If P is distinct from A, then $\overrightarrow{AP}$ lies in the plane and is perpendicular to the vector $\overrightarrow{AB} \times \overrightarrow{AC}$; if P and A are the same point, then $\overrightarrow{AP}$ is a null vector. In either case,

$$\overrightarrow{AP} \cdot (\overrightarrow{AB} \times \overrightarrow{AC}) = 0. \tag{5.9}$$

Equation (5.9) represents another vector form of the equation of a plane through three points.

Since $\overrightarrow{AP} = [x - x_1, y - y_1, z - z_1]$, $\overrightarrow{AB} = [x_2 - x_1, y_2 - y_1, z_2 - z_1]$, and $\overrightarrow{AC} = [x_3 - x_1, y_3 - y_1, z_3 - z_1]$, equation (5.9) may be expressed in the coordinate form

$$\begin{vmatrix} x - x_1 & y - y_1 & z - z_1 \\ x_2 - x_1 & y_2 - y_1 & z_2 - z_1 \\ x_3 - x_1 & y_3 - y_1 & z_3 - z_1 \end{vmatrix} = 0. \tag{5.10}$$

Note that since $\overrightarrow{AB} \times \overrightarrow{AC}$ is a vector perpendicular to the plane determined by A, B, and C, the components of $\overrightarrow{AB} \times \overrightarrow{AC}$ constitute a set of direction numbers of any line perpendicular to the plane.

Example 1. Find the equation of the plane that contains the points $A:(1, 3, -1)$, $B:(-2, 1, 5)$, and $C:(3, 2, 6)$.

Let $P:(x, y, z)$ be a general point in the plane. Then $\overrightarrow{AP} = [x - 1, y - 3, z + 1]$, $\overrightarrow{AB} = [-3, -2, 6]$, $\overrightarrow{AC} = [2, -1, 7]$, and

$$\overrightarrow{AP} \cdot (\overrightarrow{AB} \times \overrightarrow{AC}) = 0.$$

By using determinants, this equation can be written as

$$\begin{vmatrix} x - 1 & y - 3 & z + 1 \\ -3 & -2 & 6 \\ 2 & -1 & 7 \end{vmatrix} = 0.$$

Expanding this determinant and simplifying, we derive the equation of the plane:

$$8x - 33y - 7z + 84 = 0.$$

Check: Substituting the coordinates of each of the points A, B, and C for x, y, and z, we obtain

$$8(1) - 33(3) - 7(-1) + 84 = 8 - 99 + 7 + 84 = 0;$$
$$8(-2) - 33(1) - 7(5) + 84 = -16 - 33 - 35 + 84 = 0;$$
$$8(3) - 33(2) - 7(6) + 84 = 24 - 66 - 42 + 84 = 0.$$

Example 2. Determine the equation of the plane passing through $M:(2, 1, 1)$, $N:(-3, 3, -1)$, and $R:(4, 1, 5)$ by use of the general coordinate form.

Since M, N, and R lie in the plane, the coordinates of each point must satisfy the equation $ax + by + cz + d = 0$. Therefore,

$$\begin{cases} a(2) + b(1) + c(1) + d = 0 \\ a(-3) + b(3) + c(-1) + d = 0 \\ a(4) + b(1) + c(5) + d = 0. \end{cases} \quad \text{(I)}$$

If $a \neq 0$, that is, if the plane is not parallel to the x axis, then

$$\begin{cases} 2 + B + C + D = 0 \\ -3 + 3B - C + D = 0 \\ 4 + B + 5C + D = 0, \end{cases} \quad \text{(II)}$$

where $B = b/a$, $C = c/a$, and $D = d/a$. Solving for B, C, and D, we obtain $B = 2$, $C = -\frac{1}{2}$, and $D = -\frac{7}{2}$. Hence

$$x + 2y - \tfrac{1}{2}z - \tfrac{7}{2} = 0;$$

that is,

$$2x + 4y - z - 7 = 0$$

is the equation of the plane through the points M, N, and R.

If the plane had been parallel to the x axis, then system (II) would have been inconsistent. In such a case, we can proceed to solve system (I) after deleting the first term of each equation, namely $a(2)$, $a(-3)$, and $a(4)$.

Exercises

Find the equation of the plane that contains the points A, B, and C.

1. A:(1, 2, 0), B:(2, 1, 1), and C:(−1, −3, 5).

2. A:(5, 4, 3), B:(3, 4, 5), and C:(6, 6, 6).

3. A:(−1, 2, 0), B:(11, −2, 5), and C:(2, −2, 3).

4. A:(0, 0, 0), B:(2, 1, −2), and C:(3, 6, 2).

In Exercises 5–8 determine the equation of the plane passing through the points M, N, and R by use of the general coordinate form.

5. M:(2, 1, 3), N:(−2, 1, −3), and R:(4, 0, 0).

6. M:(2, 1, −2), N:(−1, 0, 1), and R:(1, 1, 1).

7. M:(1, 2, 0), N:(2, 2, 1), and R:(3, 1, 2).

8. M:(−1, −1, 2), N:(−3, 4, 1), and R:(2, 1, 5).

9. Determine a unit vector perpendicular to the plane that contains the points A:(3, 0, 2), B:(1, −1, 4), and C:(5, 1, 1).

10. Show that the equation of the plane that contains the noncollinear points (x_1, y_1, z_1), (x_2, y_2, z_2), and (x_3, y_3, z_3) may be written in the form

$$\begin{vmatrix} x & y & z & 1 \\ x_1 & y_1 & z_1 & 1 \\ x_2 & y_2 & z_2 & 1 \\ x_3 & y_3 & z_3 & 1 \end{vmatrix} = 0.$$

11. Use the results of Exercise 10 to find the equation of the plane determined by the points A:(1, −1, 1), B:(2, 2, −2), and C:(−3, 3, 3).

12. Show that the points A:(3, −2, 4), B:(2, 1, 5), C:(1, −3, 3), and D:(0, 0, 4) are coplanar.

13. Do the points A:(1, 1, 1), B:(1, 2, −1), and C:(1, 3, −3) determine a unique plane? Is it meaningful to write a set of parametric equations of the plane in this case? Explain your answer.

14. A plane passes through P_0:(6, 1, 5) and is perpendicular to the two planes $x - y + z + 5 = 0$ and $2y - 3z - 11 = 0$. What is the equation of the plane?

15. Find the equation of the plane that contains the points R:(2, 1, 3) and S:(1, 0, −6) and whose y intercept is twice the value of its x intercept.

5.4 PARALLEL AND PERPENDICULAR PLANES

The condition that two planes be parallel or perpendicular can be expressed in terms of the relationship among the coefficients of x, y, and z.

> **Example 1.** Find the equation of the plane π which passes through the point P_0:(6, 3, 4) and is parallel to the plane $2x + y - 2z + 8 = 0$.
>
> The vector $[2, 1, -2]$ is a vector perpendicular to both planes. Hence the equation of the plane π is of the form
>
> $$2x + y - 2z + d = 0.$$
>
> The constant d can be determined by a substitution of the coordinates of P_0 for x, y, and z respectively since they must satisfy the equation of the plane. Hence
>
> $$2(6) + (3) - 2(4) + d = 0,$$
> $$d = -7.$$
>
> The equation of the plane π is
>
> $$2x + y - 2z - 7 = 0.$$

In general, two planes are parallel if and only if vectors perpendicular to each plane are parallel. The following theorem is implied by the argument of Example 1. The proof is left to the reader as Exercise 11.

> **Theorem 5.2.** *Two planes $a_1x + b_1y + c_1z + d_1 = 0$ and $a_2x + b_2y + c_2z + d_2 = 0$ are parallel (or coincide) if and only if*
>
> $$\frac{a_1}{a_2} = \frac{b_1}{b_2} = \frac{c_1}{c_2} = t$$
>
> *where t is a nonzero real number.*

Example 2. Show that the planes $x - 3y + 2z + 6 = 0$ and $2x - 6y + 3z - 11 = 0$ are not parallel.

A vector perpendicular to the plane $x - 3y + 2z + 6 = 0$ is $[1, -3, 2]$; a vector perpendicular to the plane $2x - 6y + 3z - 11 = 0$ is $[2, -6, 3]$. Since $[1, -3, 2] \neq t[2, -6, 3]$ for any nonzero real number t, the vectors are not parallel; hence the planes are not parallel.

Example 3. Show that the planes $3x + 4y - 2z + 10 = 0$ and $2x + y + 5z - 13 = 0$ are perpendicular.

The vector $[3, 4, -2]$ is a vector perpendicular to the plane $3x + 4y - 2z + 10 = 0$; the vector $[2, 1, 5]$ is a vector perpendicular to the plane $2x + y + 5z - 13 = 0$. The two given planes are perpendicular if and only if vectors perpendicular to each plane are themselves perpendicular. Since

$$[3, 4, -2] \cdot [2, 1, 5] = (3)(2) + (4)(1) + (-2)(5) = 0,$$

the vectors are perpendicular; hence the planes are perpendicular.

Theorem 5.3. *Two planes* $a_1x + b_1y + c_1z + d_1 = 0$ *and* $a_2x + b_2y + c_2z + d_2 = 0$ *are perpendicular if and only if*

$$a_1a_2 + b_1b_2 + c_1c_2 = 0.$$

The proof of Theorem 5.3 is left to the reader as Exercise 12.

Exercises

Find the equation of the plane which passes through the point P_0 and is parallel to the given plane.

1. P_0:$(1, 4, 3)$; $12x - 4y + 7z - 10 = 0$.

2. P_0:$(-3, -1, 2)$; $3x + 2y + z + 4 = 0$.

3. P_0:$(0, 2, 5)$; $x - 3y + 6z - 1 = 0$.

4. P_0:$(4, 1, -1)$; $8x - 3y + 1 = 0$.

In Exercises 5–8 determine whether the planes whose equations are given are parallel or perpendicular.

5. $x + 4y - 2z = 0$ and $3x + 12y - 6z + 4 = 0$.

6. $x - y + z - 6 = 0$ and $x + y - z + 6 = 0$.

7. $4x - 3y + z = 0$ and $3x + 2y - 6z + 2 = 0$.

8. $3x - 2y + z + 2 = 0$ and $3x + 4y - 7z + 1 = 0$.

9. For what value of c is the plane $2x - 3y + 7z + 4 = 0$ perpendicular to the plane $-4x - 3y + cz + 5 = 0$?

10. Determine the equation of the plane containing the points $A:(6, -1, 4)$ and $B:(5, 3, 2)$ and which is perpendicular to the plane $3x - 6y + 2z - 4 = 0$.

11. Prove Theorem 5.2.

12. Prove Theorem 5.3.

5.5   THE ANGLE BETWEEN TWO PLANES

The procedure for finding the measure of the angle between two lines was presented in §3.11. An analogous procedure can be used to find the measure of the angle between two planes. The procedure is dependent upon the fact that the coefficients a, b, and c in the equation of the plane $ax + by + cz + d = 0$ are components of a vector perpendicular to the plane.

When two planes intersect, two pairs of supplementary dihedral angles are formed. The measures of these angles are θ and $\pi - \theta$. As a matter of convenience, by "the angle between two planes" we shall mean the acute angle formed by the planes.

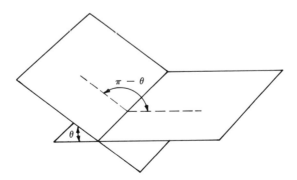

Figure 5.6

Let the planes $a_1x + b_1y + c_1z + d_1 = 0$ and $a_2x + b_2y + c_2z + d_2 = 0$ intersect to form an acute angle whose measure is θ. Vectors $\vec{n}_1$ and $\vec{n}_2$ perpendicular to the planes are $\vec{n}_1 = [a_1, b_1, c_1]$ and $\vec{n}_2 = [a_2, b_2, c_2]$ respectively. Furthermore, the measure of the angle formed by the vectors is equal to θ or $\pi - \theta$ depending upon the orientation of the vectors, as shown in Figures 5.7 and 5.8 respectively. In either case, the cosine of the acute angle can be determined by using the relationship

$$|\vec{n}_1 \cdot \vec{n}_2| = |\vec{n}_1|\,|\vec{n}_2|\cos\theta.$$

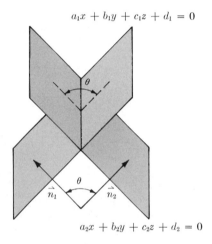

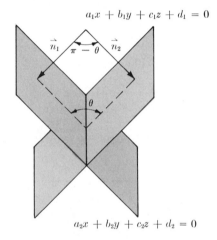

$$a_1x + b_1y + c_1z + d_1 = 0$$

$$a_2x + b_2y + c_2z + d_2 = 0$$

Figure 5.7

Figure 5.8

Therefore,

$$\cos\theta = \frac{|\vec{n}_1 \cdot \vec{n}_2|}{|\vec{n}_1|\,|\vec{n}_2|};$$

whereby

$$\cos\theta = \frac{|a_1a_2 + b_1b_2 + c_1c_2|}{\sqrt{a_1{}^2 + b_1{}^2 + c_1{}^2}\sqrt{a_2{}^2 + b_2{}^2 + c_2{}^2}}. \tag{5.11}$$

Example 1. Find the cosine of the angle between the planes $-2x + 2y + z + 1 = 0$ and $4x + 3y + 5 = 0$.

Using equation (5.11), we have

$$\cos\theta = \frac{|(-2)(4) + (2)(3) + (1)(0)|}{\sqrt{(-2)^2 + 2^2 + 1^2}\sqrt{4^2 + 3^2 + 0^2}}$$

$$= \frac{|-8 + 6 + 0|}{\sqrt{9}\sqrt{25}} = \frac{2}{15}.$$

Example 2. Find the measures of the dihedral angles that are formed when the planes $3x - 2y + 6z + 5 = 0$ and $3x + 5y - 8z + 3 = 0$ intersect.

Vectors $\vec{n_1}$ and $\vec{n_2}$ perpendicular to the planes are respectively $\vec{n_1} = [3, -2, 6]$ and $\vec{n_2} = [3, 5, -8]$. The angle θ between the two vectors is given by the relationship

$$\cos \theta = \frac{\vec{n_1} \cdot \vec{n_2}}{|\vec{n_1}|\,|\vec{n_2}|}$$

$$= \frac{(3)(3) + (-2)(5) + (6)(-8)}{\sqrt{3^2 + (-2)^2 + 6^2}\sqrt{3^2 + 5^2 + (-8)^2}}$$

$$= \frac{-49}{\sqrt{49}\sqrt{98}} = -\frac{1}{\sqrt{2}}.$$

Thus $\theta = 3\pi/4$. Hence the measures of the two pairs of dihedral angles formed by the given planes are $\pi/4$ and $3\pi/4$.

Exercises

In Exercises 1–4 find the cosine of the angle between the given planes.

1. $3x - 6y + 2z + 1 = 0$ and $2x + 2y + z + 1 = 0$.

2. $4x + 3y + 2z - 7 = 0$ and $8x + 6y + 4z + 3 = 0$.

3. $4x - 3y + 10 = 0$ and $3x + 4y + z - 1 = 0$.

4. $x + y + z - 5 = 0$ and $3x + 2y - z = 0$.

5.   Find the measure of the acute angle formed by the intersecting planes $2x + 2y - z - 6 = 0$ and $4x + y + z + 1 = 0$.

6.   Find the value of b such that the planes $3x + by + 6z + 8 = 0$ and $2x + by - z + 11 = 0$ intersect to form an angle whose measure is $\pi/2$.

5.6   DISTANCE OF A POINT FROM A PLANE

Consider any plane $ax + by + cz + d = 0$, and let $P_1:(x_1, y_1, z_1)$ be any point in space. In order to determine the shortest distance of the point P_1 from the plane, choose an arbitrary point $P_0:(x_0, y_0, z_0)$ in the plane. The

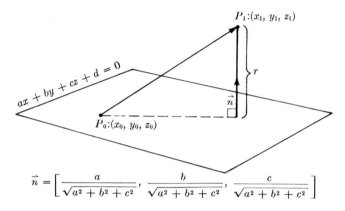

$$\vec{n} = \left[\frac{a}{\sqrt{a^2 + b^2 + c^2}}, \frac{b}{\sqrt{a^2 + b^2 + c^2}}, \frac{c}{\sqrt{a^2 + b^2 + c^2}}\right]$$

Figure 5.9

shortest distance, r, as shown in Figure 5.9, will be the length of the projection of $\overrightarrow{P_0P_1}$ on $\vec{n}$ where $\vec{n}$ is a unit vector perpendicular to the plane. Now,

$$r = |\overrightarrow{P_0P_1} \cdot \vec{n}|$$

$$= \left| [x_1 - x_0, y_1 - y_0, z_1 - z_0] \right.$$

$$\left. \cdot \left[\frac{a}{\sqrt{a^2 + b^2 + c^2}}, \frac{b}{\sqrt{a^2 + b^2 + c^2}}, \frac{c}{\sqrt{a^2 + b^2 + c^2}}\right] \right|$$

$$= \left| \frac{a(x_1 - x_0) + b(y_1 - y_0) + c(z_1 - z_0)}{\sqrt{a^2 + b^2 + c^2}} \right|$$

$$= \frac{|ax_1 + by_1 + cz_1 - ax_0 - by_0 - cz_0|}{\sqrt{a^2 + b^2 + c^2}}.$$

Since P_0 lies in the plane $ax + by + cz + d = 0$, then $ax_0 + by_0 + cz_0 + d = 0$ and

$$r = \frac{|ax_1 + by_1 + cz_1 + d|}{\sqrt{a^2 + b^2 + c^2}}. \tag{5.12}$$

Example 1. Find the distance of the point P_1: $(1, 3, -2)$ from the plane $2x + 2y - z + 3 = 0$.

By equation (5.12),

$$r = \frac{|2(1) + 2(3) - (-2) + 3|}{\sqrt{2^2 + 2^2 + (-1)^2}} = \frac{13}{3}.$$

Example 2. Determine the members of the family of parallel planes $3x - 12y + 4z + d = 0$ such that the distance of P_1:$(1, 3, 2)$ from the planes is 2.

By equation (5.12),

$$2 = \frac{|3(1) - 12(3) + 4(2) + d|}{\sqrt{3^2 + (-12)^2 + 4^2}} = \frac{|d - 25|}{13}.$$

Therefore,

$$|d - 25| = 26,$$
$$d = 51 \text{ or } -1.$$

Thus each of the planes $3x - 12y + 4z + 51 = 0$ and $3x - 12y + 4z - 1 = 0$ is such that the distance of P_1:(1, 3, 2) from the plane is 2.

Exercises

In Exercises 1–4 find the distance of the point P_1 from the given plane.

1. P_1:(2, -1, 5); $2x + 2y - z - 3 = 0$.

2. P_1:(5, 0, -2); $2x + y - z = 0$.

3. P_1:(2, 3, -2); $4x + y - 8z + 9 = 0$.

4. P_1:(3, 2, -1); $2x - y + 2z + 9 = 0$.

5. Determine the values of x if the distance of the point P_1:(x, 3, 2) from the plane $6x - 7y + 6x - 12 = 0$ is 3.

6. Determine the value of y if the distance of the point P_1:(4, y, 3) from the plane $2x + 6y - 3z - 13 = 0$ is 4, and if the point is in the same half-space determined by the plane as is the origin.

7. Determine the members of the family of parallel planes $4x - 8y + z + d = 0$ such that the distance of P_1:(1, 1, 0) from the planes is 2.

8. Derive a formula representing the distance of the origin from the plane $ax + by + cz + d = 0$.

9. Use the results of Exercise 8 to find the distance of the origin from the plane $6x + 6y - 7z + 33 = 0$.

10. The equation $x \cos \alpha + y \cos \beta + z \cos \gamma - p = 0$, where a unit vector perpendicular to the plane is $[\cos \alpha, \cos \beta, \cos \gamma]$ and $p \geq 0$, is called the *normal form* of the equation of a plane. Prove that p is equal to the distance of the origin from the plane.

11. Use the results of Exercise 10 to write the equation of the plane $x - y + \sqrt{2}z + 4 = 0$ in normal form. Use this normal form to find the distance of the origin from the plane.

12. Find the equations of the planes perpendicular to each of the planes $x + y - 4z - 15 = 0$ and $x + 3y + 4z + 13 = 0$ and at a distance 2 from the origin.

5.7 DISTANCE BETWEEN TWO PARALLEL PLANES

Consider the problem of finding the distance between the two parallel planes

$$4x - y + 8z - 3 = 0 \qquad \text{and} \qquad 4x - y + 8z + 15 = 0.$$

The procedure of §5.6 can be applied to solve this problem. Let $P_1:(x_1, y_1, z_1)$ be any point in the plane $4x - y + 8z - 3 = 0$. Then the distance r between the two parallel planes is equal to the distance of P_1 from the plane $4x - y + 8z + 15 = 0$:

$$r = \frac{|4x_1 - y_1 + 8z_1 + 15|}{\sqrt{4^2 + (-1)^2 + 8^2}} = \frac{|4x_1 - y_1 + 8z_1 + 15|}{9}.$$

Since P_1 lies in the plane $4x - y + 8z + 3 = 0$, then $4x_1 - y_1 + 8z_1 - 3 = 0$ and

$$r = \frac{|3 + 15|}{9} = 2.$$

A formula can be obtained for the distance r between the two parallel planes

$$ax + by + cz + d_1 = 0 \qquad \text{and} \qquad ax + by + cz + d_2 = 0$$

by a generalization of the above procedure. Let $P_1:(x_1, y_1, z_1)$ be any point in the plane $ax + by + cz + d_1 = 0$. Then the distance r between the two planes is equal to the distance of the point P_1 from the plane $ax + by + cz + d_2 = 0$:

$$r = \frac{|ax_1 + by_1 + cz_1 + d_2|}{\sqrt{a^2 + b^2 + c^2}}.$$

Since P_1 lies in the plane $ax + by + cz + d_1 = 0$, then $ax_1 + by_1 + cz_1 + d_1 = 0$ and

$$r = \frac{|d_2 - d_1|}{\sqrt{a^2 + b^2 + c^2}}. \tag{5.13}$$

Note that equation (5.13) can be used to find the distance between two parallel planes only if the equations of the planes are written so that the two sets of coefficients of x, y, and z are respectively identical.

Example. Determine the distance between the planes $2x - y - z + 2 = 0$ and $6x - 3y - 3z + 10 = 0$.

The two planes are parallel since

$$\frac{2}{6} = \frac{-1}{-3} = \frac{-1}{-3}.$$

If we multiply the members of the equation of the first plane by 3, then the variables x, y, and z in the equations of both planes will contain identical coefficients respectively:

$$6x - 3y - 3z + 6 = 0,$$
$$6x - 3y - 3z + 10 = 0.$$

By equation (5.13), the distance r between the given parallel planes can now be determined:

$$r = \frac{|10 - 6|}{\sqrt{6^2 + (-3)^2 + (-3)^2}} = \frac{4}{3\sqrt{6}}.$$

Exercises

In Exercises 1–4 determine the distance between each pair of planes.

1. $x + 2y - 2z + 4 = 0$ and $x + 2y - 2z - 14 = 0$.

2. $x - y + 2z = 3$ and $2x - 2y + 4z = 12$.

3. $3x + 2y - 10z + 5 = 0$ and $6x + 4y + z - 12 = 0$.

4. $7x - 4y + 4z - 34 = 0$ and $7x - 4y + 4z - 7 = 0$.

5. Find the equations of the parallel planes 6 units from the plane whose equation is $3x + 12y - 4z + 7 = 0$.

6. Determine the equations of the pair of planes that bisect the supplementary dihedral angles formed when the planes $a_1x + b_1y + c_1z + d_1 = 0$ and $a_2x + b_2y + c_2z + d_2 = 0$ intersect.

7. Use the results of Exercise 6 to find the equations of the planes that bisect the dihedral angles formed when the planes $2x + y - 2z - 4 = 0$ and $2x + 6y + 3z = 0$ intersect.

8. Use the results of Exercise 6 to prove that the angle bisectors of the dihedral angles formed by any two distinct intersecting planes are perpendicular.

9. Verify the results of Exercise 8 for the angle bisectors of the planes $8x - 4y - z + 2 = 0$ and $9x + 6y + 2z + 7 = 0$.

5.8   THE EQUATION OF A SPHERE

A *sphere* is a set of points in space which are equidistant from a fixed point called the *center*. The distance from the center to any point on the sphere is called the *radius*. The equation of a sphere can be derived in a manner completely analogous to the derivation of the equation of a circle in §4.3.

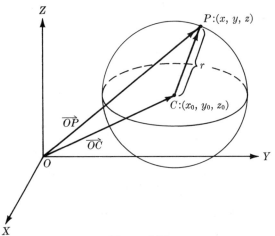

Figure 5.10

Let $P:(x, y, z)$ be any point on the sphere with center at $C:(x_0, y_0, z_0)$ and radius r, as shown in Figure 5.10. Then

$$\vec{OP} - \vec{OC} = \vec{CP} \tag{5.14}$$

where $|CP| = r$. Taking the scalar product of each member of equation (5.14) with itself, we have

$$(\vec{OP} - \vec{OC}) \cdot (\vec{OP} - \vec{OC}) = \vec{CP} \cdot \vec{CP},$$

$$(\vec{OP} - \vec{OC}) \cdot (\vec{OP} - \vec{OC}) = r^2. \tag{5.15}$$

Equation (5.15) represents a vector form of the equation of a sphere. Since $\vec{OP} = [x, y, z]$ and $\vec{OC} = [x_0, y_0, z_0]$, then

$$\vec{OP} - \vec{OC} = [x - x_0, y - y_0, z - z_0],$$

and equation (5.15) may be written as

$$(x - x_0)^2 + (y - y_0)^2 + (z - z_0)^2 = r^2. \tag{5.16}$$

Equation (5.16) represents a coordinate form of the equation of a sphere with center at $C:(x_0, y_0, z_0)$ and radius r.

Example 1. Determine the equation of the sphere with center at $C:(5, 1, -2)$ and radius 4.

Setting $x_0 = 5$, $y_0 = 1$, $z_0 = -2$, and $r = 4$ in equation (5.16), we have

$$(x - 5)^2 + (y - 1)^2 + (z + 2)^2 = 4^2,$$
$$x^2 + y^2 + z^2 - 10x - 2y + 4z + 14 = 0,$$

which is the equation of the sphere.

Example 2. Determine the center and the radius of the sphere whose equation is

$$x^2 + y^2 + z^2 - 6x + 2y - 4z - 11 = 0.$$

Rearranging the terms of the equation, we have

$$x^2 - 6x + y^2 + 2y + z^2 - 4z = 11.$$

Completing the squares in x, y, and z, we obtain

$$(x^2 - 6x + 9) + (y^2 + 2y + 1) + (z^2 - 4z + 4) = 25,$$
$$(x - 3)^2 + (y + 1)^2 + (z - 2)^2 = 5^2.$$

The center of the sphere is at the point $C:(3, -1, 2)$, and the radius is equal to 5.

If the binomial expressions in equation (5.16) are expanded, the equation of a sphere can be expressed in the equivalent form

$$x^2 + y^2 + z^2 + Dx + Ey + Fz + G = 0. \tag{5.17}$$

The equation of every sphere is of this form. However, not every equation of this form has a sphere as its graph. If equation (5.17) represents a sphere, the center is at $\left(-\dfrac{D}{2}, -\dfrac{E}{2}, -\dfrac{F}{2}\right)$ and the radius is $\dfrac{\sqrt{D^2 + E^2 + F^2 - 4G}}{2}$.

Exercises

Determine the equation of the sphere with center at C and radius equal to r.

1. $C:(2, 1, 5)$; $r = 3$.
2. $C:(5, 0, -2)$; $r = 1$.
3. $C:(-1, 2, 3)$; $r = 5$.
4. $C:(1, -8, 1)$; $r = 4$.
5. $C:(0, 0, 0)$; $r = 3$.
6. $C:(0, 0, 1)$; $r = 2$.

In Exercises 7–12 find the coordinates of the center and the radius of the sphere whose equation is given.

7. $x^2 + y^2 + z^2 - 6x = 0.$

8. $x^2 + y^2 + z^2 - 2y + 4z - 4 = 0.$

9. $3x^2 + 3y^2 + 3z^2 + 12x + 6y - 6z - 57 = 0.$

10. $2x^2 + 2y^2 + 2z^2 + x - 3y + 5z = 0.$

11. $x^2 + y^2 + z^2 - 9 = 0.$

12. $4x^2 + 4y^2 + 4z^2 - 4x - 4y - 4z - 1 = 0.$

13. Find the equation of the sphere with center at $C:(4, 3, 3)$ and which passes through the point $P_0:(-2, -6, 1)$.

14. Find the equation of the sphere with diameter AB where $A:(5, 4, 0)$ and $B:(1, -2, 2)$.

15. Determine the equation of the set of points $P:(x, y, z)$ such that $\overrightarrow{AP} \cdot \overrightarrow{BP} = 0$ where $A:(1, 5, -4)$ and $B:(7, 1, 4)$.

16. Show that the equation of the set of points $P:(x, y, z)$ whose distance from $A:(1, 2, 0)$ is twice the distance from $B:(-3, 1, -1)$ is a sphere.

In Exercises 17 and 18 determine the equation of the sphere that contains the noncoplanar points M, N, R, and S.

17. $M:(0, 0, 0)$, $N:(2, 0, 0)$, $R:(1, 0, 1)$, and $S:(1, 1, 0)$.

18. $M:(3, 4, 12)$, $N:(-4, 3, -12)$, $R:(0, 13, 0)$, and $S:(12, 0, -5)$.

19. Describe the set of points whose coordinates satisfy the statement (a) $x^2 + y^2 + z^2 < 1$; (b) $x^2 + y^2 + z^2 \leq 1$.

5.9 TANGENT PLANES TO A SPHERE

A plane that intersects a sphere at one and only one point $T:(x_1, y_1, z_1)$ is called a *tangent plane* to the sphere. The point T is called the *point of tangency*. To determine the equation of the plane tangent at T, let $P:(x, y, z)$ be a general point on the plane, and let $C:(x_0, y_0, z_0)$ be the center of the sphere. Then $\overrightarrow{TP}$ is a vector in the tangent plane and is perpendicular to the radius

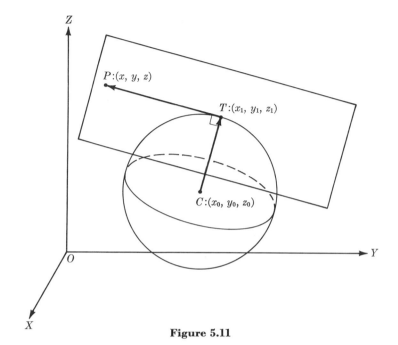

Figure 5.11

vector $\overrightarrow{CT}$, as shown in Figure 5.11. The point P is a point on the tangent plane if and only if

$$\overrightarrow{TP} \cdot \overrightarrow{CT} = 0. \tag{5.18}$$

This equation represents a vector form of the tangent plane. Since $\overrightarrow{TP} = [x - x_1,\ y - y_1,\ z - z_1]$ and $\overrightarrow{CT} = [x_1 - x_0,\ y_1 - y_0,\ z_1 - z_0]$, then, by using equation (5.18),

$$(x - x_1)(x_1 - x_0) + (y - y_1)(y_1 - y_0) + (z - z_1)(z_1 - z_0) = 0 \tag{5.19}$$

represents a coordinate form of the equation of the plane tangent at $T:(x_1, y_1, z_1)$ to the sphere with center at $C:(x_0, y_0, z_0)$.

> **Example.** Find the equation of the plane tangent at $T:(6, 2, 4)$ to the sphere with center at $C:(-1, 1, 2)$.
>
> Using equation (5.19), we find that the equation of the tangent plane is
>
> $$(x - 6)(6 + 1) + (y - 2)(2 - 1) + (z - 4)(4 - 2) = 0;$$
>
> that is,
>
> $$7x + y + 2z - 52 = 0.$$

Exercises

Find the equation of the plane tangent at T to the sphere with center at C.

1. $T:(1, 0, 2)$; $C:(1, 1, 1)$.   3. $T:(1, 2, -1)$; $C:(0, 0, 0)$.

2. $T:(0, 0, 0)$; $C:(2, 2, 1)$.   4. $T:(-1, 3, 3)$; $C:(-1, 4, 4)$.

In Exercises 5 and 6 determine the equation of the plane tangent at T to the sphere whose equation is given.

5. $T:(3, -2, 5)$; $x^2 + y^2 + z^2 + 6x - 8y + 4z + 13 = 0$.

6. $T:(0, 2, 8)$; $x^2 + y^2 + z^2 - 2x + 4y - 76 = 0$.

7. Find the equation of the plane tangent at $T:(x_1, y_1, z_1)$ to the sphere whose equation is $x^2 + y^2 + z^2 = r^2$.

8. Find the equations of the distinct planes π_1 and π_2 that are parallel to the plane $2x + 6y + 3z = 0$ and tangent to the sphere whose equation is $x^2 + y^2 + z^2 - 2x - 2y - 2z - 1 = 0$.

9. Determine the values of d such that the plane $2x - y - 2z + d = 0$ is tangent to the sphere $x^2 + y^2 + z^2 - 6x + 8y - 12z + 45 = 0$.

10. Determine the equation of the sphere with center at $C:(2, 2, 1)$ that is tangent to the plane $3x + 4y + 12z = 0$.

5.10 THE EQUATION OF A LINE IN SPACE

The various vector forms and coordinate forms of the equation of a line in a plane were derived in Chapter 3. Many of these derivations can be extended to obtain the equation of a line in three-dimensional space subject to similar conditions. The following examples illustrate some of these extensions.

Example 1. Determine a set of parametric equations of the line that contains the point $P_0:(4, -1, 6)$ and is parallel to the vector $\vec{n}$ where $\vec{n} = [1, 5, 3]$.

Let $P:(x, y, z)$ be a general point on the line. Then

$$\vec{P_0P} = t\vec{n}$$

where t is an arbitrary real number. Hence

$$[x - 4, y + 1, z - 6] = t[1, 5, 3]$$

and

$$\begin{cases} x - 4 = t \\ y + 1 = 5t \\ z - 6 = 3t, \end{cases}$$

which is equivalent to

$$\begin{cases} x = 4 + t \\ y = -1 + 5t \\ z = 6 + 3t. \end{cases}$$

In general, a set of *parametric equations* of a line in space is of the form

$$\begin{cases} x = x_0 + at \\ y = y_0 + bt \\ z = z_0 + ct \end{cases} \tag{5.20}$$

where t is an arbitrary real number, (x_0, y_0, z_0) is a point on the line, and $(a : b : c)$ is a set of direction numbers of the line.

If each equation of (5.20) is solved for t, it follows that

$$\frac{x - x_0}{a} = \frac{y - y_0}{b} = \frac{z - z_0}{c}, \tag{5.21}$$

provided that $abc \neq 0$. The set of equations (5.21) is often referred to as the *symmetric form* of the equation of a line in space. If $abc = 0$, the symmetric form of the equation of a line does not exist; if $abc = 0$, the line is parallel to at least one coordinate reference plane.

Example 2. Determine the equation of the line ℓ passing through the points $A : (x_0, y_0, z_0)$ and $B : (x_1, y_1, z_1)$.

If $P : (x, y, z)$ is a general point on line ℓ, then, by Theorem 2.7,

$$\overrightarrow{OP} = t\overrightarrow{OA} + (1 - t)\overrightarrow{OB}$$

where t is an arbitrary real number. Thus

$$[x, y, z] = t[x_0, y_0, z_0] + (1 - t)[x_1, y_1, z_1]$$
$$= [tx_0 + (1 - t)x_1, ty_0 + (1 - t)y_1, tz_0 + (1 - t)z_1].$$

Equating corresponding components, we have

$$\begin{cases} x = tx_0 + (1 - t)x_1 \\ y = ty_0 + (1 - t)y_1 \\ z = tz_0 + (1 - t)z_1, \end{cases} \tag{5.22}$$

which represents a set of parametric equations of a line through two given points. Provided that $x_0 \neq x_1$, $y_0 \neq y_1$, and $z_0 \neq z_1$, the equation of the line can be written in the symmetric form

$$\frac{x - x_1}{x_0 - x_1} = \frac{y - y_1}{y_0 - y_1} = \frac{z - z_1}{z_0 - z_1} \qquad (5.23)$$

by solving each equation of (5.22) for t. Equation (5.23) is often referred to as the *two-point form* of the equation of a line in space.

Exercises

1. Determine a set of parametric equations of the line that contains the point P_0:(4, 2, 5) and is parallel to the vector $\vec{n}$ where $\vec{n} = [3, 1, 2]$.

2. If possible, determine the symmetric form of the equation of a line passing through P_0:(2, 1, −1) and parallel to the vector $\vec{n}$ where $\vec{n} = [1, 2, 2]$.

3. Use the two-point form to find the equation of the line that contains the points A:(4, 3, 4) and B:(−2, 5, 1).

4. Determine a set of parametric equations of the line through the point P_0:(6, −3, 1) and parallel to the y axis.

5. Find a set of direction numbers of the line whose parametric equations are
$$\begin{cases} x = 3 + 2t \\ y = 5 - 3t \\ z = -1. \end{cases}$$

6. Find a set of direction cosines of the line
$$\frac{x - 3}{6} = \frac{y + 4}{6} = \frac{z - 5}{7}.$$

7. Determine the symmetric form of the equation of the line through the point P_0:(1, −2, 7) and parallel to the line
$$\frac{x + 3}{4} = \frac{y + 1}{3} = \frac{z - 1}{1}.$$

8. Determine a set of parametric equations of the line through the point P_0:(1, 0, 4) and parallel to the line that contains the points A:(6, 3, 7) and B:(2, -1, -1).

9. Find the equation of the line through the point P_0:(2, 2, 3) and perpendicular to the plane $3x - y + 5z - 2 = 0$ in   (a) parametric form; (b) symmetric form.

10. Find the equation of the line through the origin and parallel to the line that contains the points A:(-4, 3, 1) and B:(6, -2, -4) in   (a) parametric form;   (b) symmetric form.

11. Determine the coordinates of the point of intersection of the line AB, where A:(6, -1, 4) and B:(2, -3, 14), and the yz plane.

12. Write in symmetric form the equation of the line determined by the origin and the point (x_1, y_1, z_1).

13. Determine c if the line

$$\frac{x - 1}{3} = \frac{y + 2}{1} = \frac{z}{c}$$

is parallel to the plane $3x + y + 2z - 6 = 0$.

14. Write a set of necessary and sufficient conditions for the line

$$\frac{x - x_0}{a} = \frac{y - y_0}{b} = \frac{z - z_0}{c}$$

and the plane $Ax + By + Cz + D = 0$ to be (a) parallel; (b) perpendicular.

15. Write a set of necessary and sufficient conditions for the lines

$$\frac{x - x_0}{a_0} = \frac{y - y_0}{b_0} = \frac{z - z_0}{c_0} \quad \text{and} \quad \frac{x - x_1}{a_1} = \frac{y - y_1}{b_1} = \frac{z - z_1}{c_1}$$

to be (a) parallel; (b) perpendicular.

Find the equation of the plane containing the point P_0 and the given line.

16. P_0:(-6, 3, -2); $\dfrac{x + 1}{3} = \dfrac{y - 3}{2} = \dfrac{z + 1}{3}$.

17. P_0:(2, 0, 2); $\begin{cases} x = -1 + t \\ y = 1 + t \\ z = 2 + t. \end{cases}$

18. P_0:(3, 1, 4); $\dfrac{x - 6}{6} = \dfrac{y + 1}{2} = \dfrac{-z}{1}$.

5.11 GENERAL FORM OF THE EQUATION OF A LINE

If two distinct planes $a_1x + b_1y + c_1z + d_1 = 0$ and $a_2x + b_2y + c_2z + d_2 = 0$ are not parallel, they intersect in a line. Thus the system of equations

$$\begin{cases} a_1x + b_1y + c_1z + d_1 = 0 \\ a_2x + b_2y + c_2z + d_2 = 0 \end{cases} \qquad (5.24)$$

represents the equation of a line. The system (5.24) is called the *general form* of the equation of a line in space. Since a given line can be represented in this manner by infinitely many pairs of planes, the general form of the equation of a line is not unique.

> **Example.** Find a symmetric form of the equation of the line defined by
>
> $$\begin{cases} 2x + y - z + 1 = 0 \\ 3x - y - z - 6 = 0. \end{cases}$$
>
> By letting $z = 0$, one solution of the system of equations may be obtained. The solution $A:(1, -3, 0)$ represents the point of intersection of the line defined by the system and the xy plane. The point of intersection of a line and a reference plane is called a *piercing point*. In a similar manner, another piercing point may be obtained by letting $y = 0$. Thus, $B:(7, 0, 15)$ is the point of intersection of the line and the zx plane. The two points A and B lie on the line of intersection of the given planes; therefore, $\vec{AB} = [6, 3, 15]$ is a vector parallel to the line. Any nonzero real multiple of the components of $\vec{AB}$, such as $(2:1:5)$, constitutes a set of direction numbers of the line AB. Hence, using (5.21) with $x_0 = 1$, $y_0 = -3$, and $z_0 = 0$, we obtain a symmetric form of the equation of line AB:
>
> $$\frac{x - 1}{2} = \frac{y + 3}{1} = \frac{z}{5}.$$

Exercises

In Exercises 1–4 find, if possible, a symmetric form of the equation of the line defined by each system of planes.

1. $\begin{cases} x - y + 3z - 8 = 0 \\ 4x + y + 2z - 2 = 0. \end{cases}$

3. $\begin{cases} 2x + 3y - z + 5 = 0 \\ x + 2y + 2z - 2 = 0. \end{cases}$

2. $\begin{cases} x - y + 2z + 3 = 0 \\ x - y - 5z - 4 = 0. \end{cases}$

4. $\begin{cases} 2x - 4y + 3z + 7 = 0 \\ 3x + 3y - 2z - 6 = 0. \end{cases}$

5. Show that

$$\left(\begin{vmatrix} b_1 & c_1 \\ b_2 & c_2 \end{vmatrix} : \begin{vmatrix} c_1 & a_1 \\ c_2 & a_2 \end{vmatrix} : \begin{vmatrix} a_1 & b_1 \\ a_2 & b_2 \end{vmatrix} \right)$$

is a set of direction numbers of the line determined by the system of planes

$$\begin{cases} a_1 x + b_1 y + c_1 z + d_1 = 0 \\ a_2 x + b_2 y + c_2 z + d_2 = 0. \end{cases}$$

6. Show that the lines defined by the systems of planes

$$\begin{cases} -3x + y + 5z + 1 = 0 \\ 4x + 6y - 3z - 15 = 0 \end{cases} \quad \text{and} \quad \begin{cases} x + y - z = 0 \\ 4x - 2y - 7z + 3 = 0 \end{cases}$$

are parallel.

7. Determine the point of intersection of the line

$$\begin{cases} x - 2y - z + 14 = 0 \\ 3x - y + 2z + 17 = 0 \end{cases}$$

and the plane $3x - 2y + 3z + 16 = 0$.

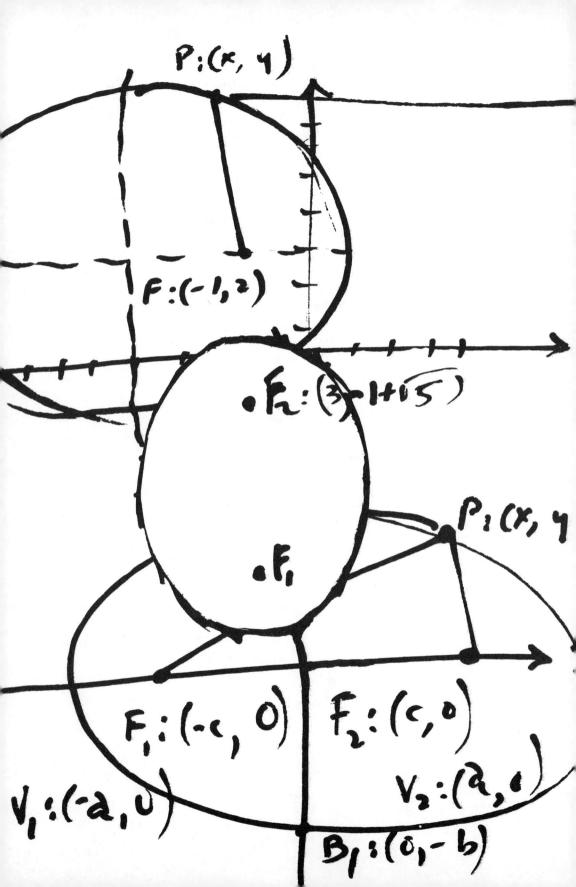

$P:(x, y)$

$F:(-1, 2)$

$F_2:(3, -1+\sqrt{5})$

$P:(x, y)$

F_1

$F_1:(-c, 0)$ $F_2:(c, 0)$

$V_1:(-a, 0)$ $V_2:(a, 0)$

$B_1:(0, -b)$

CONIC SECTIONS

6.1 A SYNTHETIC APPROACH

Let ℓ be a line passing through a point V. The set of points on the lines passing through V and making an angle whose measure is θ with line ℓ is called a *right circular cone* (Figure 6.1). The point V is called the *vertex* of the cone; the line ℓ is called the *axis* of the cone. Each line on the cone is called an *element*, or *generator*, of the cone. The vertex separates the cone into two parts called the *nappes* of the cone. The vertex is common to both nappes.

The intersections of a right circular cone and a plane form a class of plane curves called *conic sections*, or *conics*. If the plane intersects only the vertex of the cone, the curve of intersection is a *point;* if the plane intersects

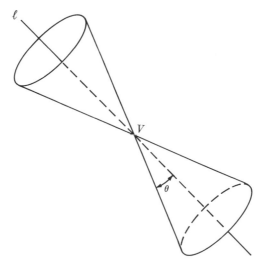

Figure 6.1

exactly one element of the cone, the curve of intersection is a *line;* if the plane contains the axis of the cone, the curve of intersection is a pair of *intersecting lines.* The point, the line, and the pair of intersecting lines are called *degenerate conics.* Every degenerate conic contains the vertex of the cone. Those curves of intersection which do not contain the vertex of the cone are called *proper conics.* The proper conics will be of primary interest to us throughout this chapter.

There are three main types of proper conics, depending upon the way in which the plane intersects the cone. If the plane intersects all the elements of one nappe of the cone, as shown in Figure 6.2, the conic is an *ellipse.* A circle is a special form of the ellipse, and is obtained when the plane intersects all the elements of one nappe of the cone and is perpendicular to the axis of the cone. If the plane intersects elements of both nappes of the cone, as shown in Figure 6.3, the conic is a *hyperbola.* If the plane is parallel to one and only one element of the cone, as shown in Figure 6.4, the conic is a *parabola.* Note that the plane must be parallel to, but not contain, the element of the cone.

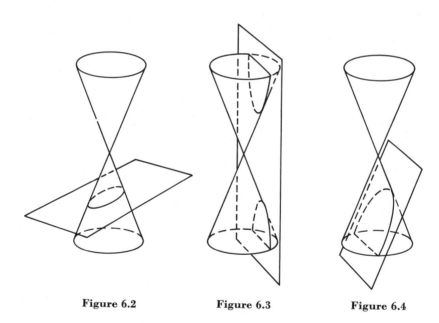

Figure 6.2   Figure 6.3   Figure 6.4

The following geometric properties of the proper conics are important in establishing an analytic approach to the study of the conics in §6.2.

Theorem 6.1. *Each point on an ellipse is such that the sum of its distances from two fixed points in the plane is a constant.*

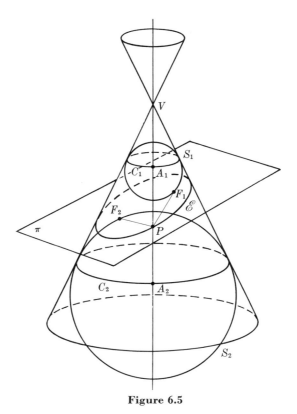

Figure 6.5

Proof: Let π be any plane that intersects a cone, as shown in Figure 6.5, to form an ellipse. Consider the spheres S_1 and S_2 to be internally tangent to the cone and tangent to the plane π at the points F_1 and F_2 respectively. The spheres S_1 and S_2 are tangent to the cone at the points which form the circles C_1 and C_2 respectively. Let P be a general point on the ellipse. The element of the cone that contains the point P, that is, the line VP, intersects the circles C_1 and C_2 at the points A_1 and A_2 respectively. Then $|PA_1| = |PF_1|$ and $|PA_2| = |PF_2|$ since the lengths of line segments tangent to a sphere from an external point are equal. Since the planes containing the circles are parallel, $|A_1A_2|$ is a constant. Furthermore,

$$|PA_1| + |PA_2| = |A_1A_2|.$$

Hence

$$|PF_1| + |PF_2| = |A_1A_2|.$$

Theorem 6.2. *Each point on a hyperbola is such that the difference of its distances from two fixed points in the plane is constant.*

The proof of Theorem 6.2 is left to the reader as Exercise 4.

Theorem 6.3. *Each point on a parabola is such that it is equidistant from a fixed line and a fixed point not on the line.*

The proof of Theorem 6.3 is left to the reader as Exercise 5.

Each of the fixed points in Theorems 6.1, 6.2, and 6.3 is called a *focus* (plural: *foci*), or *focal point*. The fixed line in Theorem 6.3 is called a *directrix*.

Exercises

1.   Graph a set of lines of the form $kx \pm \sqrt{1 - k^2}\, y = 1$ for different values of k. Identify the conic associated with the set.

2.   Repeat Exercise 1 using the set of lines of the form $kx + \dfrac{1}{k}y = 2$.

3.   Repeat Exercise 1 using the set of lines of the form $2kx - y = k^2$.

4.   Prove Theorem 6.2. (Hint: The spheres internally tangent to the cone are contained within different nappes of the cone.)

5.   Prove Theorem 6.3. (Hint: Consider a single sphere internally tangent to the cone and tangent to the intersecting plane. The fixed line is the line common to the intersecting plane and the plane that contains the circle of tangent points. The fixed point is the point of tangency common to the sphere and the intersecting plane.)

6.   Assume the converse of Theorem 6.1. Prove that the intersection of a right circular cylinder and a plane that meets each element of the cylinder is an ellipse.

6.2   AN ANALYTIC APPROACH

The set of points whose coordinates satisfy the equation $f(x, y) = 0$ is the plane curve defined by the equation. A plane curve may consist of a set of real points or not depending upon whether or not its equation is satisfied by a set of real number pairs. If no real points lie on the plane curve, we shall call the plane curve *imaginary*.

In §6.1 we define the conic sections by purely geometric conditions. It is possible to define the conic sections in a purely algebraic manner as the graphs of the general equation of the second degree in two variables.* Using the two variables x and y, we can write the equation of a conic section in the form

$$ax^2 + 2bxy + cy^2 + 2dx + 2ey + f = 0, \tag{6.1}$$

where a, b, c, d, e, and f are real numbers. If the graphs of equation (6.1) are defined to be the conic sections, then there exist nine basic conic sections, of which two are imaginary. For later reference we shall list the conic sections as follows:

(1) Real ellipse
(2) Imaginary ellipse
(3) Hyperbola
(4) Parabola
(5) Point
(6) Intersecting lines
(7) Coincident lines
(8) Real parallel lines
(9) Imaginary parallel lines

It is not our purpose in this chapter to study the conic sections by a study of the general equation (6.1). By appropriate changes of the coordinate reference system, it is possible to transform the general equation of the conic sections into one of two *standard*, or *canonical*, *forms:*

$$Ax^2 + Cy^2 = F; \tag{6.2}$$
$$Ax^2 + Ey = 0. \tag{6.3}$$

(The procedure by which this is accomplished is presented in §8.10.) In the remaining sections of this chapter, we shall discuss the properties of the conic sections by studying the equations of the conics in the simple canonical forms. In the discussion of these equations, an interchange of variables is possible which does not affect the fundamental characteristics to be examined. For example, equation (6.3) could have been written in the form

$$Ay^2 + Ex = 0,$$

in which case the roles of the variables x and y would be interchanged.

---

* Note that the imaginary curves and the real parallel lines obtained from an analytic definition of the conics are not obtained by way of the synthetic approach. The coincident lines obtained from the analytic definition, however, "correspond" to the line obtained by the synthetic approach.

In the next two sections, we interrupt our study of the conics to discuss some properties of graphs of equations in general. These properties will be useful in our study of the conics.

6.3 SYMMETRY

Certain geometric properties are useful in sketching the graph of an equation. One such property is *symmetry*, if it exists. Special cases of two types of symmetry will be considered in this section. The first type of symmetry is symmetry with respect to a line.

> *Symmetry with respect to a line:* Two points P and P' are said to be symmetric with respect to a line ℓ if ℓ is the perpendicular bisector of line segment PP'. The line ℓ is called the *axis of symmetry*.

Consider the polynomial function represented by the equation $y = x^n$ where n is an even positive integer. Let x equal $-a$ or a. Since $(-a)^n = a^n$ when n is an even positive integer, we find that $y = a^n$ in both cases. Consider the two general points $P:(-a, a^n)$ and $P':(a, a^n)$ on the graph of the function, as shown in Figure 6.6. Now, the line segment PP' is parallel to the x axis since the ordinate values of the points are equal. Furthermore, the points are both $|a|$ units away from the y axis. Hence the y axis contains the midpoint of the line segment PP' and is perpendicular to it. For each point (x, x^n),

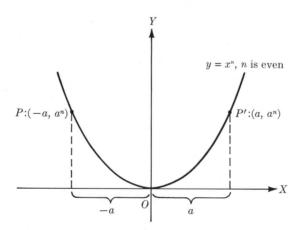

Figure 6.6

an "image" point or *symmetric point* $(-x, x^n)$ exists with respect to the y axis. In this case we say that the y axis is a vertical axis of symmetry for the graph of the function $y = x^n$.

In general, if any function $f(x)$ has the property that $f(x) = f(-x)$ for all values in the domain of the function, then the y axis is a *vertical axis of symmetry*. The functions for which this is true are called *even functions*.

Example 1. Determine the equation of the axis of symmetry for the points P:(2, 3) and P':(6, 9).

From the definition, the axis of symmetry ℓ passes through the midpoint of line segment PP'. The coordinates of the midpoint are $\left(\dfrac{2 + 6}{2}, \dfrac{3 + 9}{2}\right)$, that is, (4, 6). Since ℓ is perpendicular to the line PP', the slope of ℓ is the negative reciprocal of the slope of line PP'. Now, the slope of PP' is $\dfrac{9 - 3}{6 - 2}$, that is, 3. Therefore, the slope of ℓ equals $-\frac{1}{3}$. The equation of line ℓ may now be written in point-slope form as $y - 6 = -\frac{1}{3}(x - 4)$. Simplifying, we have

$$x + 3y - 22 = 0$$

as the equation of the axis of symmetry.

If the replacement of y by $-y$ in an equation relating x and y does not change the form of the equation, then the graph of the equation is symmetric with respect to the x axis; that is, the x axis is an axis of symmetry.

Example 2. Show that the graph of the relation $9x^2 + 16y^2 = 144$ is symmetric with respect to both the x axis and the y axis.

If x is replaced by $-x$ and y is replaced by $-y$ in the given equation, then the equation becomes

$$9(-x)^2 + 16(-y)^2 = 144,$$

that is,

$$9x^2 + 16y^2 = 144.$$

Since this equation is equivalent to the given equation, the graph is symmetric with respect to both the x axis and the y axis.

Consider the graph of $9x^2 + 16y^2 = 144$. Note that you could sketch the graph in the first quadrant by using a table of values. By using the fact that the graph is symmetric with respect to the y axis, the graph of the equation in the second quadrant can be readily obtained. By using the fact that the graph is symmetric with respect to the x axis, the graph of the equation in the third and fourth quadrants can be readily obtained.

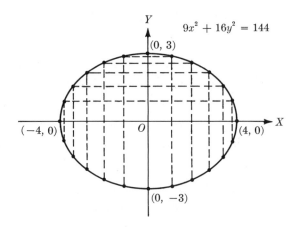

Figure 6.7

The second type of symmetry is symmetry with respect to a point.

> *Symmetry with respect to a point:* Two points P and P' are said to be symmetric with respect to a third point M if M is the midpoint of the line segment PP'.

If each point P on the graph of a function has a symmetric point P' with respect to a third point M, then the graph of the function is said to be symmetric with respect to the point M.

Consider the polynomial function $y = x^n$ where n is an odd positive integer (Figure 6.8). We can associate with each point $P:(a, a^n)$ on the graph of the function a point $P':(-a, -a^n)$ also on the graph. By use of the midpoint formula, the midpoint of line segment PP' is the origin $(0, 0)$. Hence the graph of the function is symmetric with respect to the origin.

The graph of any function $f(x)$ with the property that $f(x) = -f(-x)$ for all values in the domain of the function is symmetric with respect to the origin.* Such functions are called *odd functions*.

---

* In general, if the replacement of x by $-x$ and y by $-y$ in an equation relating x and y does not change the form of the equation, then the graph of the equation is symmetric with respect to the origin.

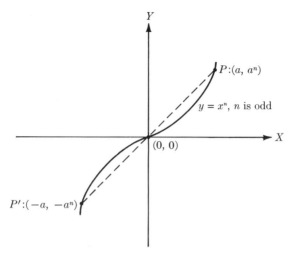

Figure 6.8

An interesting theorem relates every function to even and odd functions.

Example 3. Prove that every function is the sum of an even function and an odd function.

Every function $f(x)$ can be written in the form

$$f(x) = \tfrac{1}{2}[f(x) + f(-x)] + \tfrac{1}{2}[f(x) - f(-x)].$$

Let $g(x) = f(x) + f(-x)$ and $h(x) = f(x) - f(-x)$. Then

$$f(x) = \tfrac{1}{2}g(x) + \tfrac{1}{2}h(x).$$

Now, $g(-x) = f(-x) + f(x)$ and $h(-x) = f(-x) - f(x)$. Since $g(x) = g(-x)$, then $g(x)$ is an even function, and since $h(x) = -h(-x)$, then $h(x)$ is an odd function. Since the constant factor $\tfrac{1}{2}$ does not affect the even or odd property of a function, $f(x)$ equals the sum of an even and an odd function.

Example 4. Show that the points $P:(3, -2)$ and $P':(5, 8)$ are symmetric with respect to the point $M:(4, 3)$.

By the midpoint formula, the point which bisects the line segment PP' has coordinates $\left(\dfrac{3 + 5}{2}, \dfrac{-2 + 8}{2}\right)$, that is, $(4, 3)$. Hence the points P and P' are symmetric with respect to M.

Example 5. Show that the relation $9x^2 + 16y^2 = 144$, as in Example 2, is symmetric with respect to the origin.

Since the graph of $9x^2 + 16y^2 = 144$ is symmetric with respect to both the x axis and the y axis, it must be symmetric to any point which they have in common. But the origin is the intersection of the two axes; hence the relation is symmetric with respect to the origin.

Exercises

1. Determine the equation of the axis of symmetry for the points $P:(3, 5)$ and $P':(-2, 1)$.

2. Show that the graph of each equation is symmetric with respect to the y axis.
   (a) $y = x^2 + 5$;
   (b) $y = x^4$;
   (c) $y \geq x^2$;
   (d) $y = 3/x^2$.

3. Show that the graph of each equation is symmetric with respect to the x axis.
   (a) $x^2 + 2y^2 = 2$;
   (b) $2x^2 + 6x - 3y^2 = 7$;
   (c) $|y| < 3$;
   (d) $y^2 = x^3$.

4. Show that the graph of each equation is symmetric with respect to the origin.
   (a) $y = x^5 - 3x^3 + 2x + 5$;
   (b) $y = 1$ if $x \geq 0$, and $y = -1$ if $x \leq 0$;
   (c) $xy = 1$;
   (d) $|x| + |y| = 1$.

5. The graph of any equation in x and y is symmetric with respect to the line $x - h = 0$ if the equation remains unchanged when $(x - h)$ is replaced by $-(x - h)$. Show that the graph of $y = (x - 5)^2$ is symmetric with respect to the line $x = 5$.

6. The graph of any equation in x and y is symmetric with respect to the line $y - k = 0$ if the equation remains unchanged when $(y - k)$ is replaced by $-(y - k)$. Show that the graph of $x = (y - 1)^2 + 5$ is symmetric with respect to the line $y = 1$.

In Exercises 7–12 determine the axes of symmetry for the graph of each equation.

7. $y = (x - 1)^2 + 2$.

8. $y = x^2 - 4x + 5$.

9. $(x - 2)^2 + (y - 3)^2 = 4$.

10. $x^2 - 6x + y^2 - 4y = 7$.

11. $2x^2 - 3y^2 + 6y = 7$.

12. $x^2 + y^2 + 2Dx + 2Ey + F = 0$.

13. The graph of an equation in x and y is symmetric with respect to the point (h, k) if the equation remains unchanged when $(x - h)$ and $(y - k)$ are replaced by $-(x - h)$ and $-(y - k)$ respectively. Show that the graph of $(x - 2)^2 + (y - 1)^2 = 3$ is symmetric with respect to the point $(2, 1)$.

In Exercises 14–19 determine the point of symmetry for the graphs of each equation.

14. $(x - 1)^2 - 2(y + 3)^2 = 6.$ **17.** $y = x^5 + x^3 - 3x + 7.$

15. $x^2 - 4x + 2y^2 - 6y = 7.$ **18.** $x^2 + 4y^2 - 2x + 2y - 33 = 0.$

16. $y = x^3 + 5.$ **19.** $x^2 + y^2 + 2Dx + 2Ey + F = 0.$

In Exercises 20–23 copy the given figure and add whatever is necessary in order that the revised figure will be symmetric with respect to the graph of the line whose equation is given.

20.

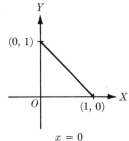

$x = 0$

Figure 6.9

22.

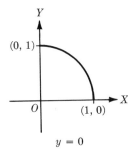

$y = 0$

Figure 6.11

21.

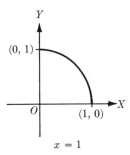

$x = 1$

Figure 6.10

23.

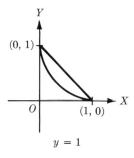

$y = 1$

Figure 6.12

24. Prove that the graph of $y = x^2 + bx + c$, where b and c are real numbers, has an axis of symmetry.

25. If the equation of the axis of symmetry of $y = 2x^2 + px + q$ is $x = 3$, find the value of p.

26. Prove that the graph of $Ax^2 + Cy^2 + 2Dx + 2Ey + F = 0$, where $AC \neq 0$, has two axes of symmetry whenever the graph exists.

In Exercises 27–32 determine whether each function is odd, even, or neither.

27. $x^5 - 3x$.

28. $x^3 + 5$.

29. $x^2 + 4$.

30. 5.

31. $|x|$.

32. $|x - 1|$.

33. Prove that the product of an odd function and an even function is an odd function. Give an example.

34. Prove that the product of two odd functions or two even functions is an even function. Give an example of each case.

6.4 INTERCEPTS AND EXTENT

In §3.6 the intercepts of a line were discussed. In general, the x *intercepts* of a plane curve are the x coordinates of the points where the curve intersects the x axis. Similarly, the y *intercepts* of a plane curve are the y coordinates of the points where the curve intersects the y axis. The intercepts may be useful in sketching the graph of an equation.

Another useful geometric property of a plane curve is that of *extent*. In order to graph the equation $y = f(x)$ or $x = g(y)$ it would be helpful to identify the range of admissible replacement values for each variable. For example, if certain ranges of values of the variable x do not yield real values of y, then these values of x define *excluded regions* of the plane for the graph of the equation. The regions of the plane in terms of the variables x and y for which the graph of the equation exists are called the *extent* of the plane curve.

> **Example.** Use the concepts of symmetry, intercepts, and extent to graph the equation $y^2 = x(x - 1)(x + 3)$.
>
> Since $(-y)^2 = y^2$, the graph of the equation is symmetric with respect to the x axis. To determine the x intercepts, let $y = 0$ in the given equation, and solve for x. Thus the x intercepts are 0, 1, and -3. Similarly, to find the y intercepts, let $x = 0$. The only y intercept is 0.

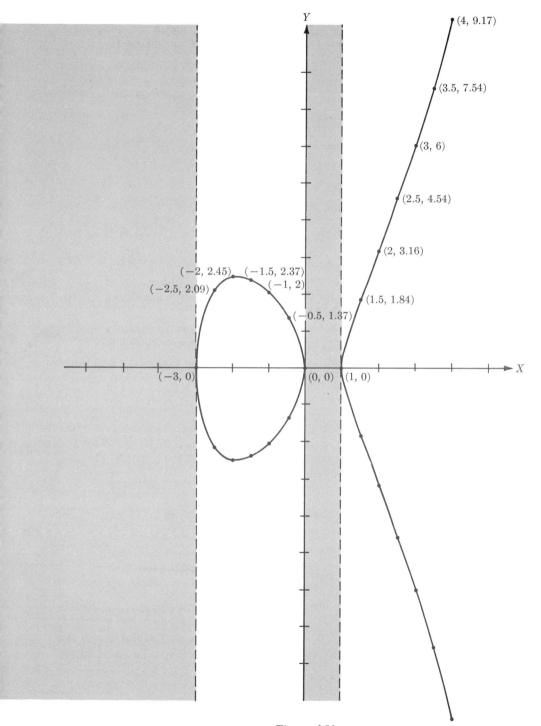

Figure 6.13

Since $y = \pm\sqrt{x(x-1)(x+3)}$, the graph of the equation is excluded from those regions of the plane for which $x(x-1)(x+3) < 0$.

If $x < -3$, then $x(x-1)(x+3) < 0$;

if $x = -3$, then $x(x-1)(x+3) = 0$;

if $-3 < x < 0$, then $x(x-1)(x+3) > 0$;

if $x = 0$, then $x(x-1)(x+3) = 0$;

if $0 < x < 1$, then $x(x-1)(x+3) < 0$;

if $x = 1$, then $x(x-1)(x+3) = 0$;

if $x > 1$, then $x(x-1)(x+3) > 0$.

Thus the graph of the equation $y^2 = x(x-1)(x+3)$ is excluded from the regions where $x < -3$ and $0 < x < 1$. The range of admissible replacement values of y is unbounded since y^2 increases as x increases. The excluded regions of the plane for the graph of the equation are shown as shaded portions in Figure 6.13.

The following table of values enables us to locate a sufficient number of points on the curve to sketch its graph.

x	-2.50	-2.00	-1.50	-1	-0.50	1.50	2.00	2.50	3	3.50	4.00
y	2.10	2.45	2.37	2	1.37	1.84	3.16	4.54	6	7.54	9.17

6.5 THE ELLIPSE

The geometric property of the ellipse presented in Theorem 6.1 suggests an alternate definition:

An *ellipse* is a set of points in a plane such that the sum of the distances of each point from two fixed points in the plane is a constant.

This definition enables us to obtain the equation of an ellipse given the foci and the sum of the distances.

Let $F_1:(-c, 0)$ and $F_2:(c, 0)$ be the *foci* of an ellipse. Let the sum of the distances from the foci of any point $P:(x, y)$ on the ellipse be equal to $2a$, where $0 < c < a$; that is,

$$|PF_1| + |PF_2| = 2a,$$

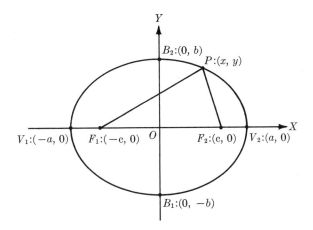

Figure 6.14

as shown in Figure 6.14. Using the distance formula, we have

$$|PF_1| = \sqrt{(x + c)^2 + y^2} \qquad \text{and} \qquad |PF_2| = \sqrt{(x - c)^2 + y^2}.$$

Therefore,

$$\sqrt{(x + c)^2 + y^2} + \sqrt{(x - c)^2 + y^2} = 2a,$$

$$\sqrt{(x + c)^2 + y^2} = 2a - \sqrt{(x - c)^2 + y^2}.$$

Squaring both members of this equation and simplifying, we obtain

$$x^2 + 2cx + c^2 + y^2 = 4a^2 - 4a\sqrt{(x - c)^2 + y^2} + x^2 - 2cx + c^2 + y^2,$$

$$a^2 - cx = a\sqrt{(x - c)^2 + y^2}.$$

Squaring and simplifying once again, we have

$$a^4 - 2a^2cx + c^2x^2 = a^2(x^2 - 2cx + c^2 + y^2),$$

$$(a^2 - c^2)x^2 + a^2y^2 = a^2(a^2 - c^2),$$

$$\frac{x^2}{a^2} + \frac{y^2}{a^2 - c^2} = 1.$$

Since $a > c$, then $a^2 - c^2$ is a positive real number. If we let $a^2 - c^2 = b^2$, then the equation of the ellipse becomes

$$\frac{x^2}{a^2} + \frac{y^2}{b^2} = 1, \tag{6.4}$$

which is the standard form of the equation of an ellipse. The coordinates of each point on the ellipse satisfy this equation. Conversely, it can be shown by reversing the preceding argument that each point whose coordinates satisfy equation (6.4) is on the ellipse. Note that equation (6.4) is of the form (6.2) with $A = 1/a^2$, $C = 1/b^2$, and $F = 1$.

Since only even powers of x and y occur in the standard form of the equation of an ellipse, the conic is symmetric with respect to both coordinate axes. Therefore, the conic is symmetric with respect to the origin, its *geometric center*.

The ellipse intersects with lines $x = k$ parallel to the y axis, provided that $|k| \leq a$ since $y^2/b^2 = 1 - k^2/a^2$ is meaningful only for these values. The ellipse intersects with lines $y = n$ parallel to the x axis, provided that $|n| \leq b$ since $x^2/a^2 = 1 - n^2/b^2$ is meaningful only for these values. Hence the ellipse is contained within the rectangular region defined by

$$\begin{cases} -a \leq x \leq a \\ -b \leq y \leq b. \end{cases}$$

The x intercepts $-a$ and a determine the *vertices* $V_1:(-a, 0)$ and $V_2:(a, 0)$ of the ellipse. The line segment V_1V_2, whose length is $2a$, is called the *major axis* of the ellipse; the line segment B_1B_2, whose length is $2b$, is called the *minor axis* of the ellipse. The positive real numbers a and b are often referred to as the *semi-major* and *semi-minor axes* respectively. (In actual fact, however, a and b are the lengths of the semi-axes.)

Example 1. Determine the standard form of the equation of the ellipse which has its geometric center at the origin, a focus at $(4, 0)$, and a major axis 10 units in length.

It is given that $a = 5$ and $c = 4$. Thus $b^2 = a^2 - c^2 = 9$; and so $b = 3$. Hence the standard form of the equation of the ellipse is

$$\frac{x^2}{25} + \frac{y^2}{9} = 1.$$

Note that the other focus is at $(-4, 0)$ and the length of the minor axis is 6. Furthermore, the vertices are at $(5, 0)$ and $(-5, 0)$.

Consider an ellipse which has its geometric center at the point $C:(h, k)$ and its major and minor axes parallel to the x axis and y axis respectively, as shown in Figure 6.15. If the lengths of the major and minor axes are $2a$ and $2b$ respectively, then the foci are $F_1:(h - c, k)$ and $F_2:(h + c, k)$ where $c^2 = a^2 - b^2$. If $P:(x, y)$ is a general point on the ellipse, then once again

$$|PF_1| + |PF_2| = 2a.$$

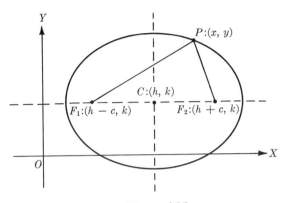

Figure 6.15

Using the distance formula, we have

$$\sqrt{(x - h + c)^2 + (y - k)^2} + \sqrt{(x - h - c)^2 + (y - k)^2} = 2a,$$

$$\sqrt{(x - h + c)^2 + (y - k)^2} = 2a - \sqrt{(x - h - c)^2 + (y - k)^2}.$$

Squaring both members of this equation and simplifying, we obtain

$$a^2 - c(x - h) = a\sqrt{(x - h - c)^2 + (y - k)^2}.$$

Squaring and simplifying once again, we have

$$(a^2 - c^2)(x - h)^2 + a^2(y - k)^2 = a^2(a^2 - c^2),$$

$$\frac{(x - h)^2}{a^2} + \frac{(y - k)^2}{a^2 - c^2} = 1,$$

$$\frac{(x - h)^2}{a^2} + \frac{(y - k)^2}{b^2} = 1, \tag{6.5}$$

where $a^2 - c^2 = b^2$. Equation (6.5) represents an ellipse with geometric center at $C:(h, k)$ and major and minor axes parallel to the coordinate axes.

Example 2. Graph the ellipse whose equation is

$$9x^2 + 4y^2 - 54x + 8y + 49 = 0.$$

State the basic characteristics of the ellipse.

Rearranging the terms of the equation, we have

$$9x^2 - 54x + 4y^2 + 8y = -49,$$

whereby

$$9(x^2 - 6x) + 4(y^2 + 2y) = -49.$$

Completing the square in x and in y respectively, we obtain

$$9(x^2 - 6x + 9) + 4(y^2 + 2y + 1) = 36,$$
$$9(x - 3)^2 + 4(y + 1)^2 = 36,$$
$$\frac{(x - 3)^2}{4} + \frac{(y + 1)^2}{9} = 1.$$

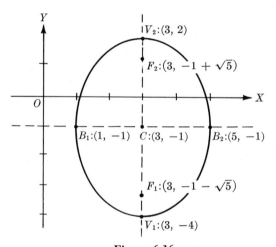

Figure 6.16

Thus the geometric center of the ellipse is $C:(3, -1)$. The major axis is parallel to the y axis, and its length is 6; the minor axis is parallel to the x axis, and its length is 4. Since $b = 3$ and $a = 2$, then $c^2 = b^2 - a^2 = 5$ and $c = \sqrt{5}$. The vertices are $V_1:(3, -1 - 3)$ and $V_2:(3, -1 + 3)$; the foci are $F_1:(3, -1 - \sqrt{5})$ and $F_2:(3, -1 + \sqrt{5})$.

Before completing the discussion of the ellipse, we make note of two other equations of the form $Ax^2 + Cy^2 = F$ where A and C have like algebraic signs. By analogy, the equation

$$\frac{x^2}{a^2} + \frac{y^2}{b^2} = -1 \tag{6.6}$$

represents an *imaginary ellipse* since no real points lie on the plane curve. The equation

$$\frac{x^2}{a^2} + \frac{y^2}{b^2} = 0 \tag{6.7}$$

represents a *point ellipse*, or simply a *point*, since the coordinates of the origin are the only coordinates that satisfy the equation.

Exercises

In Exercises 1–4 graph the ellipse whose equation is given. State the basic characteristics of each ellipse.

1. $\dfrac{x^2}{64} + \dfrac{y^2}{100} = 1.$

2. $\dfrac{(x+3)^2}{25} + \dfrac{(y-4)^2}{16} = 1.$

3. $25x^2 + 9y^2 - 225 = 0.$

4. $x^2 + 2y^2 + 4x + 4y + 4 = 0.$

5. Determine the equation of the ellipse which has its geometric center at the origin, a focus at $(-2, 0)$, and a major axis 6 units in length.

6. Determine the equation of the ellipse which has its foci at $F_1:(-1, 4)$ and $F_2:(11, 4)$, and a minor axis 10 units in length.

7. Determine the equation of the ellipse which has its vertices at the points $V_1:(3, 2)$ and $V_2:(3, -8)$, and one focus at $(3, 0)$.

8. Determine the equation of the ellipse which has its geometric center at the origin, major axis on the y axis, and contains the points $(\sqrt{2}, 4)$ and $(1, -3\sqrt{2})$.

9. Find the equation of an ellipse whose geometric center is $C:(1, -4)$ and whose semi-axes are 3 and 5.

10. Find the equation of the set of points in a plane such that the sum of the distances of each point from the points $(0, 1)$ and $(8, 1)$ is 12.

11. Find the values of k for which the line $y = k$ intersects the ellipse $9x^2 + 4y^2 - 16y - 20 = 0.$

12. State the conditions placed upon a and b if equation (6.4) represents a circle. Describe the position of the foci if the ellipse is a circle.

13. Find the equation of the ellipse whose axes are parallel to the coordinate axes and which contains the points $(2, 9)$, $(1, 11)$, $(-2, 13)$, and $(-5, -5)$. (Hint: Note that equation (6.5) can be expressed in the form $Ax^2 + Cy^2 + Dx + Ey + F = 0.$)

14. A line segment AB whose length is 12 units moves in such a way that A is always on the x axis and B is on the y axis. Determine the equation of the locus of a point P on the line segment, where P is 4 units from A.

15. A line segment perpendicular to the major axis of an ellipse at a focal point and whose endpoints lie on the ellipse is called a *latus rectum* of the ellipse. Determine the length of a latus rectum of the ellipse $b^2x^2 + a^2y^2 = a^2b^2$ where $a > b$.

16. The *eccentricity* e of the ellipse $\dfrac{x^2}{a^2} + \dfrac{y^2}{a^2 - c^2} = 1$ is defined by the equation $e = c/a$. Discuss the range of values for e. Describe as a function of e the relative shape of the members of a family of ellipses with a fixed value a.

17. Determine the eccentricity of an ellipse whose major axis is twice as long as its minor axis.

18. Derive the equation of the ellipse whose foci are $F_1:(-h, -h)$ and $F_2:(h, h)$, and for which the sum of the distances of any point on the ellipse from the foci is equal to $2a$.

6.6 THE HYPERBOLA

The geometric property of the hyperbola presented in Theorem 6.2 suggests an alternate definition:

> A *hyperbola* is a set of points in a plane such that the difference of the distances of each point from two fixed points in the plane is a constant.

As in the case of the ellipse, this definition enables us to obtain the equation of a hyperbola given the foci and the difference of the distances.

Let $F_1:(-c, 0)$ and $F_2:(c, 0)$ be the *foci* of a hyperbola. Let the difference of the distances from the foci of any point $P:(x, y)$ on the hyperbola be equal to $2a$, where $0 < a < c$; that is,

$$\big|\, |PF_1| - |PF_2| \,\big| = 2a,$$

as shown in Figure 6.17. This equation is equivalent to

$$|PF_1| - |PF_2| = \pm 2a.$$

Using the distance formula, we have

$$\sqrt{(x + c)^2 + y^2} - \sqrt{(x - c)^2 + y^2} = \pm 2a,$$
$$\sqrt{(x + c)^2 + y^2} = \pm 2a + \sqrt{(x - c)^2 + y^2}.$$

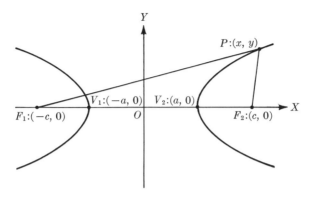

Figure 6.17

Squaring both members of this equation and simplifying, we obtain

$$x^2 + 2cx + c^2 + y^2 = 4a^2 \pm 4a\sqrt{(x-c)^2 + y^2} + x^2 - 2cx + c^2 + y^2,$$
$$a^2 - cx = \pm a\sqrt{(x-c)^2 + y^2}.$$

Squaring and simplifying once again, we have

$$a^4 - 2a^2cx + c^2x^2 = a^2(x^2 - 2cx + c^2 + y^2),$$
$$(c^2 - a^2)x^2 - a^2y^2 = a^2(c^2 - a^2),$$
$$\frac{x^2}{a^2} - \frac{y^2}{c^2 - a^2} = 1.$$

Since $a < c$, then $c^2 - a^2$ is a positive real number, say b^2. Thus the equation of the hyperbola becomes

$$\frac{x^2}{a^2} - \frac{y^2}{b^2} = 1, \tag{6.8}$$

which is a standard form of the equation of a hyperbola. The coordinates of each point on the hyperbola satisfy this equation. Conversely, it can be shown that each point whose coordinates satisfy equation (6.8) is on the hyperbola.

As in the case of the ellipse, the hyperbola is symmetric with respect to both coordinate axes, and hence the origin is its *geometric center*. The ellipse and the hyperbola are the only two proper conics having a geometric center.

The x intercepts $-a$ and a determine the *vertices* $V_1:(-a, 0)$ and $V_2:(a, 0)$ of the hyperbola. The line segment V_1V_2, whose length is $2a$, is called the *transverse axis* of the hyperbola. The line segment B_1B_2, whose length is $2b$, is called the *conjugate axis* of the hyperbola.

If the foci of the hyperbola are at $(0, -c)$ and $(0, c)$, the standard form of the equation of the hyperbola is

$$\frac{y^2}{a^2} - \frac{x^2}{b^2} = 1. \tag{6.9}$$

In this case, the transverse axis lies along the y axis, and the conjugate axis lies along the x axis. In either case, the standard form of the equation of the hyperbola is of the form (6.2) where A and C have different algebraic signs and F equals 1.

The hyperbola (6.8) intersects with lines $x = k$ parallel to the y axis, provided that $|k| \geq a$ since $y^2/b^2 = k^2/a^2 - 1$ is meaningful only for these values. Hence the hyperbola does not exist within the region $-a < x < a$. The hyperbola always intersects with lines $y = n$ parallel to the x axis since $x^2/a^2 = n^2/b^2 + 1$ is meaningful for all values of n.

In discussing the graph of an ellipse it is useful to identify the rectangular region within which the set of points is contained. In discussing the graph of a hyperbola it will be useful to identify a pair of intersecting lines which determine the region within which the set of points is contained.

Consider the hyperbola whose equation is $\frac{x^2}{a^2} - \frac{y^2}{b^2} = 1$. Since $\frac{y^2}{b^2} = \frac{x^2}{a^2} - 1$ and $\frac{x^2}{a^2} - 1 < \frac{x^2}{a^2}$, then

$$-\frac{x}{a} < \frac{y}{b} < \frac{x}{a} \qquad \text{for} \quad x > 0;$$

$$-\frac{x}{a} > \frac{y}{b} > \frac{x}{a} \qquad \text{for} \quad x < 0.$$

Hence if $x > 0$, the graph of the hyperbola lies below the line $y = \frac{b}{a}x$ and above the line $y = -\frac{b}{a}x$. If $x < 0$, the graph of the hyperbola lies above the line $y = \frac{b}{a}x$ and below the line $y = -\frac{b}{a}x$. The pair of intersecting lines $y = \frac{b}{a}x$ and $y = -\frac{b}{a}x$ are called the *asymptotes* of the hyperbola. Furthermore, note that the equation of the hyperbola $\frac{x^2}{a^2} - \frac{y^2}{b^2} = 1$ can be expressed in the form

$$y = \pm\frac{b}{a}\sqrt{x^2 - a^2}.$$

For increasing values of $|x|$, the expression $\pm\frac{b}{a}\sqrt{x^2 - a^2}$ approaches $\pm\frac{b}{a}x$, that is, the points (x, y) on the graph of the hyperbola approximate better

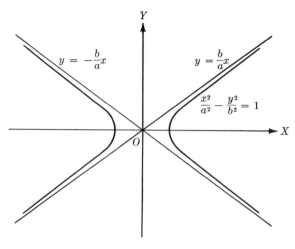

Figure 6.18

the points on the asymptotes, as indicated in Figure 6.18. Finally, note that the equations of the asymptotes of the hyperbola $\dfrac{x^2}{a^2} - \dfrac{y^2}{b^2} = 1$ can be obtained by considering the related equation $\dfrac{x^2}{a^2} - \dfrac{y^2}{b^2} = 0$, which is of the form $Ax^2 + Cy^2 = F$ where A and C have different algebraic signs and F equals 0.

Example 1. Graph the hyperbola whose equation is $25x^2 - 144y^2 = 3600$. State the basic characteristics of the hyperbola.

The equation of the hyperbola can be written in standard form as

$$\frac{x^2}{144} - \frac{y^2}{25} = 1; \qquad \text{that is,} \qquad \frac{x^2}{12^2} - \frac{y^2}{5^2} = 1.$$

Thus $a = 12$, $b = 5$, $c^2 = a^2 + b^2 = 169$, and $c = 13$. The vertices are at $V_1:(-12, 0)$ and $V_2:(12, 0)$; the foci are at $F_1:(-13, 0)$ and $F_2:(13, 0)$. The transverse axis lies along the x axis and is 24 units in length; the conjugate axis lies along the y axis and is 10 units in length.

The equations of the asymptotes are given by the related equation

$$\frac{x^2}{144} - \frac{y^2}{25} = 0.$$

Hence

$$y = \frac{5}{12}\,x \qquad \text{and} \qquad y = -\frac{5}{12}\,x$$

are the equations of the asymptotes, as shown in Figure 6.19.

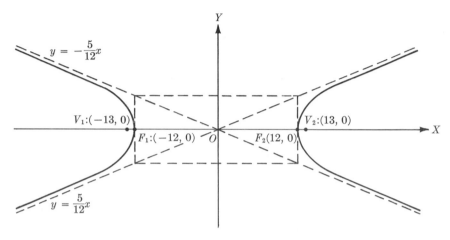

Figure 6.19

Example 2. Determine the equation of the hyperbola passing through the point $P_1:(3, 2)$ and whose asymptotes are $y = \pm\frac{4}{3}x$.

The asymptotes of the hyperbola $\dfrac{x^2}{a^2} - \dfrac{y^2}{b^2} = F$, where F is any nonzero real number, are given by the equation $\dfrac{x^2}{a^2} - \dfrac{y^2}{b^2} = 0$. Now,

$$\frac{x^2}{a^2} - \frac{y^2}{b^2} = \left(\frac{x}{a} - \frac{y}{b}\right)\left(\frac{x}{a} + \frac{y}{b}\right).$$

If each factor of the right-hand member of this equation is set equal to zero, the equation of an asymptote is formed. Since the equations of the asymptotes in this example are $3y - 4x = 0$ and $3y + 4x = 0$, the equation of the hyperbola is of the form

$$(3y - 4x)(3y + 4x) = F.$$

Substituting the coordinates of P_1, we have

$$(6 - 12)(6 + 12) = F = -108.$$

Hence the required equation of the hyperbola is

$$(3y - 4x)(3y + 4x) = -108;$$

that is,

$$16x^2 - 9y^2 = 108.$$

The equation of a hyperbola whose geometric center is at $C:(h, k)$ and whose transverse and conjugate axes, of lengths $2a$ and $2b$ respectively, are parallel to the coordinate axes is of the form

$$\frac{(x - h)^2}{a^2} - \frac{(y - k)^2}{b^2} = 1 \qquad (6.10)$$

or

$$\frac{(y - k)^2}{a^2} - \frac{(x - h)^2}{b^2} = 1. \qquad (6.11)$$

These equations can be determined in a completely analogous manner to those of the ellipse and are left to the reader as Exercises 11 and 12. The graphs of (6.10) and (6.11) are shown in Figures 6.20 and 6.21 respectively.

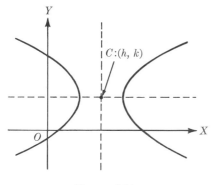

Figure 6.20

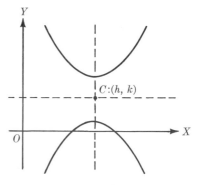

Figure 6.21

Exercises

In Exercises 1–4 graph the hyperbola whose equation is given. State the basic characteristics of each hyperbola.

1. $\dfrac{x^2}{16} - \dfrac{y^2}{9} = 1.$

2. $\dfrac{(x - 1)^2}{49} - \dfrac{(y + 2)^2}{625} = 1.$

3. $9x^2 - y^2 - 36 = 0.$

4. $4x^2 - 9y^2 - 24x + 36y - 1 = 0.$

5. Determine the equation of the hyperbola which has its geometric center at the origin, a focus at $(2\sqrt{13}, 0)$, and a transverse axis 12 units in length.

6. Determine the equation of the hyperbola which has its foci at $F_1:(-2, 1)$ and $F_2:(14, 1)$ and a conjugate axis 6 units in length.

7. Determine the equation of the hyperbola passing through the point $P_1:(5, 7)$ and whose asymptotes are $y = \pm\sqrt{2}x$.

8. Determine the equation of the hyperbola which has its geometric center at the origin, a vertex at $(4, 0)$, and for which the equation of one asymptote is $3x + 4y = 0$.

9. Find the equation of the set of points in a plane such that the difference of the distances of each point from the points $(4, -3)$, and $(4, 11)$ is 8.

10. Derive equation (6.9).

11. Derive equation (6.10).

12. Derive equation (6.11).

13. Find the values of k for which the line $x = k$ intersects the hyperbola $4x^2 - 9y^2 + 8x - 36y - 68 = 0$.

14. A hyperbola whose transverse and conjugate axes are of equal length is called an *equilateral hyperbola*. Prove that the asymptotes of an equilateral hyperbola are perpendicular.

15. Find the equation of an equilateral hyperbola having vertices at $V_1:(-1, 1)$ and $V_2:(1, 1)$.

16. Two hyperbolas are called *conjugate hyperbolas* if the transverse and conjugate axes of one are the conjugate and transverse axes of the other respectively. Find the conjugate hyperbola of $\dfrac{x^2}{8} - \dfrac{y^2}{2} = 1$. Discuss the relationship of the asymptotes of conjugate hyperbolas in general.

17. A line segment perpendicular to the transverse axis of a hyperbola at a focal point and whose endpoints lie on the hyperbola is called a *latus rectum* of the hyperbola. Determine the length of a latus rectum of the hyperbola $b^2x^2 - a^2y^2 = a^2b^2$.

18. The *eccentricity e* of the hyperbola $\dfrac{x^2}{a^2} - \dfrac{y^2}{c^2 - a^2} = 1$ is defined by the equation $e = c/a$. Discuss the range of values for e. Describe as a function of e the relative shape of the members of a family of hyperbolas with a fixed value a.

19. State the relationship between the eccentricity of a hyperbola and its conjugate.

20. Prove that the product of the distances of each point on the hyperbola $b^2x^2 - a^2y^2 = a^2b^2$ from the two asymptotes is a constant.

6.7 THE PARABOLA

The geometric property of the parabola presented in Theorem 6.3 suggests an alternate definition:

> A *parabola* is a set of points in a plane such that each point is equidistant from a fixed line and a fixed point not on the line.

It is understood that the fixed point (the *focus*) and the fixed line (the *directrix*) lie in the same plane. By means of this definition we are able to obtain the equation of a parabola given the focus and the directrix.

Let $F:(p, 0)$ be the focus of a parabola, and let $x = -p$ be the directrix. If each point $P:(x, y)$ on the parabola is equidistant from the focus and the directrix, then

$$|PF| = |PN|,$$

where line segment PN is perpendicular to the directrix, as shown in Figure 6.22. Using the distance formula, we have

$$\sqrt{(x - p)^2 + y^2} = \sqrt{(x + p)^2}.$$

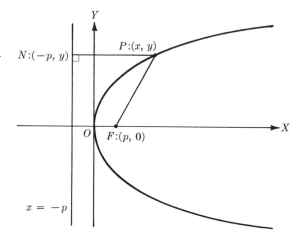

Figure 6.22

Squaring both members of this equation and simplifying, we obtain

$$y^2 = 4px, \tag{6.12}$$

which is a standard form of the equation of a parabola. The coordinates of each point on the parabola satisfy this equation. Conversely, it can be shown that each point whose coordinates satisfy equation (6.12) is on the parabola. Note that this equation is of the form $Ay^2 + Ex = 0$.

From the form of equation (6.12) it is evident that the parabola is symmetric with respect to the x axis. The point where the parabola intersects the axis of symmetry is called the *vertex* of the parabola. Thus the vertex of the parabola defined by equation (6.12) is the origin. If $p > 0$, as shown in Figure 6.22, then the replacement values of x are such that $x \geq 0$ since y^2 is always nonnegative. Furthermore, the values of y^2 increase as the values of x increase. Hence the parabola is a curve open to the right. If $p < 0$, the replacement values of x are such that $x \leq 0$, and the parabola is a curve open to the left.

If the focus of a parabola is at the point $(0, p)$ on the y axis, and the directrix is the line $y = -p$ parallel to the x axis, then the standard form of the equation of the parabola is

$$x^2 = 4py. \tag{6.13}$$

If $p > 0$, the parabola opens upward, as shown in Figure 6.23; if $p < 0$, the parabola opens downward, as shown in Figure 6.24. The axis of symmetry in each case is the y axis.

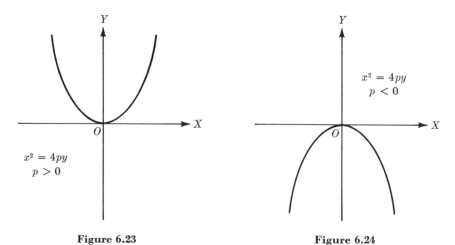

Figure 6.23   Figure 6.24

Example 1. Determine the standard form of the equation of the parabola whose focus is at $F:(0, -3)$ and whose directrix is $y = 3$.

Since the focus is on the y axis, the directrix is parallel to the x axis, and the vertex is at the origin, the equation of the parabola is of the form $x^2 = 4py$. It is given that $p = -3$; hence the desired equation is $x^2 = -12y$.

Consider a parabola with vertex at the point $V:(h, k)$. Let the focus be n units to the right of the vertex V, as shown in Figure 6.25; that is,

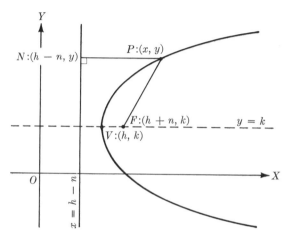

Figure 6.25

the focus is at the point $F:(h + n, k)$. It follows that the directrix is the line $x = h - n$. If $P:(x, y)$ is a general point on the parabola, then

$$|PF| = |PN|,$$

$$\sqrt{[x - (h + n)]^2 + (y - k)^2} = \sqrt{[x - (h - n)]^2},$$

$$[x - (h + n)]^2 + (y - k)^2 = [x - (h - n)]^2,$$

$$[(x - h) - n]^2 + (y - k)^2 = [(x - h) + n]^2,$$

$$(x - h)^2 - 2n(x - h) + n^2 + (y - k)^2 = (x - h)^2 + 2n(x - h) + n^2,$$

$$(y - k)^2 = 4n(x - h). \qquad (6.14)$$

Equation (6.14) represents a parabola with vertex at $V:(h, k)$ and focus at $F:(h + n, k)$. The axis of symmetry is the line $y = k$, and the curve opens to the right.

If the focus $F:(h - n, k)$ is n units to the left of the vertex $V:(h, k)$, the equation of the parabola is of the form

$$(y - k)^2 = -4n(x - h). \qquad (6.15)$$

The axis of symmetry is once again the line $y = k$. However, the curve opens to the left. If the focus $F:(h, k + n)$ is n units above the vertex

$V:(h, k)$, the equation of the parabola is of the form

$$(x - h)^2 = 4n(y - k), \tag{6.16}$$

and the curve opens upward. If the focus $F:(h, k - n)$ is n units below the vertex $V:(h, k)$, the equation of the parabola is of the form

$$(x - h)^2 = -4n(y - k), \tag{6.17}$$

and the curve opens downward. The axis of symmetry of the parabolas defined by equations (6.16) and (6.17) is the line $x = h$.

Example 2. Graph the parabola whose equation is

$$y^2 + 8x + 2y - 23 = 0.$$

State the basic characteristics of the parabola.

Rearranging terms of the equation, we have

$$y^2 + 2y = -8x + 23.$$

Completing the square in y, we obtain

$$y^2 + 2y + 1 = -8x + 24,$$
$$(y + 1)^2 = -8(x - 3).$$

The equation of the parabola is of the form $(y - k)^2 = -4n(x - h)$ with $h = 3$, $k = -1$, and $n = 2$. Thus the vertex of the parabola is the point $V:(3, -1)$, and the axis of symmetry is the line $y = -1$. The focus is the point $F:(1, -1)$, and the directrix is the line $x = 5$. The graph of the parabola is a curve open to the left.

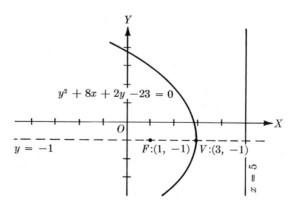

Figure 6.26

Exercises

In Exercises 1–4 graph the parabola whose equation is given. State the basic characteristics of each parabola.

1. $y^2 = -6x$.

3. $x^2 + 6x - 2y + 1 = 0$.

2. $(x - 2)^2 = -12(y + 1)$.

4. $y^2 + 4x - 8 = 0$.

5. Determine the equation of the parabola whose focus is at $F:(6, -1)$ and whose directrix is $x = 2$.

6. Determine the equation of the parabola with vertex at $V:(-3, 0)$ and focus at $F:(-3, -2)$.

7. Determine the equation of the parabola which has its vertex at the origin, the y axis as the axis of symmetry, and contains the point $(3, -3)$.

8. Find the equation of the parabola whose axis of symmetry is parallel to the y axis and which passes through the points $(2, 10)$, $(-4, 7)$, and $(0, 5)$.

9. Derive equation (6.13).

11. Derive equation (6.16).

10. Derive equation (6.15).

12. Derive equation (6.17).

13. Find the equation of the set of points in a plane such that the ratio e of the distances of each point from $F:(4, 0)$ and the y axis is   (a) $\frac{1}{3}$; (b) $\frac{1}{2}$;   (c) $\frac{2}{3}$;   (d) $\frac{3}{4}$.   State the type of conic determined in each case.

14. Repeat Exercise 13 for e equal to   (a) $\frac{4}{3}$;   (b) $\frac{3}{2}$;   (c) 2;   (d) 3.

15. The line segment perpendicular to the axis of symmetry of a parabola at the focus and whose endpoints lie on the parabola is called the *latus rectum* of the parabola. Determine the length of the latus rectum of the parabola $y^2 = 4px$.

16. Derive the equation of the parabola whose latus rectum has $A:(-2, 3)$ and $B:(6, 3)$ for its endpoints.

17. Determine the equation of the line tangent at $P_1:(x_1, y_1)$ to the parabola $y^2 = 4px$.

18. Use the results of Exercise 17 to show that the angle APF has the same measure as the angle BPC, where the line AB is tangent at P to the parabola, the point F is the focus of the parabola, and the line PC is parallel to the axis of symmetry (Figure 6.27).

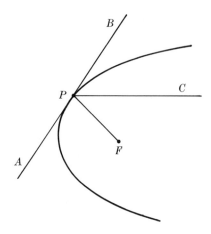

Figure 6.27

6.8 COMMENTS

It was mentioned in §6.2 that by appropriate changes of the coordinate reference system, it is possible to transform the general equation of the conic sections into one of two standard forms:

$$Ax^2 + Cy^2 = F; \qquad (6.18)$$

$$Ax^2 + Ey = 0. \qquad (6.19)$$

In this section we shall briefly summarize the algebraic conditions under which each of the conics can be represented by either (6.18) or (6.19). This information will be useful in §8.10 when the conditions under which each of the conics is represented by the general equation of the second degree is discussed.

Consider equation (6.18). If both A and C are nonzero and agree in algebraic sign, then the equation represents a real ellipse, an imaginary ellipse, or a point, depending upon whether F agrees in sign with A and C, differs in sign from them, or is zero respectively. If both A and C are nonzero but differ in algebraic sign, then the equation represents a hyperbola or a pair of intersecting lines, depending upon whether F is nonzero or equal to zero respectively.

Suppose A or C, but not both, is zero. There is no loss of generality in assuming that $C = 0$. If $F \neq 0$, then equation (6.18) represents a pair of real parallel lines or a pair of imaginary parallel lines, depending upon whether A and F agree or differ in sign respectively.

If A and E are both nonzero, equation (6.19) represents a parabola. If $E = 0$, then the equation represents a pair of coincident lines.

Exercises

Determine the conic represented by each equation.

1. $x^2 + 4y^2 = 36.$
2. $x^2 - 4x + 6 = 0.$
3. $x^2 - y^2 = 10.$
4. $y^2 - 5x^2 = 0.$
5. $y^2 - 2y + 1 = 0.$
6. $5x^2 + 10y^2 = 0.$
7. $x^2 - y^2 + 14x + 48 = 0.$
8. $3x^2 + 2y^2 + 6 = 0.$
9. $x^2 - 6x + y - 3 = 0.$
10. $x^2 + y^2 + 8x - 6y + 25 = 0.$
11. $y^2 + 6x + 9 = 0.$
12. $x^2 - y^2 - 2x + 5 = 0.$
13. $x^2 + 4x - 1 = 0.$
14. $x^2 + y^2 + 4x + 4y = 0.$
15. $7x^2 + 3y^2 - 28x + 30y + 82 = 0.$
16. $4x^2 - 9y^2 + 2x + 9y - 2 = 0.$

6.9   ECCENTRICITY

An alternate analytic approach to the definition of the proper conic sections considered in §6.5, §6.6, and §6.7 is possible, as suggested by Exercises 13 and 14 of §6.7:

> A *proper conic* is a set of points in a plane such that the ratio
> e of the distances of each point from a fixed point and a fixed
> line is a constant:
>   (i)   If $e < 1$, the conic is an *ellipse*.
>   (ii) If $e = 1$, the conic is a *parabola*.
>   (iii) If $e > 1$, the conic is a *hyperbola*.

Once again, it is understood that the fixed point (the *focus* of the conic) and the fixed line (the *directrix* of the conic) lie in the same plane. It is also assumed that the focus does not lie on the directrix. The constant ratio e is called the *eccentricity* of the conic.

The following argument demonstrates that the above definition of the proper conic sections in terms of eccentricity is consistent with our previous analytic definitions.

Let $F:(p, 0)$ be the focus of the conic, and let the y axis be the directrix. If the ratio of the distances of each point $P:(x, y)$ on the conic from the focus and from the directrix is equal to the constant e, then

$$\frac{\sqrt{(x - p)^2 + y^2}}{\sqrt{x^2}} = e,$$

whereby

$$x^2 - 2px + p^2 + y^2 = e^2 x^2,$$

$$(1 - e^2)x^2 + y^2 - 2px + p^2 = 0. \tag{6.20}$$

Note that this equation is a second degree equation in x and y and hence represents a conic under our previous analytic definition.

(i) Consider $e < 1$. Then $1 - e^2 > 0$ and equation (6.20) can be written as

$$x^2 - \frac{2p}{1 - e^2}\, x + \frac{y^2}{1 - e^2} = \frac{-p^2}{1 - e^2}.$$

Completing the square in x, we obtain

$$\left(x^2 - \frac{2p}{1 - e^2}\, x + \frac{p^2}{(1 - e^2)^2}\right) + \frac{y^2}{1 - e^2} = \frac{-p^2}{1 - e^2} + \frac{p^2}{(1 - e^2)^2},$$

$$\left(x - \frac{p}{1 - e^2}\right)^2 + \frac{y^2}{1 - e^2} = \frac{e^2 p^2}{(1 - e^2)^2},$$

$$\frac{\left(x - \dfrac{p}{1 - e^2}\right)^2}{\dfrac{e^2 p^2}{(1 - e^2)^2}} + \frac{y^2}{\dfrac{e^2 p^2}{1 - e^2}} = 1.$$

This last equation is of the form

$$\frac{(x - h)^2}{a^2} + \frac{y^2}{b^2} = 1,$$

where $h = \dfrac{p}{1 - e^2}$, $a^2 = \dfrac{e^2 p^2}{(1 - e^2)^2}$, and $b^2 = \dfrac{e^2 p^2}{1 - e^2}$, and thus represents an

ellipse. Since $c^2 = a^2 - b^2 = \dfrac{e^4 p^2}{(1 - e^2)^2}$, then $c^2/a^2 = e^2$ and $c/a = e$, the eccentricity of the ellipse.

(ii) Consider $e = 1$. As a result of the definition of a parabola in §6.7, equation (6.20) obviously represents a parabola. The equation of the parabola is

$$y^2 = 2p\left(x - \frac{p}{2}\right).$$

The vertex is at $V:\left(\frac{p}{2}, 0\right)$ and the axis of symmetry is the x axis.

(iii)   Consider $e > 1$. Then $e^2 - 1 > 0$ and equation (6.20) can be written as

$$x^2 + \frac{2p}{e^2 - 1}x - \frac{y^2}{e^2 - 1} = \frac{p^2}{e^2 - 1}.$$

Completing the square in x, we obtain

$$\left(x^2 + \frac{2p}{e^2 - 1}x + \frac{p^2}{(e^2 - 1)^2}\right) - \frac{y^2}{e^2 - 1} = \frac{p^2}{e^2 - 1} + \frac{p^2}{(e^2 - 1)^2},$$

$$\left(x + \frac{p}{e^2 - 1}\right)^2 - \frac{y^2}{e^2 - 1} = \frac{e^2 p^2}{(e^2 - 1)^2},$$

$$\frac{\left(x + \dfrac{p}{e^2 - 1}\right)^2}{\dfrac{e^2 p^2}{(e^2 - 1)^2}} - \frac{y^2}{\dfrac{e^2 p^2}{e^2 - 1}} = 1.$$

This last equation is of the form

$$\frac{(x - h)^2}{a^2} - \frac{y^2}{b^2} = 1,$$

where $h = -\dfrac{p}{e^2 - 1}$, $a^2 = \dfrac{e^2 p^2}{(e^2 - 1)^2}$, and $b^2 = \dfrac{e^2 p^2}{e^2 - 1}$, and thus represents a hyperbola.

Example. Determine the equation of the ellipse with focus at $F:(-1, 2)$, directrix $x = 5$, and eccentricity $\frac{1}{2}$. State the basic characteristics of the ellipse.

Let $P:(x, y)$ be a general point on the ellipse. From the definition of an ellipse in terms of the eccentricity e of the conic,

$$|PF| = e|PN|,$$

as shown in Figure 6.28. Thus, using the distance formula, we have

$$\sqrt{(x + 1)^2 + (y - 2)^2} = \tfrac{1}{2}\sqrt{(x - 5)^2}.$$

Squaring both members of this equation and simplifying, we obtain

$$(x + 1)^2 + (y - 2)^2 = \tfrac{1}{4}(x - 5)^2,$$
$$x^2 + 2x + 1 + y^2 - 4y + 4 = \tfrac{1}{4}(x^2 - 10x + 25),$$
$$3x^2 + 4y^2 + 18x - 16y - 5 = 0.$$

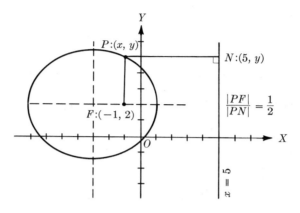

Figure 6.28

Completing the square in x and in y respectively, we obtain
$$3(x^2 + 6x + 9) + 4(y^2 - 4y + 4) = 48,$$
$$3(x + 3)^2 + 4(y - 2)^2 = 48,$$
$$\frac{(x + 3)^2}{16} + \frac{(y - 2)^2}{12} = 1.$$

The geometric center of the ellipse is the point $C:(-3, 2)$. Since $a = 4$ and $b = 2\sqrt{3}$, the major axis is parallel to the x axis, and its length is 8; the minor axis is parallel to the y axis, and its length is $4\sqrt{3}$. The vertices are the points $V_1:(-7, 2)$ and $V_2:(1, 2)$; the endpoints of the minor axis are at $B_1:(-3, 2 - 2\sqrt{3})$ and $B_2:(-3, 2 + 2\sqrt{3})$. Since $c/a = e$, then $c = ea = \frac{1}{2} \cdot 4 = 2$, and the foci are the points $F_1:(-5, 2)$ and $F_2:(-1, 2)$.

Exercises

1. Determine the equation of the ellipse with focus at $F:(0, 2)$, directrix $y = 7$, and eccentricity $\frac{2}{3}$. State the basic characteristics of the ellipse.
2. Determine the equation of the ellipse with focus at $F:(0, -2)$, directrix $y = -7$, and eccentricity $\frac{2}{3}$. Compare this equation with the results of Exercise 1.

3. Given a set of points in a plane such that the ratio of the distances of each point from $(-2, 5)$ and the x axis is $\frac{3}{2}$, find the equation of the locus.

4. Determine the equation of the set of points that divide the ordinates of the points on the circle $x^2 + y^2 = 100$ in the ratio $\frac{3}{5}$. Graph the equation.

5. Determine the equation of the hyperbola with vertices at $V_1:(-4, 0)$ and $V_2:(4, 0)$, and eccentricity $\frac{5}{2}$.

6. Find the equation of the ellipse which has its geometric center at $(8, 1)$, a vertex at $(0, 1)$, and whose eccentricity equals $\frac{1}{2}$.

7. Find the eccentricity of the hyperbola $x^2 - 4y^2 + 4x + 8y - 16 = 0$.

8. Find the eccentricity of the ellipse $8x^2 + 9y^2 - 16x - 64 = 0$.

9. The earth's orbit is an ellipse with the sun at one of the foci. If the semi-major axis of the elliptical path is taken to be 93,000,000 miles, and the eccentricity is approximately $\frac{1}{62}$, find the approximate greatest and least distances of the earth from the sun.

10. Determine the equation of a set of points in a plane such that the ratio e of the distances of each point from the origin and the y axis is a constant where   (a) $e < 1$;   (b) $e = 1$;   (c) $e > 1$.   Describe the locus.

6.10   POLAR COORDINATE FORM OF THE CONICS

It is possible to express the equation of a proper conic in polar coordinate form by using the definition of a conic in terms of eccentricity. Consider a polar coordinate reference system. Let $P:(r, \theta)$ be a general point on the conic whose focus is the pole and whose directrix ℓ is perpendicular to the polar axis and p units to the left of the pole, as shown in Figure 6.29. By the definition of a proper conic presented in §6.9,

$$|OP| = e|PN|.$$

Since $|OP| = r$ and $|PN| = p + r \cos \theta$,

$$r = e(p + r \cos \theta),$$

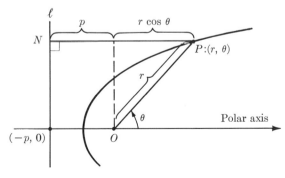

Figure 6.29

which is equivalent to

$$r = \frac{ep}{1 - e \cos \theta}. \tag{6.21}$$

This equation is a standard *polar coordinate form of the equation of a proper conic*. Equation (6.21) represents an ellipse if $0 < e < 1$, a parabola if $e = 1$, and a hyperbola if $e > 1$.

If the directrix is chosen so that it is perpendicular to the polar axis and p units to the right of the pole (the focus), the polar coordinate form of the proper conic is

$$r = \frac{ep}{1 + e \cos \theta}. \tag{6.22}$$

If the directrix is chosen so that it is parallel to the polar axis and p units from the pole (the focus), the polar coordinate form of the proper conic is either

$$r = \frac{ep}{1 + e \sin \theta} \tag{6.23}$$

or

$$r = \frac{ep}{1 - e \sin \theta}, \tag{6.24}$$

depending upon whether the directrix is above or below the polar axis respectively.

Example. Graph the conic whose equation in polar coordinate form is

$$r = \frac{6}{3 - 3 \sin \theta}.$$

The given polar equation can be expressed in standard form by dividing both the numerator and the denominator by 3:

$$r = \frac{2}{1 - \sin \theta}.$$

Now, $e = 1$; thus $ep = 2$ implies $p = 2$. Since $e = 1$, the equation represents a parabola. The focus of the parabola is at the pole; the directrix is parallel to the polar axis and 2 units below it.

The following table of values enables us to locate a sufficient number of points on the parabola to sketch its graph.

θ	0	$\frac{\pi}{6}$	$\frac{\pi}{4}$	$\frac{\pi}{3}$	$\frac{\pi}{2}$	$\frac{2\pi}{3}$	$\frac{3\pi}{4}$	$\frac{5\pi}{6}$	π	$\frac{7\pi}{6}$	$\frac{5\pi}{4}$	$\frac{4\pi}{3}$	$\frac{3\pi}{2}$	$\frac{5\pi}{3}$	$\frac{7\pi}{4}$	$\frac{11\pi}{6}$
r	2	4	6.83	14.93	—	14.93	6.83	4	2	1.33	1.17	1.07	1	1.07	1.17	1.33

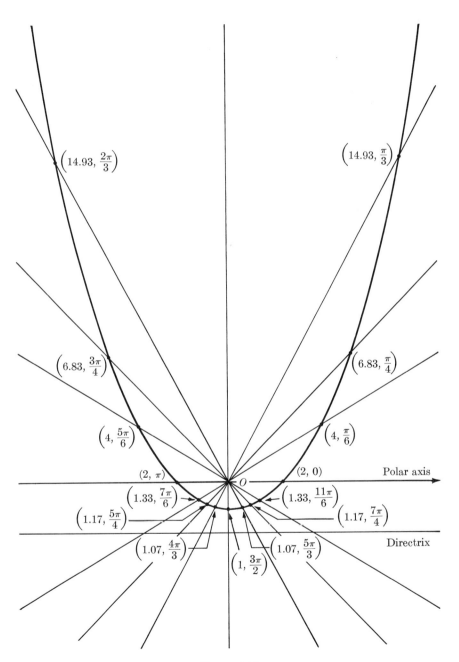

Figure 6.30

Exercises

In Exercises 1–14 graph each conic.

1. $r = \dfrac{8}{1 + \cos\theta}$.

2. $r = \dfrac{12}{2 - \cos\theta}$.

3. $r = \dfrac{9}{3 - \sin\theta}$.

4. $r = \dfrac{6}{1 + 2\sin\theta}$.

5. $r = \dfrac{-20}{4 + 2\cos\theta}$.

6. $r = \dfrac{-2}{2 - 2\sin\theta}$.

7. $r = \dfrac{10}{\cos\theta - 1}$.

8. $r = \dfrac{8}{2 + 6\cos\theta}$.

9. $r = \dfrac{8}{\sin\theta - 1}$.

10. $r = \dfrac{4}{1 + \sin\theta}$.

11. $r = \dfrac{6}{4 + 3\cos\theta}$.

12. $r = \dfrac{12}{1 - 2\cos\theta}$.

13. $r = \dfrac{20}{5 + 4\sin\theta}$.

14. $r = \dfrac{-12}{1 + 4\cos\theta}$.

15. Show that the length of the major axis of the ellipse

$$r = \frac{ep}{1 - e\cos\theta},$$

where $e < 1$, is $2ep/(1 - e^2)$.

16. Show that the length of the transverse axis of the hyperbola

$$r = \frac{ep}{1 - e\cos\theta},$$

where $e > 1$, is $2ep/(e^2 - 1)$.

17. Determine the polar coordinate form of the equation of the ellipse with focus at the pole, directrix $r\cos\theta = -6$, and eccentricity $\frac{2}{3}$.

18. Find the polar coordinate form of the equation of the parabola whose focus is the pole and whose directrix is $r\sin\theta = 4$.

19. Find the polar coordinate form of the equation of the parabola whose vertex is the pole and whose focus is the point $(a, 0)$. Verify your results by determining the rectangular Cartesian coordinate form of the equation of the parabola.

20. Show that the polar coordinate form of the equation of the circle determined by the points $(0, 0)$, $(a, 0)$, and $\left(b, \dfrac{\pi}{2}\right)$ is

$$r = a \cos \theta + b \sin \theta.$$

21. Graph the equation $r = \dfrac{8}{1 - 2 \cos \theta}$ using only positive values of r.

22. Discuss the graph of the polar equation

$$r = \frac{ep}{1 - e \cos \theta},$$

where $e > 1$ and only positive values of r are considered.

23. Show that the length of the latus rectum of the parabola

$$r = \frac{ep}{1 - e \cos \theta},$$

where $e = 1$, is $2ep$.

24. Show that a polar coordinate form of the equation of the parabola whose latus rectum is 10 is $r = \dfrac{5}{1 - \sin \theta}$.

25. Determine the length of a latus rectum of the ellipse $r = \dfrac{6}{5 - 2 \cos \theta}$.

MATRIX ALGEBRA

7.1 DEFINITIONS

Rectangular arrays of elements such as

$$\begin{pmatrix} 3 & 5 \\ 4 & -1 \end{pmatrix}, \quad \begin{pmatrix} 2 & 0 \\ 1 & 6 \\ 7 & 3 \end{pmatrix}, \quad \text{and} \quad \begin{pmatrix} a_{11} & a_{12} & \cdots & a_{1n} \\ a_{21} & a_{22} & \cdots & a_{2n} \\ \cdots \cdots \cdots \cdots \cdots \\ a_{m1} & a_{m2} & \cdots & a_{mn} \end{pmatrix}$$

are called *matrices* (singular: *matrix*). A matrix of m rows and n columns is called a matrix of *order m by n*. A *square matrix* is a matrix in which the numbers of rows is equal to the number of columns. The order of a square matrix of n rows and n columns is usually referred to simply as n. The element of the ith row and jth column is designated a_{ij}. For example, the matrix

$$\begin{pmatrix} 2 & -1 & 1 & 4 \\ 6 & 0 & -2 & 3 \\ -3 & -4 & 0 & 5 \end{pmatrix}$$

is a matrix of order 3 by 4, and the element a_{23} is -2. If the elements of a matrix are real numbers, as in the above matrix, then the matrix is called a *real matrix*. Hereafter, by "matrix" we shall mean real matrix. Furthermore, we shall be concerned primarily with square real matrices.

Matrices are denoted symbolically by $A, B, C, \ldots$ or by $((a_{ij}))$, $((b_{ij}))$, $((c_{ij})), \ldots$.

Two matrices A and B are *equal* if and only if they are of the same order and corresponding elements are equal.

Example. Construct a square matrix $((a_{ij}))$ of order 3 where $a_{ij} = 2i + j$.

$$a_{11} = 2(1) + 1 = 3, \quad a_{12} = 2(1) + 2 = 4, \quad a_{13} = 2(1) + 3 = 5,$$
$$a_{21} = 2(2) + 1 = 5, \quad a_{22} = 2(2) + 2 = 6, \quad a_{23} = 2(2) + 3 = 7,$$
$$a_{31} = 2(3) + 1 = 7, \quad a_{32} = 2(3) + 2 = 8, \quad a_{33} = 2(3) + 3 = 9.$$

Therefore,

$$((a_{ij})) = \begin{pmatrix} 3 & 4 & 5 \\ 5 & 6 & 7 \\ 7 & 8 & 9 \end{pmatrix}.$$

Exercises

1. State the order of each matrix.

   (a) $\begin{pmatrix} 4 & 0 \\ 1 & 0 \end{pmatrix}$;

   (b) $\begin{pmatrix} 1 & 5 \\ 4 & 4 \\ -2 & 6 \end{pmatrix}$;

   (c) $\begin{pmatrix} 5 & -1 & -2 \\ 3 & 4 & 7 \end{pmatrix}$;

   (d) $\begin{pmatrix} 2 & 0 & 0 \\ 0 & 1 & 0 \\ 0 & 2 & 0 \end{pmatrix}.$

2. In the matrix $((a_{ij}))$, what is the position of the elements for which
   (a) $i = 2$;   (b) $j = 3$;   (c) $i = j$;   (d) $i > j$?

3. Construct a square matrix $((a_{ij}))$ of order 3 where $a_{ij} = i^2 - 2j$ for all pairs of values i and j.

4. Construct a matrix $((a_{ij}))$ of order 2 by 3 where $a_{ij} = i + j - 1$ for all pairs of values i and j.

5. Determine whether or not the following pairs of matrices are equal.

   (a) $\begin{pmatrix} 3 & 6 \\ 2 & -1 \end{pmatrix}$ and $\begin{pmatrix} 3 & 6 & 0 \\ 2 & -1 & 0 \end{pmatrix}$;

   (b) $\begin{pmatrix} \sqrt{4} & 5 \\ 3 & 1 \end{pmatrix}$ and $\begin{pmatrix} 2 & \sqrt{16}+1 \\ \sqrt{9} & 1 \end{pmatrix}.$

7.2   ADDITION OF MATRICES

We define the *sum* of two matrices A and B of the same order to be a matrix C of the same order such that each element c_{ij} of C is the sum of the corresponding elements a_{ij} and b_{ij} of A and B respectively. That is, $A + B = C$ where $a_{ij} + b_{ij} = c_{ij}$ for all pairs of values i and j. In general, the sum of any finite number of matrices of the same order can be obtained by adding the corresponding elements.

Since each element in a sum of matrices is the algebraic sum of corresponding elements, it follows that matrix addition is commutative and associative; that is,

$$A + B = B + A \tag{7.1}$$

and

$$(A + B) + C = A + (B + C). \tag{7.2}$$

If the elements of a matrix are all zero, the matrix is called a *null matrix*, or *zero matrix*, and is denoted by 0. A null matrix 0 of order m by n is such that $A + 0 = 0 + A = A$ for every matrix A of order m by n.

The product of a real number t and a matrix A is defined as a matrix whose elements are the products of t and the corresponding elements of A. That is, if $A = ((a_{ij}))$, then

$$t((a_{ij})) = ((ta_{ij})) \tag{7.3}$$

for all pairs of values i and j. It should be clear from the definition of the multiplication of a matrix by a real number that linear combinations of matrices with real coefficients obey the following laws:

$$tA = At; \tag{7.4}$$

$$sA + tA = (s + t)A; \tag{7.5}$$

$$stA = s(tA) = t(sA); \tag{7.6}$$

$$t(A + B) = tA + tB; \tag{7.7}$$

where s and t are real numbers and A and B are matrices of the same order. Furthermore, the cancellation law holds; that is, $tA = 0$ implies that either $t = 0$ or A is a null matrix.

Example 1. Find the sum of matrices A and B where

$$A = \begin{pmatrix} 3 & 1 \\ 2 & -4 \end{pmatrix} \quad \text{and} \quad B = \begin{pmatrix} 2 & 0 \\ 1 & 6 \end{pmatrix}.$$

$$A + B = \begin{pmatrix} 3 + 2 & 1 + 0 \\ 2 + 1 & -4 + 6 \end{pmatrix} = \begin{pmatrix} 5 & 1 \\ 3 & 2 \end{pmatrix}.$$

Example 2. Find the product $2A$ where

$$A = \begin{pmatrix} 3 & 1 & 0 \\ 5 & -2 & -1 \end{pmatrix}.$$

$$2A = \begin{pmatrix} 2(3) & 2(1) & 2(0) \\ 2(5) & 2(-2) & 2(-1) \end{pmatrix} = \begin{pmatrix} 6 & 2 & 0 \\ 10 & -4 & -2 \end{pmatrix}.$$

A matrix of order 1 by n is called a *row matrix*, or *row vector*. A matrix of order m by 1 is called a *column matrix*, or *column vector*. There exists a one-to-one correspondence between the two-dimensional vectors $[a_1, a_2]$ and the row vectors $(a_1 \quad a_2)$ of order 1 by 2; there exists a one-to-one correspondence between the three-dimensional vectors $[a_1, a_2, a_3]$ and the row vectors $(a_1 \quad a_2 \quad a_3)$ of order 1 by 3. Similarly, each two-dimensional vector corresponds to a column vector of order 2 by 1; each three-dimensional vector corresponds to a column vector of order 3 by 1.

Example 3. Find the column vector $\begin{pmatrix} x \\ y \end{pmatrix}$ such that

$$\begin{pmatrix} x \\ y \end{pmatrix} + \begin{pmatrix} 3 \\ 8 \end{pmatrix} = \begin{pmatrix} 7 \\ 5 \end{pmatrix}.$$

By the definitions of addition of matrices and equality of matrices,

$$\begin{pmatrix} x \\ y \end{pmatrix} + \begin{pmatrix} 3 \\ 8 \end{pmatrix} = \begin{pmatrix} x + 3 \\ y + 8 \end{pmatrix} = \begin{pmatrix} 7 \\ 5 \end{pmatrix}$$

if and only if $x + 3 = 7$ and $y + 8 = 5$. Hence

$$\begin{pmatrix} x \\ y \end{pmatrix} = \begin{pmatrix} 4 \\ -3 \end{pmatrix}.$$

Exercises

1. Find $A + B$, $3A$, and $A - 2B$ where

$$A = \begin{pmatrix} 5 & 0 & 1 \\ -2 & 7 & 0 \end{pmatrix} \quad \text{and} \quad B = \begin{pmatrix} 1 & 2 & 3 \\ -1 & 3 & -2 \end{pmatrix}.$$

2. Verify the associative law of addition of matrices for

$$A = \begin{pmatrix} 1 & 6 \\ 8 & -4 \end{pmatrix}, \quad B = \begin{pmatrix} 2 & 3 \\ -1 & 0 \end{pmatrix}, \quad \text{and} \quad C = \begin{pmatrix} 7 & -3 \\ -4 & 4 \end{pmatrix}.$$

3. Prove that the addition of real matrices is commutative.

4. Prove that for every matrix A of order m by n,

$$A + (-A) = 0.$$

5. Find the additive inverse of each matrix.

(a) $\begin{pmatrix} 1 & 6 \\ -3 & 8 \end{pmatrix}$;

(b) $\begin{pmatrix} a & b & c \\ d & e & f \end{pmatrix}$.

6. Determine the elements a_{ij} such that

$$\begin{pmatrix} 2 & 1 & -4 \\ 3 & 0 & 6 \end{pmatrix} + \begin{pmatrix} a_{11} & a_{12} & a_{13} \\ a_{21} & a_{22} & a_{23} \end{pmatrix} = \begin{pmatrix} 10 & 7 & -2 \\ 5 & 15 & 6 \end{pmatrix}.$$

7. Verify equation (7.5) where $s = 3$, $t = -2$, and $A = \begin{pmatrix} 3 & 2 \\ -1 & 5 \end{pmatrix}$.

8. Verify equation (7.7) where $t = 2$, $A = \begin{pmatrix} 3 & -2 \\ 1 & -4 \\ 6 & 5 \end{pmatrix}$, and $B = \begin{pmatrix} 0 & 1 \\ -3 & 2 \\ 4 & 1 \end{pmatrix}$.

7.3 MATRIX MULTIPLICATION

Consider a system of linear equations such as

$$\begin{cases} 2x + y - 3z = 3 \\ x + 3y + 4z = 2 \\ 4x + 5y - 2z = 4. \end{cases}$$

By a process of successive elimination of variables through addition and subtraction, a unique solution, if one exists, may be found. Such a process places the emphasis on the values of the coefficients. Consider the following scheme of representing the above system of equations:

$$\begin{pmatrix} 2 & 1 & -3 \\ 1 & 3 & 4 \\ 4 & 5 & -2 \end{pmatrix} \begin{pmatrix} x \\ y \\ z \end{pmatrix} = \begin{pmatrix} 3 \\ 2 \\ 4 \end{pmatrix}. \tag{7.8}$$

In this representation, the coefficients, the variables, and the constants can be expressed in matrix form. The square *matrix of coefficients* may be considered as an operator acting upon the column matrix of variables x, y, and z in such a way as to produce the column matrix representing the constants. The operation of matrix multiplication is suggested by the arrangement. Note that

$$\begin{pmatrix} 2x + y - 3z \\ x + 3y + 4z \\ 4x + 5y - 2z \end{pmatrix} = \begin{pmatrix} 3 \\ 2 \\ 4 \end{pmatrix} \tag{7.9}$$

is a valid matrix equation, representing the given system of linear equations. In order that (7.8) and (7.9) represent the same system of linear equations, it must follow that

$$\begin{pmatrix} 2 & 1 & -3 \\ 1 & 3 & 4 \\ 4 & 5 & -2 \end{pmatrix} \begin{pmatrix} x \\ y \\ z \end{pmatrix} = \begin{pmatrix} 2x + y - 3z \\ x + 3y + 4z \\ 4x + 5y - 2z \end{pmatrix}.$$

If we were to multiply the elements of the first row of the matrix of coefficients by the elements of the column matrix of variables, element by element in order, and then sum the products, we would obtain

$$(2)(x) + (1)(y) + (-3)(z); \quad \text{that is,} \quad 2x + y - 3z.$$

Similarly, if we sum the products of the elements of the second row of the matrix of coefficients by the elements of the column matrix of variables, we would obtain

$$(1)(x) + (3)(y) + (4)(z); \quad \text{that is,} \quad x + 3y + 4z.$$

Finally, summing the products of the elements of the third row of the matrix of coefficients by the elements of the column matrix of variables, we would have

$$(4)(x) + (5)(y) + (-2)(z); \quad \text{that is,} \quad 4x + 5y - 2z.$$

The definition of matrix multiplication is suggested by this argument. Let $A = ((a_{ij}))$ be a matrix of order m by n, and let $B = ((b_{ij}))$ be a matrix of order n by r. In general, we define the *product* AB to be a matrix C of order m by r, where $C = ((c_{ij}))$, such that

$$c_{ij} = a_{i1}b_{1j} + a_{i2}b_{2j} + \cdots + a_{in}b_{nj}$$

for all pairs of values i and j. Thus the element in the ith row and jth column of the product matrix AB is obtained by summing the products of the elements in the ith row of A by the elements in the jth column of B.

It is evident from the general definition of matrix multiplication that two matrices can be multiplied only when they are *conformable;* that is, the number of columns in the first matrix must be equal to the number of rows in the second matrix.

Example 1. Verify that, in general, matrix multiplication is not commutative. Take

$$A = \begin{pmatrix} 2 & 6 \\ 4 & 3 \end{pmatrix} \quad \text{and} \quad B = \begin{pmatrix} 1 & 5 \\ -2 & 0 \end{pmatrix}.$$

By definition,

$$AB = \begin{pmatrix} 2 & 6 \\ 4 & 3 \end{pmatrix} \begin{pmatrix} 1 & 5 \\ -2 & 0 \end{pmatrix}$$

$$= \begin{pmatrix} (2)(1) + (6)(-2) & (2)(5) + (6)(0) \\ (4)(1) + (3)(-2) & (4)(5) + (3)(0) \end{pmatrix}$$

$$= \begin{pmatrix} -10 & 10 \\ -2 & 20 \end{pmatrix};$$

$$BA = \begin{pmatrix} 1 & 5 \\ -2 & 0 \end{pmatrix} \begin{pmatrix} 2 & 6 \\ 4 & 3 \end{pmatrix}$$

$$= \begin{pmatrix} (1)(2) + (5)(4) & (1)(6) + (5)(3) \\ (-2)(2) + (0)(4) & (-2)(6) + (0)(3) \end{pmatrix}$$

$$= \begin{pmatrix} 22 & 21 \\ -4 & -12 \end{pmatrix}.$$

Hence $AB \neq BA$.

While matrix multiplication is in general not commutative, two other familiar laws of the algebra of real numbers hold for matrix multiplication. It can be shown that the multiplication of matrices is distributive with respect to addition:

$$A(B + C) = AB + AC; \tag{7.10}$$
$$(A + B)C = AC + BC. \tag{7.11}$$

Of great importance is the fact that the multiplication of matrices is associative:

$$(AB)C = A(BC). \tag{7.12}$$

Example 2. Verify that $A(B + C) = AB + AC$. Take

$$A = \begin{pmatrix} 1 & 4 \\ 3 & 0 \\ 2 & 5 \end{pmatrix}, \quad B = \begin{pmatrix} 5 & -1 \\ 6 & 2 \end{pmatrix}, \quad \text{and} \quad C = \begin{pmatrix} 3 & -3 \\ 7 & 1 \end{pmatrix}.$$

$$A(B + C) = \begin{pmatrix} 1 & 4 \\ 3 & 0 \\ 2 & 5 \end{pmatrix} \left[\begin{pmatrix} 5 & -1 \\ 6 & 2 \end{pmatrix} + \begin{pmatrix} 3 & -3 \\ 7 & 1 \end{pmatrix} \right]$$

$$= \begin{pmatrix} 1 & 4 \\ 3 & 0 \\ 2 & 5 \end{pmatrix} \begin{pmatrix} 8 & -4 \\ 13 & 3 \end{pmatrix} = \begin{pmatrix} 60 & 8 \\ 24 & -12 \\ 81 & 7 \end{pmatrix};$$

$$AB + AC = \begin{pmatrix} 1 & 4 \\ 3 & 0 \\ 2 & 5 \end{pmatrix} \begin{pmatrix} 5 & -1 \\ 6 & 2 \end{pmatrix} + \begin{pmatrix} 1 & 4 \\ 3 & 0 \\ 2 & 5 \end{pmatrix} \begin{pmatrix} 3 & -3 \\ 7 & 1 \end{pmatrix}$$

$$= \begin{pmatrix} 29 & 7 \\ 15 & -3 \\ 40 & 8 \end{pmatrix} + \begin{pmatrix} 31 & 1 \\ 9 & -9 \\ 41 & -1 \end{pmatrix} = \begin{pmatrix} 60 & 8 \\ 24 & -12 \\ 81 & 7 \end{pmatrix}.$$

Hence $A(B + C) = AB + AC$.

The elements d_{ii} of a square matrix D are called the *diagonal elements* of D and are said to lie on the *main diagonal*, or *principal diagonal*. A square matrix such as

$$D = \begin{pmatrix} d_{11} & 0 & \cdots & 0 \\ 0 & d_{22} & \cdots & 0 \\ \cdots & \cdots & \cdots & \cdots \\ 0 & 0 & \cdots & d_{nn} \end{pmatrix}$$

is called a *diagonal matrix;* that is, every element d_{ij}, where $i \neq j$, is equal to zero in a diagonal matrix. If all d_{ii} are equal, the diagonal matrix is called a *scalar matrix*.

A scalar matrix where $d_{ii} = 1$ is called an *identity matrix*, or *unit matrix*. For example,

$$\begin{pmatrix} 1 & 0 \\ 0 & 1 \end{pmatrix}, \quad \begin{pmatrix} 1 & 0 & 0 \\ 0 & 1 & 0 \\ 0 & 0 & 1 \end{pmatrix}, \quad \text{and} \quad \begin{pmatrix} 1 & 0 & 0 & 0 \\ 0 & 1 & 0 & 0 \\ 0 & 0 & 1 & 0 \\ 0 & 0 & 0 & 1 \end{pmatrix}$$

are identity matrices. An identity matrix, denoted by I, has the property that

$$AI = IA = A \tag{7.13}$$

where A is a square matrix and I is the identity matrix of the same order as A. It should be noted that if A is a matrix of order m by n, the *pre-multiplication* identity matrix is of order m by m, while the *postmultiplication* identity matrix is of order n by n. For example, if

$$A = \begin{pmatrix} 2 & 3 & 1 \\ 5 & 0 & 4 \end{pmatrix},$$

then

$$\begin{pmatrix} 1 & 0 \\ 0 & 1 \end{pmatrix} \begin{pmatrix} 2 & 3 & 1 \\ 5 & 0 & 4 \end{pmatrix} = \begin{pmatrix} 2 & 3 & 1 \\ 5 & 0 & 4 \end{pmatrix}$$

and

$$\begin{pmatrix} 2 & 3 & 1 \\ 5 & 0 & 4 \end{pmatrix} \begin{pmatrix} 1 & 0 & 0 \\ 0 & 1 & 0 \\ 0 & 0 & 1 \end{pmatrix} = \begin{pmatrix} 2 & 3 & 1 \\ 5 & 0 & 4 \end{pmatrix}.$$

Exercises

1. Find AB where

$$A = \begin{pmatrix} 3 & -1 & 0 \\ 2 & 6 & 3 \\ 1 & 7 & 2 \end{pmatrix} \quad \text{and} \quad B = \begin{pmatrix} 1 & -1 \\ 2 & 1 \\ 0 & 4 \end{pmatrix}.$$

2. If the orders of matrices A, B, C, and D are 2 by 3, 3 by 4, 2 by 5, and 4 by 2 respectively, state all possible products involving two of these matrices.

3. Verify that matrix multiplication is not commutative. Take

$$A = \begin{pmatrix} 2 & 6 \\ 1 & -3 \end{pmatrix} \quad \text{and} \quad B = \begin{pmatrix} 4 & -1 \\ 2 & 2 \end{pmatrix}.$$

4. Verify equation (7.10) where

$$A = \begin{pmatrix} 6 & -1 \\ 3 & 2 \end{pmatrix}, \quad B = \begin{pmatrix} 5 & 4 \\ 1 & 0 \end{pmatrix}, \quad \text{and} \quad C = \begin{pmatrix} 2 & -1 \\ -1 & 3 \end{pmatrix}.$$

5. Verify equation (7.11) where

$$A = \begin{pmatrix} 5 & 1 \\ 2 & 3 \end{pmatrix}, \quad B = \begin{pmatrix} 4 & -4 \\ 0 & 2 \end{pmatrix}, \quad \text{and} \quad C = \begin{pmatrix} 2 & 1 & 0 \\ 1 & 6 & -3 \end{pmatrix}.$$

6. Verify that matrix multiplication is associative. Take

$$A = \begin{pmatrix} -4 & 2 \\ 1 & 3 \\ 0 & -1 \end{pmatrix}, \quad B = \begin{pmatrix} 5 & 4 \\ 1 & 0 \end{pmatrix}, \quad \text{and} \quad C = \begin{pmatrix} 0 & -2 & 1 & 2 \\ 4 & 3 & 0 & 1 \end{pmatrix}.$$

7. Can the product of two nonsquare matrices be a square matrix? If so, under what conditions?

8. Find the matrix products AB and BA of the row vector $A = (3 \quad -4)$ and the column vector $B = \begin{pmatrix} 2 \\ 1 \end{pmatrix}$.

9. Find $\begin{pmatrix} \cos \theta & -\sin \theta \\ \sin \theta & \cos \theta \end{pmatrix} \begin{pmatrix} \cos \phi & -\sin \phi \\ \sin \phi & \cos \phi \end{pmatrix}$.

10. Find A^2, A^3, A^4, . . . , A^n where

$$A = \begin{pmatrix} \dfrac{1}{2} & -\dfrac{\sqrt{3}}{2} \\ \dfrac{\sqrt{3}}{2} & \dfrac{1}{2} \end{pmatrix}.$$

11. Given $A = \begin{pmatrix} 5 & 1 \\ 3 & 0 \end{pmatrix}$ and $B = \begin{pmatrix} 1 & 4 \\ 0 & 1 \end{pmatrix}$, show that

$$(A + B)(A + B) \neq A^2 + 2AB + B^2.$$

12. Determine under what conditions $(A + B)(A - B) = A^2 - B^2$.

13. Find all matrices A such that

(a) $A \begin{pmatrix} 3 & 0 \\ -2 & 0 \end{pmatrix} = \begin{pmatrix} 0 & 0 \\ 0 & 0 \end{pmatrix};$ (b) $\begin{pmatrix} 1 & 0 \\ 1 & 0 \end{pmatrix} A = \begin{pmatrix} 2 & 0 & 0 \\ 4 & 0 & 0 \end{pmatrix}.$

14. Find two square matrices A and B of order 2 such that $AB = 0$, but $A \neq 0$ and $B \neq 0$.

15. Show that $AB = BA = I$ where

$$A = \begin{pmatrix} 3 & 0 & -2 \\ 3 & 1 & -2 \\ -1 & 0 & 1 \end{pmatrix} \quad \text{and} \quad B = \begin{pmatrix} 1 & 0 & 2 \\ -1 & 1 & 0 \\ 1 & 0 & 3 \end{pmatrix}.$$

16. Solve the matrix equation

$$\begin{pmatrix} 3 & 1 \\ 8 & 4 \end{pmatrix} \begin{pmatrix} w & x \\ y & z \end{pmatrix} = \begin{pmatrix} 1 & 0 \\ 0 & 1 \end{pmatrix}.$$

17. Prove that the product of two square diagonal matrices of the same order is commutative.

18. What is the effect of premultiplication and postmultiplication of a square matrix of order n by a conformable square diagonal matrix? By a conformable scalar matrix?

19. We define the *trace* of a square matrix to be the sum of its diagonal elements. Prove that the trace of the sum $A + B$ equals the sum of the trace of A and the trace of B.

7.4 SYMMETRIC AND SKEW-SYMMETRIC MATRICES

A real matrix $((a_{ij}))$ is called a *symmetric matrix* if $a_{ij} = a_{ji}$ for all pairs of values i and j. For example,

$$\begin{pmatrix} 6 & 3 & 0 \\ 3 & -1 & 5 \\ 0 & 5 & 7 \end{pmatrix}$$

is a symmetric matrix of order 3. A matrix $((a_{ij}))$ is called a *skew-symmetric matrix* if $a_{ij} = -a_{ji}$ for all pairs of values i and j. The matrix

$$\begin{pmatrix} 0 & 6 & -2 & 3 \\ -6 & 0 & 4 & 0 \\ 2 & -4 & 0 & 5 \\ -3 & 0 & -5 & 0 \end{pmatrix}$$

is a skew-symmetric matrix of order 4.

For a matrix to be symmetric or skew-symmetric, it must necessarily be a square matrix. In addition, each element lying along the principal diagonal of a skew-symmetric matrix must be zero since $a_{ii} = -a_{ii}$ if and only if $a_{ii} = 0$.

We may discuss symmetric and skew-symmetric matrices in terms of the operation of *transposition*, whereby the rows and columns of a given matrix A are interchanged. The resulting matrix is called the *transpose* of the original matrix, and is denoted by A^T. That is, if $A = ((a_{ij}))$, then $A^\mathsf{T} = ((a_{ji}))$. Note that the transpose of a column matrix is a row matrix, and the transpose of a row matrix is a column matrix.

If $a_{ij} = a_{ji}$ for all pairs of values i and j of matrix A, then A is a symmetric matrix, and the transposition of A leaves the matrix unaltered. For example,

$$\text{if} \quad A = \begin{pmatrix} a & h & g & r \\ h & b & f & s \\ g & f & c & t \\ r & s & t & d \end{pmatrix}, \quad \text{then} \quad A^\mathsf{T} = \begin{pmatrix} a & h & g & r \\ h & b & f & s \\ g & f & c & t \\ r & s & t & d \end{pmatrix};$$

hence $A^\mathsf{T} = A$.

If $a_{ij} = -a_{ji}$ for all pairs of values i and j of matrix A, then A is a skew-symmetric matrix, and the transposition of A changes the sign of all the elements of A. For example,

$$\text{if} \quad A = \begin{pmatrix} 0 & -a & b \\ a & 0 & -c \\ -b & c & 0 \end{pmatrix}, \quad \text{then} \quad A^\mathsf{T} = \begin{pmatrix} 0 & a & -b \\ -a & 0 & c \\ b & -c & 0 \end{pmatrix};$$

hence $A^\mathsf{T} = -A$.

The following theorems are true for matrices in general and will be accepted without proof.

Theorem 7.1. *For any matrix, the transposition operation is reflexive:*

$$(A^\mathsf{T})^\mathsf{T} = A.$$

Theorem 7.2. *The transpose of the sum (or difference) of two matrices is equal to the sum (or difference) of their transposes:*

$$(A + B)^\mathsf{T} = A^\mathsf{T} + B^\mathsf{T}.$$

Theorem 7.3. *The transpose of the product of two matrices is equal to the product of their transposes in reverse order:*

$$(AB)^\mathsf{T} = B^\mathsf{T}A^\mathsf{T}.$$

Theorem 7.4. *The product of any matrix and its transpose is a symmetric matrix:*

$$AA^\mathsf{T} = B, \qquad where \quad B^\mathsf{T} = B.$$

The following theorems are true for square matrices in general.

Theorem 7.5. *The sum of any square matrix and its transpose is a symmetric matrix:*

$$A + A^\mathsf{T} = B, \qquad where \quad B^\mathsf{T} = B.$$

Proof: If $B = A + A^\mathsf{T}$, then

$$B^\mathsf{T} = (A + A^\mathsf{T})^\mathsf{T}.$$

By Theorem 7.2,

$$B^\mathsf{T} = A^\mathsf{T} + (A^\mathsf{T})^\mathsf{T}.$$

By Theorem 7.1,

$$B^\mathsf{T} = A^\mathsf{T} + A.$$

Since the addition of matrices is commutative,

$$B^\mathsf{T} = A + A^\mathsf{T}.$$

Hence $B^\mathsf{T} = B$.

Theorem 7.6. *The difference of any square matrix and its transpose is a skew-symmetric matrix:*

$$A - A^\mathsf{T} = B, \qquad where \quad B^\mathsf{T} = -B.$$

Proof: If $B = A - A^\mathsf{T}$, then

$$B^\mathsf{T} = (A - A^\mathsf{T})^\mathsf{T}.$$

By Theorem 7.2,

$$B^\mathsf{T} = A^\mathsf{T} - (A^\mathsf{T})^\mathsf{T}.$$

By Theorem 7.1,

$$B^\mathsf{T} = A^\mathsf{T} - A.$$

Hence $B^\mathsf{T} = -B$.

It is always possible to express a square matrix as the sum of a symmetric matrix and a skew-symmetric matrix. Consider any matrix A expressed in the form

$$A = \tfrac{1}{2}(A + A^\mathsf{T}) + \tfrac{1}{2}(A - A^\mathsf{T}). \qquad (7.14)$$

We have already proved that $A + A^\mathsf{T}$ is a symmetric matrix and $A - A^\mathsf{T}$ is a skew-symmetric matrix. Since the multiplication of a matrix by a real number does not affect the symmetric nature of the matrix, then $\tfrac{1}{2}(A + A^\mathsf{T})$

is a symmetric matrix, $\frac{1}{2}(A - A^\mathsf{T})$ is a skew-symmetric matrix, and A is the sum of a symmetric and a skew-symmetric matrix.

Example 1. Given $A = \begin{pmatrix} 4 & 1 & 3 \\ -2 & 0 & 5 \\ 1 & 1 & 6 \end{pmatrix}$, find the sum of A and its transpose.

By interchanging the rows and columns of A, we have

$$A^\mathsf{T} = \begin{pmatrix} 4 & -2 & 1 \\ 1 & 0 & 1 \\ 3 & 5 & 6 \end{pmatrix}.$$

Therefore,

$$A + A^\mathsf{T} = \begin{pmatrix} 4+4 & 1+(-2) & 3+1 \\ -2+1 & 0+0 & 5+1 \\ 1+3 & 1+5 & 6+6 \end{pmatrix}$$

$$= \begin{pmatrix} 8 & -1 & 4 \\ -1 & 0 & 6 \\ 4 & 6 & 12 \end{pmatrix}.$$

Note that the result is a symmetric matrix.

Example 2. Find the symmetric and skew-symmetric matrices whose sum is the matrix A where

$$A = \begin{pmatrix} 6 & 1 & 4 \\ 2 & 5 & 8 \\ 0 & 3 & 1 \end{pmatrix}.$$

Using equation (7.14), write each element a_{ij} of the matrix A in the form

$$a_{ij} = \tfrac{1}{2}(a_{ij} + a_{ji}) + \tfrac{1}{2}(a_{ij} - a_{ji}).$$

Then

$$A = \frac{1}{2}\begin{pmatrix} 6+6 & 1+2 & 4+0 \\ 2+1 & 5+5 & 8+3 \\ 0+4 & 3+8 & 1+1 \end{pmatrix} + \frac{1}{2}\begin{pmatrix} 6-6 & 1-2 & 4-0 \\ 2-1 & 5-5 & 8-3 \\ 0-4 & 3-8 & 1-1 \end{pmatrix}$$

$$= \begin{pmatrix} 6 & \frac{3}{2} & 2 \\ \frac{3}{2} & 5 & \frac{11}{2} \\ 2 & \frac{11}{2} & 1 \end{pmatrix} + \begin{pmatrix} 0 & -\frac{1}{2} & 2 \\ \frac{1}{2} & 0 & \frac{5}{2} \\ -2 & -\frac{5}{2} & 0 \end{pmatrix}.$$

Exercises

1. Determine whether each matrix is symmetric, skew-symmetric, or neither.

    (a) $\begin{pmatrix} 0 & -2 & 1 \\ 2 & 0 & 6 \\ -1 & 6 & 0 \end{pmatrix}$;

    (b) $\begin{pmatrix} 0 & 3 \\ 3 & 0 \end{pmatrix}$;

    (c) $\begin{pmatrix} 3 & 0 & 0 \\ 0 & 2 & 0 \\ 0 & 0 & 5 \end{pmatrix}$;

    (d) $\begin{pmatrix} 0 & 1 \\ -1 & 0 \end{pmatrix}$;

    (e) $\begin{pmatrix} 0 & 0 & 0 \\ 0 & 0 & 0 \\ 0 & 0 & 0 \end{pmatrix}$;

    (f) $\begin{pmatrix} 4 & -1 & 0 \\ -1 & 6 & 0 \end{pmatrix}$;

    (g) $\begin{pmatrix} 0 & 2 & 4 \\ 6 & 0 & 6 \\ 4 & 2 & 0 \end{pmatrix}$;

    (h) $\begin{pmatrix} 5 & -2 & 4 \\ 2 & 0 & -3 \\ -4 & 3 & 1 \end{pmatrix}$.

2. Verify Theorem 7.3 where

    $$A = \begin{pmatrix} -1 & 2 & 3 \\ 4 & -5 & 6 \end{pmatrix} \quad \text{and} \quad B = \begin{pmatrix} 1 & -3 \\ 2 & -1 \\ 3 & 0 \end{pmatrix}.$$

3. Verify Theorem 7.4 where $A = \begin{pmatrix} 5 & 1 \\ 1 & 3 \end{pmatrix}$.

4. Write the matrix

    $$\begin{pmatrix} 3 & -1 & 0 \\ 4 & 2 & 1 \\ -2 & 3 & 1 \end{pmatrix}$$

    as the sum of a symmetric matrix and a skew-symmetric matrix.

5. Prove Theorem 7.1.

6. Prove Theorem 7.2.

7. Prove Theorem 7.3.

8. Prove Theorem 7.4.

9. Prove that if A and B are symmetric matrices, then AB is a symmetric matrix if and only if $AB = BA$.

10. Prove that if A and B are skew-symmetric matrices, then AB is a symmetric matrix if and only if $AB = BA$.

7.5   INVERSE OF A MATRIX

Consider any square matrix $A = ((a_{ij}))$. As noted in §2.9, there is associated with the square array of elements a_{ij} a real number. In terms of the matrix A, we shall refer to this real number as the *determinant of the matrix* and shall denote that determinant by $\det A$ or $\|a_{ij}\|$. The determinant of a matrix plays a fundamental role in the process of obtaining the multiplicative inverse, if it exists, of a square matrix. The *multiplicative inverse* of matrix A, denoted by A^{-1}, is that matrix for which $AA^{-1} = A^{-1}A = I$. In this section we illustrate a process of obtaining the multiplicative inverse of a square matrix of order 3. The process can be easily extended for square matrices of any order n.

Let $A = ((a_{ij}))$ be any square matrix of order 3. From a study of determinants we know that $\det A$ is equal to the sum of the products of the elements of any row and their cofactors:

$$\det A = a_{11}A_{11} + a_{12}A_{12} + a_{13}A_{13},$$
$$\det A = a_{21}A_{21} + a_{22}A_{22} + a_{23}A_{23},$$
$$\det A = a_{31}A_{31} + a_{32}A_{32} + a_{33}A_{33},$$

where A_{ij} is the cofactor of the element a_{ij}. Recall from Exercise 10 of §2.9 that if two rows of a determinant are identical, then the value of the determinant is 0. Thus the sum of the products of the elements of any row with the cofactors of the corresponding elements of another row is 0 since the sum represents the expansion of a determinant in which two rows are identical:

$$a_{11}A_{21} + a_{12}A_{22} + a_{13}A_{23} = 0,$$
$$a_{11}A_{31} + a_{12}A_{32} + a_{13}A_{33} = 0,$$
$$a_{21}A_{11} + a_{22}A_{12} + a_{23}A_{13} = 0,$$
$$a_{21}A_{31} + a_{22}A_{32} + a_{23}A_{33} = 0,$$
$$a_{31}A_{11} + a_{32}A_{12} + a_{33}A_{13} = 0,$$
$$a_{31}A_{21} + a_{32}A_{22} + a_{33}A_{23} = 0.$$

We may express the above nine equations by the single matrix equation

$$\begin{pmatrix} a_{11} & a_{12} & a_{13} \\ a_{21} & a_{22} & a_{23} \\ a_{31} & a_{32} & a_{33} \end{pmatrix} \begin{pmatrix} A_{11} & A_{21} & A_{31} \\ A_{12} & A_{22} & A_{32} \\ A_{13} & A_{23} & A_{33} \end{pmatrix} = \det A \begin{pmatrix} 1 & 0 & 0 \\ 0 & 1 & 0 \\ 0 & 0 & 1 \end{pmatrix}. \tag{7.15}$$

This equation can be expressed in more concise notation as

$$((a_{ij}))((A_{ij}))^{\mathsf{T}} = \det A \cdot I. \tag{7.16}$$

Note that the matrix $((A_{ij}))^\intercal$ is the transpose of the matrix obtained by replacing each element of $((a_{ij}))$ by its cofactor. Since $A = ((a_{ij}))$, equation (7.16) can also be written as

$$A((A_{ij}))^\intercal = \det A \cdot I, \tag{7.17}$$

whereby

$$A \frac{((A_{ij}))^\intercal}{\det A} = I, \tag{7.18}$$

provided that $\det A \neq 0$. Thus, since $AA^{-1} = I$,

$$A^{-1} = \frac{((A_{ij}))^\intercal}{\det A}, \tag{7.19}$$

provided that the determinant of matrix A is nonzero.

It should be mentioned that we have shown only that $\frac{((A_{ij}))^\intercal}{\det A}$ is the *right-hand inverse* of matrix A. However, if the preceding argument is presented in terms of the elements of the columns instead of the rows, it can be shown that

$$\frac{((A_{ij}))^\intercal}{\det A} A = I. \tag{7.20}$$

It is important to note that the inverse expressed by equation (7.19) is defined only for square matrices.

Example 1. Determine A^{-1}, if it exists, where

$$A = \begin{pmatrix} 1 & -2 & -5 \\ 0 & 2 & 8 \\ -1 & 1 & 2 \end{pmatrix}.$$

Since $\det A = \begin{vmatrix} 1 & -2 & -5 \\ 0 & 2 & 8 \\ -1 & 1 & 2 \end{vmatrix} = 2$, the multiplicative in-

verse of matrix A exists. The cofactors of the elements of A are

$$A_{11} = \begin{vmatrix} 2 & 8 \\ 1 & 2 \end{vmatrix}, \qquad A_{12} = -\begin{vmatrix} 0 & 8 \\ -1 & 2 \end{vmatrix}, \qquad A_{13} = \begin{vmatrix} 0 & 2 \\ -1 & 1 \end{vmatrix},$$

$$A_{21} = -\begin{vmatrix} -2 & -5 \\ 1 & 2 \end{vmatrix}, \qquad A_{22} = \begin{vmatrix} 1 & -5 \\ -1 & 2 \end{vmatrix}, \qquad A_{23} = -\begin{vmatrix} 1 & -2 \\ -1 & 1 \end{vmatrix},$$

$$A_{31} = \begin{vmatrix} -2 & -5 \\ 2 & 8 \end{vmatrix}, \qquad A_{32} = -\begin{vmatrix} 1 & -5 \\ 0 & 8 \end{vmatrix}, \qquad A_{33} = \begin{vmatrix} 1 & -2 \\ 0 & 2 \end{vmatrix}.$$

We now determine the transpose of the matrix of cofactors, which is

$$((A_{ij}))^\mathsf{T} = \begin{pmatrix} A_{11} & A_{21} & A_{31} \\ A_{12} & A_{22} & A_{32} \\ A_{13} & A_{23} & A_{33} \end{pmatrix} = \begin{pmatrix} -4 & -1 & -6 \\ -8 & -3 & -8 \\ 2 & 1 & 2 \end{pmatrix}.$$

Thus

$$A^{-1} = \frac{((A_{ij}))^\mathsf{T}}{\det A} = \begin{pmatrix} -2 & -\dfrac{1}{2} & -3 \\ -4 & -\dfrac{3}{2} & -4 \\ 1 & \dfrac{1}{2} & 1 \end{pmatrix}.$$

Check:

$$A A^{-1} = \begin{pmatrix} 1 & -2 & -5 \\ 0 & 2 & 8 \\ -1 & 1 & 2 \end{pmatrix} \begin{pmatrix} -2 & -\dfrac{1}{2} & -3 \\ -4 & -\dfrac{3}{2} & -4 \\ 1 & \dfrac{1}{2} & 1 \end{pmatrix} = \begin{pmatrix} 1 & 0 & 0 \\ 0 & 1 & 0 \\ 0 & 0 & 1 \end{pmatrix}.$$

Example 2. Determine A^{-1}, if it exists, where

$$A = \begin{pmatrix} 2 & 4 \\ 4 & 8 \end{pmatrix}.$$

Since $\det A = \begin{vmatrix} 2 & 4 \\ 4 & 8 \end{vmatrix} = 16 - 16 = 0$, the multiplicative inverse of A does not exist.

Example 3. Solve the system of linear equations

$$\begin{cases} 2x + y = 5 \\ x + 3y = 10 \end{cases}$$

by the use of matrices.

The system of linear equations can be expressed by the single matrix equation

$$\begin{pmatrix} 2 & 1 \\ 1 & 3 \end{pmatrix} \begin{pmatrix} x \\ y \end{pmatrix} = \begin{pmatrix} 5 \\ 10 \end{pmatrix}.$$

Since the multiplicative inverse of

$$\begin{pmatrix} 2 & 1 \\ 1 & 3 \end{pmatrix} \quad \text{is} \quad \begin{pmatrix} \dfrac{3}{5} & -\dfrac{1}{5} \\ -\dfrac{1}{5} & \dfrac{2}{5} \end{pmatrix},$$

then

$$\begin{pmatrix} \frac{3}{5} & -\frac{1}{5} \\ -\frac{1}{5} & \frac{2}{5} \end{pmatrix} \begin{pmatrix} 2 & 1 \\ 1 & 3 \end{pmatrix} \begin{pmatrix} x \\ y \end{pmatrix} = \begin{pmatrix} \frac{3}{5} & -\frac{1}{5} \\ -\frac{1}{5} & \frac{2}{5} \end{pmatrix} \begin{pmatrix} 5 \\ 10 \end{pmatrix},$$

$$\begin{pmatrix} 1 & 0 \\ 0 & 1 \end{pmatrix} \begin{pmatrix} x \\ y \end{pmatrix} = \begin{pmatrix} 1 \\ 3 \end{pmatrix},$$

$$\begin{pmatrix} x \\ y \end{pmatrix} = \begin{pmatrix} 1 \\ 3 \end{pmatrix}.$$

Hence, by the definition of equality of matrices, the solution is $x = 1$ and $y = 3$.

Example 4. Prove that the multiplicative inverse of a matrix, if it exists, is unique.

Let A be a square matrix with a multiplicative inverse A^{-1}. Let B be any other multiplicative inverse of A. Since $AA^{-1} = I$ and $AB = I$, it follows that

$$AA^{-1} = AB.$$

By the associative property of matrix multiplication,

$$A^{-1}(AA^{-1}) = A^{-1}(AB),$$
$$(A^{-1}A)A^{-1} = (A^{-1}A)B,$$
$$IA^{-1} = IB,$$
$$A^{-1} = B.$$

Hence, if it exists, the multiplicative inverse of a matrix is unique.

A matrix whose inverse exists is sometimes called *nonsingular;* a matrix whose inverse does not exist is called *singular.*

Exercises

Determine the multiplicative inverse, if it exists, of each matrix.

1. $\begin{pmatrix} 10 & 7 \\ 8 & 6 \end{pmatrix}$.

2. $\begin{pmatrix} 1 & 2 \\ 0 & 0 \end{pmatrix}$.

3. $\begin{pmatrix} 2 & 5 & 8 \\ 1 & 3 & 5 \\ 0 & 2 & 10 \end{pmatrix}$.

4. $\begin{pmatrix} 1 & 6 & 6 \\ 0 & 2 & 12 \\ 0 & 0 & 3 \end{pmatrix}$.

5. $\begin{pmatrix} \cos\theta & -\sin\theta \\ \sin\theta & \cos\theta \end{pmatrix}$.

6. $\begin{pmatrix} 0 & a \\ -a & 0 \end{pmatrix}$.

7. $\begin{pmatrix} a & 0 & 0 \\ 0 & b & 0 \\ 0 & 0 & c \end{pmatrix}$.

8. $\begin{pmatrix} \frac{2}{3} & -\frac{2}{3} & \frac{1}{3} \\ \frac{1}{3} & \frac{2}{3} & \frac{2}{3} \\ \frac{2}{3} & \frac{1}{3} & -\frac{2}{3} \end{pmatrix}$.

In Exercises 9 and 10 solve each system of linear equations by the use of matrices.

9. $\begin{cases} 2x + 3y = 5 \\ x + 2y = 4. \end{cases}$

10. $\begin{cases} 2x + y + z = 8 \\ 5x - y - z = -1 \\ 10x + 3y - 2z = -2. \end{cases}$

11. Let $A = \begin{pmatrix} a & b \\ c & d \end{pmatrix}$ and $B = \begin{pmatrix} e & f \\ g & h \end{pmatrix}$. Prove that

$$\det (AB) = \det A \cdot \det B.$$

(This is valid for any square matrices A and B of the same order.)

12. Verify the results of Exercise 11 for

$$A = \begin{pmatrix} 6 & 2 \\ 2 & 1 \end{pmatrix} \quad \text{and} \quad B = \begin{pmatrix} 3 & 1 \\ 4 & 2 \end{pmatrix}.$$

13. Find the general form of the multiplicative inverse of the matrix

$\begin{pmatrix} a & b \\ c & d \end{pmatrix}$ where $ad - bc \neq 0$.

14. Find $\det ((a_{ij}))$ if matrix $((a_{ij}))$ is of order n and $a_{ij} = 0$ for every pair of values i and j such that $i > j$.

15. Prove that $(A^{-1})^{-1} = A$.

16. Prove that $(AB)^{-1} = B^{-1}A^{-1}$.

17. Verify the results of Exercise 16 for

$$A = \begin{pmatrix} 3 & 1 \\ 4 & 2 \end{pmatrix} \quad \text{and} \quad B = \begin{pmatrix} 4 & 5 \\ 2 & 3 \end{pmatrix}.$$

18. Prove that if $AB = AC$ and the multiplicative inverse of A exists, then $B = C$.

19. Prove that the transpose of A^{-1} equals the inverse of A^{T}.

20. Verify the results of Exercise 19 for

$$A = \begin{pmatrix} 2 & 0 & 2 \\ 2 & 0 & 1 \\ 0 & 1 & 0 \end{pmatrix}.$$

7.6 ORTHOGONAL MATRICES

A real matrix A for which $AA^{\mathsf{T}} = A^{\mathsf{T}}A = I$ is called an *orthogonal matrix*. By definition, it immediately follows that an orthogonal matrix must necessarily be a square matrix. Furthermore, $A^{-1} = A^{\mathsf{T}}$; that is, the inverse and the transpose of an orthogonal matrix are equal.

Let $A = \begin{pmatrix} a & b \\ c & d \end{pmatrix}$ be any orthogonal matrix of order 2. Then

$$\begin{pmatrix} a & b \\ c & d \end{pmatrix}\begin{pmatrix} a & c \\ b & d \end{pmatrix} = \begin{pmatrix} 1 & 0 \\ 0 & 1 \end{pmatrix},$$

$$\begin{pmatrix} a^2 + b^2 & ac + bd \\ ac + bd & c^2 + d^2 \end{pmatrix} = \begin{pmatrix} 1 & 0 \\ 0 & 1 \end{pmatrix};$$

that is, $a^2 + b^2 = 1$, $c^2 + d^2 = 1$, and $ac + bd = 0$. Since $a^2 + b^2 = 1$ and $c^2 + d^2 = 1$, the row vectors of orthogonal matrix A are unit vectors. Since $ac + bd = 0$, the row vectors of A are orthogonal vectors. In general, if A is an orthogonal matrix of order n, any two row vectors of A are orthogonal, and each row vector is a unit vector.

Furthermore, by the results of Exercise 11 of §7.5,

$$\det\left[\begin{pmatrix} a & b \\ c & d \end{pmatrix}\begin{pmatrix} a & c \\ b & d \end{pmatrix}\right] = \det\begin{pmatrix} a & b \\ c & d \end{pmatrix} \cdot \det\begin{pmatrix} a & c \\ b & d \end{pmatrix} = \det\begin{pmatrix} 1 & 0 \\ 0 & 1 \end{pmatrix}.$$

Since $\det\begin{pmatrix} a & b \\ c & d \end{pmatrix} = \det\begin{pmatrix} a & c \\ b & d \end{pmatrix}$ and $\det\begin{pmatrix} 1 & 0 \\ 0 & 1 \end{pmatrix} = 1$, $\left[\det\begin{pmatrix} a & b \\ c & d \end{pmatrix}\right]^2 = 1$;

hence $\det\begin{pmatrix} a & b \\ c & d \end{pmatrix} = \pm 1$. In general, if A is an orthogonal matrix of order n, then $\det A = \pm 1$. If $\det A = 1$, matrix A is called a *proper orthogonal matrix;* if $\det A = -1$, matrix A is called an *improper orthogonal matrix*.

Example 1. Verify that matrix A is a proper orthogonal matrix where

$$A = \begin{pmatrix} \dfrac{1}{\sqrt{6}} & -\dfrac{1}{\sqrt{6}} & \dfrac{2}{\sqrt{6}} \\[2mm] \dfrac{1}{\sqrt{2}} & \dfrac{1}{\sqrt{2}} & 0 \\[2mm] -\dfrac{1}{\sqrt{3}} & \dfrac{1}{\sqrt{3}} & \dfrac{1}{\sqrt{3}} \end{pmatrix}.$$

$$AA^\mathsf{T} = \begin{pmatrix} \dfrac{1}{\sqrt{6}} & -\dfrac{1}{\sqrt{6}} & \dfrac{2}{\sqrt{6}} \\ \dfrac{1}{\sqrt{2}} & \dfrac{1}{\sqrt{2}} & 0 \\ -\dfrac{1}{\sqrt{3}} & \dfrac{1}{\sqrt{3}} & \dfrac{1}{\sqrt{3}} \end{pmatrix} \begin{pmatrix} \dfrac{1}{\sqrt{6}} & \dfrac{1}{\sqrt{2}} & -\dfrac{1}{\sqrt{3}} \\ -\dfrac{1}{\sqrt{6}} & \dfrac{1}{\sqrt{2}} & \dfrac{1}{\sqrt{3}} \\ \dfrac{2}{\sqrt{6}} & 0 & \dfrac{1}{\sqrt{3}} \end{pmatrix}$$

$$= \begin{pmatrix} 1 & 0 & 0 \\ 0 & 1 & 0 \\ 0 & 0 & 1 \end{pmatrix}.$$

Therefore, A is an orthogonal matrix. Furthermore,

$$\det A = -\frac{1}{\sqrt{2}} \begin{vmatrix} -\dfrac{1}{\sqrt{6}} & \dfrac{2}{\sqrt{6}} \\ \dfrac{1}{\sqrt{3}} & \dfrac{1}{\sqrt{3}} \end{vmatrix} + \frac{1}{\sqrt{2}} \begin{vmatrix} \dfrac{1}{\sqrt{6}} & \dfrac{2}{\sqrt{6}} \\ -\dfrac{1}{\sqrt{3}} & \dfrac{1}{\sqrt{3}} \end{vmatrix}$$

$$= -\frac{1}{\sqrt{2}}\left(-\frac{1}{\sqrt{2}}\right) + \frac{1}{\sqrt{2}}\left(\frac{1}{\sqrt{2}}\right) = 1.$$

Hence A is a proper orthogonal matrix.

Example 2. Prove that the product of two orthogonal matrices is an orthogonal matrix.

Let A and B be two orthogonal matrices of the same order. Then

$$\begin{aligned} (AB)^\mathsf{T} &= B^\mathsf{T}A^\mathsf{T} && \text{(by Theorem 7.3)} \\ &= B^{-1}A^{-1} && \text{(since } A \text{ and } B \text{ are orthogonal matrices)} \\ &= (AB)^{-1}. && \text{(by the results of Exercise 16 of §7.5)} \end{aligned}$$

Hence AB is an orthogonal matrix.

Exercises

In Exercises 1–4 determine whether each matrix is a proper orthogonal matrix, an improper orthogonal matrix, or neither.

1. $\begin{pmatrix} \dfrac{24}{25} & -\dfrac{7}{25} \\ \dfrac{7}{25} & \dfrac{24}{25} \end{pmatrix}.$

2. $\begin{pmatrix} \dfrac{\sqrt{2}}{2} & \dfrac{\sqrt{2}}{2} & 0 \\ 0 & 0 & 1 \\ -\dfrac{\sqrt{2}}{2} & \dfrac{\sqrt{2}}{2} & 0 \end{pmatrix}.$

3. $\begin{pmatrix} \cos\theta & -\sin\theta \\ \sin\theta & \cos\theta \end{pmatrix}.$

4. $\begin{pmatrix} \dfrac{1}{3} & -\dfrac{2}{3} & \dfrac{2}{3} \\ \dfrac{2}{3} & -\dfrac{1}{3} & -\dfrac{2}{3} \\ \dfrac{2}{3} & \dfrac{2}{3} & \dfrac{2}{3} \end{pmatrix}.$

5. Verify that the product of two orthogonal matrices A and B is an orthogonal matrix where

$$A = \begin{pmatrix} \dfrac{4}{5} & -\dfrac{3}{5} \\ \dfrac{3}{5} & \dfrac{4}{5} \end{pmatrix} \quad \text{and} \quad B = \begin{pmatrix} \dfrac{5}{13} & \dfrac{12}{13} \\ -\dfrac{12}{13} & \dfrac{5}{13} \end{pmatrix}.$$

6. Determine all orthogonal matrices of order 2 whose elements are either 0 or 1.

7. Prove that the inverse of an orthogonal matrix is an orthogonal matrix.

8. Prove that the product of two improper orthogonal matrices of order n is a proper orthogonal matrix.

9. Prove that every proper orthogonal matrix of order 2 is of the form

$$\begin{pmatrix} \cos\theta & -\sin\theta \\ \sin\theta & \cos\theta \end{pmatrix}.$$

10. Prove that if $\begin{pmatrix} a & b \\ c & d \end{pmatrix}$ is an orthogonal matrix, then $a^2 + c^2 = 1$, $b^2 + d^2 = 1$, and $ab + cd = 0$.

7.7   RANK OF A MATRIX

Given any matrix A of m rows and n columns, we may obtain square matrices of order r by selecting any r rows and r columns of the matrix. These matrices are called *submatrices* of the matrix A. The order of the largest submatrix having a nonzero determinant is called the *rank* of the matrix. It is immediately evident that the rank of a matrix cannot be zero unless every element is zero. Nor can the rank exceed either m or n, whichever is the smaller.

Example 1. Determine the rank of the matrix A where

$$A = \begin{pmatrix} 2 & 1 & 3 & 0 \\ -1 & 4 & 1 & 3 \\ 3 & 6 & 7 & 3 \end{pmatrix}.$$

Since the order of matrix A is 3 by 4, the rank of the matrix cannot be greater than 3. However, the determinant of each of the submatrices

$$\begin{pmatrix} 2 & 1 & 3 \\ -1 & 4 & 1 \\ 3 & 6 & 7 \end{pmatrix}, \begin{pmatrix} 2 & 1 & 0 \\ -1 & 4 & 3 \\ 3 & 6 & 3 \end{pmatrix}, \begin{pmatrix} 2 & 3 & 0 \\ -1 & 1 & 3 \\ 3 & 7 & 3 \end{pmatrix}, \text{ and } \begin{pmatrix} 1 & 3 & 0 \\ 4 & 1 & 3 \\ 6 & 7 & 3 \end{pmatrix}$$

is zero. Hence the rank cannot be 3. Since the submatrix $\begin{pmatrix} 2 & 1 \\ -1 & 4 \end{pmatrix}$ has a nonzero determinant, the rank of matrix A is 2.

Consider a system of three linear equations in the three variables x, y, and z:

$$\begin{cases} a_{11}x + a_{12}y + a_{13}z = c_1 \\ a_{21}x + a_{22}y + a_{23}z = c_2 \\ a_{31}x + a_{32}y + a_{33}z = c_3. \end{cases} \tag{7.21}$$

The system can be expressed in matrix form as

$$\begin{pmatrix} a_{11} & a_{12} & a_{13} \\ a_{21} & a_{22} & a_{23} \\ a_{31} & a_{32} & a_{33} \end{pmatrix} \begin{pmatrix} x \\ y \\ z \end{pmatrix} = \begin{pmatrix} c_1 \\ c_2 \\ c_3 \end{pmatrix}. \tag{7.22}$$

In addition to the *matrix of coefficients*

$$\begin{pmatrix} a_{11} & a_{12} & a_{13} \\ a_{21} & a_{22} & a_{23} \\ a_{31} & a_{32} & a_{33} \end{pmatrix}, \tag{7.23}$$

we shall define the matrix composed of the elements a_{ij} of (7.23) and the constants c_i of (7.21) attached as an additional column to be the *augmented matrix* of the system; that is,

$$\begin{pmatrix} a_{11} & a_{12} & a_{13} & c_1 \\ a_{21} & a_{22} & a_{23} & c_2 \\ a_{31} & a_{32} & a_{33} & c_3 \end{pmatrix} \tag{7.24}$$

is the augmented matrix of (7.21).

In order to determine the solutions, if they exist, of a system of linear equations such as (7.21), three simple operations may be performed to convert the system to an equivalent system:

(i)   Two equations may be interchanged.

(ii) The terms of any equation may be multiplied by a nonzero real number.

(iii)   A nonzero real multiple of the terms of one equation may be added to the corresponding terms of another equation of the system.

Essentially, the solution of the system of linear equations (7.21) consists of performing the above operations until the system can be represented in matrix form as

$$\begin{pmatrix} 1 & 0 & 0 \\ 0 & 1 & 0 \\ 0 & 0 & 1 \end{pmatrix} \begin{pmatrix} x \\ y \\ z \end{pmatrix} = \begin{pmatrix} k_1 \\ k_2 \\ k_3 \end{pmatrix},$$

which indicates k_1, k_2, and k_3 as the solution of the system. The augmented matrix of the system takes the form

$$\begin{pmatrix} 1 & 0 & 0 & k_1 \\ 0 & 1 & 0 & k_2 \\ 0 & 0 & 1 & k_3 \end{pmatrix}.$$

Therefore, the solution of the system may be obtained by considering only the augmented matrix

$$\begin{pmatrix} a_{11} & a_{12} & a_{13} & c_1 \\ a_{21} & a_{22} & a_{23} & c_2 \\ a_{31} & a_{32} & a_{33} & c_3 \end{pmatrix}$$

in an attempt to reduce it to the diagonal form

$$\begin{pmatrix} 1 & 0 & 0 & k_1 \\ 0 & 1 & 0 & k_2 \\ 0 & 0 & 1 & k_3 \end{pmatrix} \tag{7.25}$$

by performing three *elementary row operations* on the matrix:

(i)   The interchange of two rows.

(ii)   Multiplication of the elements of any row by a nonzero real number.

(iii)   Addition of a nonzero real multiple of the elements of any row onto the corresponding elements of another row.

The elementary row operations performed on an augmented matrix are completely analogous to the ordinary processes used in solving systems of equations by the method of eliminating variables.

It is important to note that the rank of a matrix is not changed by an elementary row operation, as a result of the theorems on determinants presented in §2.9.

It may not always be possible to reduce the augmented matrix of a system of linear equations such as (7.24) to a diagonal form such as (7.25) by means of the elementary row operations. In that event, it may be that a unique solution of the system does not exist. Consider a system of m linear equations in n variables where $m > n$. Denote the rank of the matrix of coefficients by r and the rank of the augmented matrix by ρ. Now, either $\rho = r$ or $\rho = r + 1$. It can be shown, although we shall only state the results here, that the system is consistent if and only if $\rho = r$. Furthermore, a unique solution exists if and only if $r = n$.

Example 2. Show that the system of linear equations

$$\begin{cases} x + y = 3 \\ 2x - y = 0 \\ x - 3y = -5 \end{cases}$$

is consistent.

The coefficient matrix $\begin{pmatrix} 1 & 1 \\ 2 & -1 \\ 1 & -3 \end{pmatrix}$ is of rank 2 since

$$\begin{vmatrix} 1 & 1 \\ 2 & -1 \end{vmatrix} \neq 0.$$

Now, it will be sufficient to show that the determinant of the augmented matrix vanishes since it is a square matrix. The determinant of the augmented matrix is equal to zero; that is,

$$\begin{vmatrix} 1 & 1 & 3 \\ 2 & -1 & 0 \\ 1 & -3 & -5 \end{vmatrix} = 0.$$

Hence the rank of the augmented matrix equals the rank of the coefficient matrix, and the system is consistent.

Note that in Example 2 only two of the equations are independent. For instance,

$$(x + y - 3) = k_1(2x - y) + k_2(x - 3y + 5),$$

where $k_1 = \frac{4}{5}$ and $k_2 = -\frac{3}{5}$. In general, the rank of a matrix is equal to the greatest number of linearly independent rows and columns.

Example 3. Solve the system of linear equations in Example 2 by performing the elementary row operations on the augmented matrix.

The augmented matrix is

$$\begin{pmatrix} 1 & 1 & 3 \\ 2 & -1 & 0 \\ 1 & -3 & -5 \end{pmatrix}.$$

Multiplying the elements of the first row by -1 and adding the results to the corresponding elements of the third row, we obtain

$$\begin{pmatrix} 1 & 1 & 3 \\ 2 & -1 & 0 \\ 0 & -4 & -8 \end{pmatrix}.$$

Similarly, by multiplying the elements of the first row by -2 and adding the results to the corresponding elements of the second row, the augmented matrix becomes

$$\begin{pmatrix} 1 & 1 & 3 \\ 0 & -3 & -6 \\ 0 & -4 & -8 \end{pmatrix}.$$

By multiplying the elements of the second row by $-\frac{1}{3}$, the augmented matrix becomes

$$\begin{pmatrix} 1 & 1 & 3 \\ 0 & 1 & 2 \\ 0 & -4 & -8 \end{pmatrix}.$$

Multiplying the elements of the second row by 4 and adding the results to the corresponding elements of the third row, we obtain

$$\begin{pmatrix} 1 & 1 & 3 \\ 0 & 1 & 2 \\ 0 & 0 & 0 \end{pmatrix}.$$

Finally, by multiplying the elements of the second row by -1 and adding the results to the corresponding elements of the first row, the augmented matrix becomes

$$\begin{pmatrix} 1 & 0 & 1 \\ 0 & 1 & 2 \\ 0 & 0 & 0 \end{pmatrix}.$$

Remember that this augmented matrix represents the system of equations

$$\begin{pmatrix} 1 & 0 \\ 0 & 1 \\ 0 & 0 \end{pmatrix} \begin{pmatrix} x \\ y \end{pmatrix} = \begin{pmatrix} 1 \\ 2 \\ 0 \end{pmatrix},$$

$$\begin{pmatrix} x \\ y \\ 0 \end{pmatrix} = \begin{pmatrix} 1 \\ 2 \\ 0 \end{pmatrix}.$$

Thus the solution is $x = 1$ and $y = 2$.

Exercises

In Exercises 1–4 determine the rank of each matrix.

1. $\begin{pmatrix} 2 & 3 & 1 & -1 \\ 6 & 9 & 4 & -3 \end{pmatrix}.$

3. $\begin{pmatrix} 1 & 1 & 2 \\ 3 & 0 & 2 \\ -1 & 2 & 2 \end{pmatrix}.$

2. $\begin{pmatrix} 2 & 1 \\ 6 & 3 \\ 0 & 4 \end{pmatrix}.$

4. $\begin{pmatrix} 5 & 2 & 3 & 7 \\ 1 & 6 & -5 & 7 \\ 3 & -10 & 13 & -7 \end{pmatrix}.$

5. Reduce the matrix $\begin{pmatrix} 1 & 1 & 0 & 3 \\ 0 & -5 & 1 & 0 \\ 4 & 3 & 0 & 6 \end{pmatrix}$ to diagonal form.

6. Find two systems of linear equations whose augmented matrices are respectively:

(a) $\begin{pmatrix} -3 & 5 & -3 & 2 \\ 2 & -1 & 1 & 3 \\ -1 & -3 & 1 & -1 \end{pmatrix};$ (b) $\begin{pmatrix} 1 & 1 & 2 & 3 \\ 3 & 0 & 2 & 2 \\ -1 & 2 & 2 & 4 \end{pmatrix}.$

7. State whether each system in Exercise 6 is   (a) consistent or inconsistent;   (b) dependent or independent.

8. What is the maximum number of elementary row operations necessary to reduce a square matrix of order n to diagonal form?

In Exercises 9–12 solve each system of linear equations by performing the elementary row operations on the augmented matrix.

9. $\begin{cases} x + y + z = 5 \\ 3x - 2y - z = 3 \\ 2x + 3y + 5z = 8. \end{cases}$

11. $\begin{cases} 3x - 7y + 2z = 1 \\ 2x - 7y - z = 1. \end{cases}$

10. $\begin{cases} w + x + y - z = 0 \\ 2w - 3x - 2y + 2z = 19 \\ w + 3x + 2y - 2z = -4 \\ 3w + x - y = -3. \end{cases}$

12. $\begin{cases} 2x + y + z = -3 \\ x - y + 2z = 0 \\ 3x - 3y + 4z = -6 \\ x + y - z = 10. \end{cases}$

Exercises 13–17 refer to a system of linear equations of the form

$$\begin{cases} a_{11}x_1 + a_{12}x_2 + \cdots + a_{1n}x_n = 0 \\ a_{21}x_1 + a_{22}x_2 + \cdots + a_{2n}x_n = 0 \\ \cdots \\ a_{m1}x_1 + a_{m2}x_2 + \cdots + a_{mn}x_n = 0, \end{cases}$$

called a system of *linear homogeneous equations*.

13. Prove that a system of linear homogeneous equations in n variables always has the trivial solution $x_1 = x_2 = \cdots = x_n = 0$.

14. Prove that a system of linear homogeneous equations in n variables has a nontrivial solution provided that the rank of the matrix of coefficients is less than n.

15. Determine whether or not each of the following systems of linear homogeneous equations has a nontrivial solution.

(a) $\begin{cases} 2x + 3y + z = 0 \\ w + 4x + 2z = 0 \\ 3w - y = 0; \end{cases}$
(b) $\begin{cases} 3x + 10y + 6z = 0 \\ x + 2y + z = 0 \\ 4x + 3y + z = 0 \\ 2x + 8y + 5z = 0. \end{cases}$

16. Show that if a system of linear homogeneous equations in n variables $x_1, x_2, \ldots, x_n$ has the nontrivial solution $x_1 = r_1, x_2 = r_2, \ldots, x_n = r_n$, then $x_1 = kr_1, x_2 = kr_2, \ldots, x_n = kr_n$, where k is any real number, is also a solution.

17. Find the nontrivial solutions, if they exist, of the systems of equations in Exercise 15.

18. (a) Show that the first elementary row operation on a square matrix A of order 3 is equivalent to a premultiplication of matrix A by one of the following matrices:

$$\begin{pmatrix} 0 & 1 & 0 \\ 1 & 0 & 0 \\ 0 & 0 & 1 \end{pmatrix}, \quad \begin{pmatrix} 0 & 0 & 1 \\ 0 & 1 & 0 \\ 1 & 0 & 0 \end{pmatrix}, \quad \text{and} \quad \begin{pmatrix} 1 & 0 & 0 \\ 0 & 0 & 1 \\ 0 & 1 & 0 \end{pmatrix}.$$

(b) Show that the second elementary row operation is equivalent to a premultiplication of matrix A by one of the following matrices:

$$\begin{pmatrix} k & 0 & 0 \\ 0 & 1 & 0 \\ 0 & 0 & 1 \end{pmatrix}, \quad \begin{pmatrix} 1 & 0 & 0 \\ 0 & k & 0 \\ 0 & 0 & 1 \end{pmatrix}, \quad \text{and} \quad \begin{pmatrix} 1 & 0 & 0 \\ 0 & 1 & 0 \\ 0 & 0 & k \end{pmatrix},$$

where k is a nonzero real number.

(c) Show that the third elementary row operation is equivalent to a premultiplication of matrix A by one of the following matrices:

$$\begin{pmatrix} 1 & k & 0 \\ 0 & 1 & 0 \\ 0 & 0 & 1 \end{pmatrix}, \quad \begin{pmatrix} 1 & 0 & k \\ 0 & 1 & 0 \\ 0 & 0 & 1 \end{pmatrix}, \quad \begin{pmatrix} 1 & 0 & 0 \\ k & 1 & 0 \\ 0 & 0 & 1 \end{pmatrix},$$

$$\begin{pmatrix} 1 & 0 & 0 \\ 0 & 1 & k \\ 0 & 0 & 1 \end{pmatrix}, \quad \begin{pmatrix} 1 & 0 & 0 \\ 0 & 1 & 0 \\ k & 0 & 1 \end{pmatrix}, \quad \text{and} \quad \begin{pmatrix} 1 & 0 & 0 \\ 0 & 1 & 0 \\ 0 & k & 1 \end{pmatrix}.$$

(These twelve matrices are called *elementary row operation matrices*.)

19. Find the product of the matrices

$$\begin{pmatrix} 0 & 1 & 0 \\ 1 & 0 & 0 \\ 0 & 0 & 1 \end{pmatrix}\begin{pmatrix} 6 & -2 & 3 & 1 \\ -2 & 0 & 1 & 2 \\ 2 & 3 & 4 & -4 \end{pmatrix}$$

without carrying out the multiplication.

20. Find all the elementary row operation matrices of order 2.

21. Express the inverse of $\begin{pmatrix} 6 & 8 \\ 1 & 4 \end{pmatrix}$ as the product of a set of elementary row operation matrices.

22. Prove that every square matrix whose inverse exists can be expressed as the product of a set of elementary row operation matrices.

7.8 SYSTEMS OF PLANES

The concept of the rank of a matrix can be applied to a discussion of systems of planes. Consider a system of two planes:

$$\begin{cases} a_1x + b_1y + c_1z + d_1 = 0 \\ a_2x + b_2y + c_2z + d_2 = 0. \end{cases}$$

If the rank r of the matrix of coefficients

$$\begin{pmatrix} a_1 & b_1 & c_1 \\ a_2 & b_2 & c_2 \end{pmatrix}$$

and the rank ρ of the augmented matrix

$$\begin{pmatrix} a_1 & b_1 & c_1 & d_1 \\ a_2 & b_2 & c_2 & d_2 \end{pmatrix}$$

are both equal to 1, the system is consistent. Since

$$\frac{a_1}{a_2} = \frac{b_1}{b_2} = \frac{c_1}{c_2} = \frac{d_1}{d_2},$$

the planes are identical.

If $r = 1$ and $\rho = 2$, the system is inconsistent, with

$$\frac{a_1}{a_2} = \frac{b_1}{b_2} = \frac{c_1}{c_2} \neq \frac{d_1}{d_2}.$$

Therefore, the planes are parallel and distinct.

If $r = \rho = 2$, the coefficients are not proportional. Hence the two planes are not parallel and must intersect in a unique line.

In an analogous fashion, in terms of the values of r and ρ, we shall proceed to characterize the geometric situations which can occur when we consider a system of three planes:

$$\begin{cases} a_1x + b_1y + c_1z + d_1 = 0 \\ a_2x + b_2y + c_2z + d_2 = 0 \\ a_3x + b_3y + c_3z + d_3 = 0. \end{cases}$$

We consider first the cases where $r = \rho$. There are three cases for which the system is consistent:

(i) If $r = \rho = 1$, the equations of the plane are identical. Hence the three planes coincide.

(ii) If $r = \rho = 2$, two of the three planes intersect in a line for which a set of direction numbers can be determined. The third plane must contain either this entire line or a single point on this line since the system is consistent. If the third plane contained a single point on this line, the coordinates of that point could be determined by Cramer's rule. But this implies that $r = 3$. Hence the three planes have a line in common if $r = \rho = 2$. Furthermore, the three planes may either be distinct or two of them may coincide.

(iii) If $r = \rho = 3$, the planes have a unique point in common, according to Cramer's rule (Figure 7.1).

A system of three or more planes which is consistent and whose augmented matrix is of rank 2 is often called a *pencil of planes*. The line of intersection of the system of planes is called the *axis of the pencil*. Thus for two nonparallel planes $f(x, y, z) = 0$ and $g(x, y, z) = 0$, the linear equation

$$k_1f(x, y, z) + k_2g(x, y, z) = 0, \qquad (7.26)$$

where k_1 and k_2 are real numbers such that k_1 and k_2 are not both zero, defines a pencil of planes through the line of intersection of these planes (Figure 7.2).

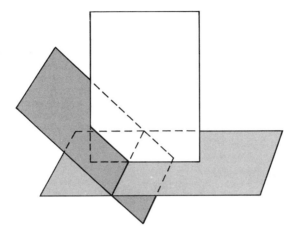

Figure 7.1

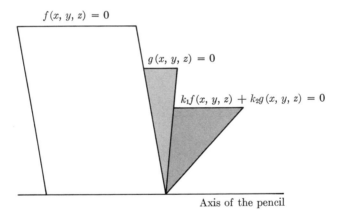

$f(x, y, z) = 0$

$g(x, y, z) = 0$

$k_1 f(x, y, z) + k_2 g(x, y, z) = 0$

Axis of the pencil

Figure 7.2

If the system of linear equations is inconsistent, one of two nontrivial cases must occur: $r = 1$ and $\rho = 2$, or $r = 2$ and $\rho = 3$. In the first case, the three planes are necessarily parallel, and at least one plane is distinct from the others (two of the three planes may be coincident). In the second case, since $r = 2$, a set of direction numbers can be determined for the line of intersection of two planes, say the first plane and second plane:

$$\left(\begin{vmatrix} b_1 & c_1 \\ b_2 & c_2 \end{vmatrix} : \begin{vmatrix} c_1 & a_1 \\ c_2 & a_2 \end{vmatrix} : \begin{vmatrix} a_1 & b_1 \\ a_2 & b_2 \end{vmatrix} \right).$$

However, since

$$a_3 \begin{vmatrix} b_1 & c_1 \\ b_2 & c_2 \end{vmatrix} + b_3 \begin{vmatrix} c_1 & a_1 \\ c_2 & a_2 \end{vmatrix} + c_3 \begin{vmatrix} a_1 & b_1 \\ a_2 & b_2 \end{vmatrix} = 0,$$

a line perpendicular to the third plane is perpendicular to that line of intersection. Hence the third plane must be parallel to the line of intersection of the first and second planes. Now, this third plane either is parallel to the first or second plane (Figure 7.3) or intersects the other two planes (Figure 7.4).

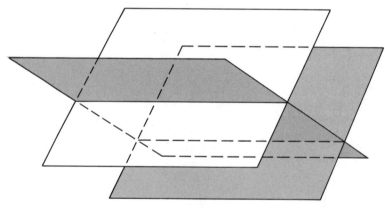

Figure 7.3

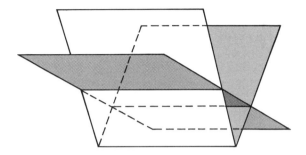

Figure 7.4

Exercises

1. Determine the relationship among the planes in each system.

(a) $\begin{cases} x - 2y + z = 5 \\ 2x - 5y + 6z = -2 \\ x + y - 2z = 3; \end{cases}$

(b) $\begin{cases} 2x + 2y + 5z = 1 \\ 8x - 3y + z = 9 \\ 4x - 5y - 2z = 1; \end{cases}$

(c) $\begin{cases} x - y + 2z = 5 \\ x - y + z = 3 \\ x - y - z = -1; \end{cases}$

(d) $\begin{cases} x + 2y + z = 5 \\ x - y - 2z = 6. \end{cases}$

2. Find the values of k for which each of the following systems of equations is consistent. Interpret each system geometrically.

(a) $\begin{cases} 2x + y + z = 5 \\ x - y + 3z = 2 \\ 3x + 3y - z = k; \end{cases}$

(b) $\begin{cases} x + y + z = 1 \\ x - y + z = 1 \\ x + y - z = k. \end{cases}$

3. Discuss geometrically a system of four planes in space in terms of the values of r and ρ.

4. Prove that six planes, each of which contains an edge of a tetrahedron and bisects the opposite edge, intersect in a point.

7.9 CHARACTERISTIC FUNCTIONS

Although the following discussion and basic results are valid for square matrices of any order n, we shall restrict this initial presentation to square matrices of orders 2 and 3.

Associated with every square matrix A of order 3, namely

$$A = \begin{pmatrix} a_{11} & a_{12} & a_{13} \\ a_{21} & a_{22} & a_{23} \\ a_{31} & a_{32} & a_{33} \end{pmatrix},$$

is a function $f(\lambda) = \det(A - \lambda I)$; that is,

$$f(\lambda) = \begin{vmatrix} a_{11} - \lambda & a_{12} & a_{13} \\ a_{21} & a_{22} - \lambda & a_{23} \\ a_{31} & a_{32} & a_{33} - \lambda \end{vmatrix}. \tag{7.27}$$

The function $f(\lambda)$ is called the *characteristic function* of matrix A. The equation $f(\lambda) = 0$, which can be expressed as

$$c_0\lambda^3 + c_1\lambda^2 + c_2\lambda + c_3 = 0, \tag{7.28}$$

is called the *characteristic equation* of A. In the case of a square matrix of order 3, it can be shown by an expansion of $f(\lambda)$ that the characteristic equation becomes

$$\lambda^3 - (a_{11} + a_{22} + a_{33})\lambda^2$$

$$+ \left(\begin{vmatrix} a_{11} & a_{12} \\ a_{21} & a_{22} \end{vmatrix} + \begin{vmatrix} a_{11} & a_{13} \\ a_{31} & a_{33} \end{vmatrix} + \begin{vmatrix} a_{22} & a_{23} \\ a_{32} & a_{33} \end{vmatrix} \right) \lambda$$

$$- \begin{vmatrix} a_{11} & a_{12} & a_{13} \\ a_{21} & a_{22} & a_{23} \\ a_{31} & a_{32} & a_{33} \end{vmatrix} = 0.$$

The roots λ_1, λ_2, and λ_3 of the characteristic equation of matrix A are called the *characteristic roots*, or *eigenvalues*, of A. We can associate with each eigenvalue λ_i a nonzero column vector $(x_1 \quad x_2 \quad x_3)^{\mathsf{T}}$ such that

$$(A - \lambda_i I)(x_1 \quad x_2 \quad x_3)^{\mathsf{T}} = 0; \tag{7.29}$$

that is,

$$\begin{pmatrix} a_{11} - \lambda_i & a_{12} & a_{13} \\ a_{21} & a_{22} - \lambda_i & a_{23} \\ a_{31} & a_{32} & a_{33} - \lambda_i \end{pmatrix} \begin{pmatrix} x_1 \\ x_2 \\ x_3 \end{pmatrix} = \begin{pmatrix} 0 \\ 0 \\ 0 \end{pmatrix}.$$

The vectors $(x_1 \quad x_2 \quad x_3)^{\mathsf{T}}$ are called the *characteristic vectors*, or *eigenvectors*, of matrix A. Many eigenvectors may be associated with each eigenvalue determined.

Example 1. Determine the characteristic equation, the eigenvalues, and a set of eigenvectors of the matrix A where

$$A = \begin{pmatrix} 1 & 2 \\ 4 & 3 \end{pmatrix}.$$

The characteristic equation of matrix A is

$$\begin{vmatrix} 1-\lambda & 2 \\ 4 & 3-\lambda \end{vmatrix} = 0;$$

that is,

$$\lambda^2 - 4\lambda - 5 = 0.$$

The eigenvalues of A are the roots of this equation:

$$\lambda_1 = -1 \quad \text{and} \quad \lambda_2 = 5.$$

Associated with λ_1 are the eigenvectors $(x_1 \quad x_2)^\mathsf{T}$ for which

$$(A - (-1)I)(x_1 \quad x_2)^\mathsf{T} = 0;$$

that is,

$$\begin{pmatrix} 2 & 2 \\ 4 & 4 \end{pmatrix}\begin{pmatrix} x_1 \\ x_2 \end{pmatrix} = \begin{pmatrix} 0 \\ 0 \end{pmatrix}.$$

Thus $x_2 = -x_1$. By conveniently choosing x_1 equal to some real number, say 1, x_2 becomes -1. Hence $(1 \quad -1)^\mathsf{T}$ is an eigenvector associated with the eigenvalue -1.

In a similar manner, for $\lambda_2 = 5$ we have

$$(A - 5I)(x_1 \quad x_2)^\mathsf{T} = 0;$$

that is,

$$\begin{pmatrix} -4 & 2 \\ 4 & -2 \end{pmatrix}\begin{pmatrix} x_1 \\ x_2 \end{pmatrix} = \begin{pmatrix} 0 \\ 0 \end{pmatrix}.$$

Thus $x_2 = 2x_1$, and $(1 \quad 2)^\mathsf{T}$ is an eigenvector associated with the eigenvalue 5.

Example 2. Determine the characteristic equation, the eigenvalues, and a set of eigenvectors of the matrix A where

$$A = \begin{pmatrix} 3 & 0 & 2 \\ 0 & 1 & 2 \\ 2 & 2 & 2 \end{pmatrix}.$$

The characteristic equation may be expressed in the form

$$\lambda^3 - (3+1+2)\lambda^2 + \left(\begin{vmatrix} 3 & 0 \\ 0 & 1 \end{vmatrix} + \begin{vmatrix} 3 & 2 \\ 2 & 2 \end{vmatrix} + \begin{vmatrix} 1 & 2 \\ 2 & 2 \end{vmatrix} \right)\lambda$$

$$- \begin{vmatrix} 3 & 0 & 2 \\ 0 & 1 & 2 \\ 2 & 2 & 2 \end{vmatrix} = 0.$$

Simplifying, we have

$$\lambda^3 - 6\lambda^2 + 3\lambda + 10 = 0,$$

$$(\lambda + 1)(\lambda - 2)(\lambda - 5) = 0.$$

Hence $\lambda_1 = -1$, $\lambda_2 = 2$, and $\lambda_3 = 5$.

For $\lambda_1 = -1$, the equation $(A - \lambda_1 I)(x_1 \quad x_2 \quad x_3)^\mathsf{T} = 0$ becomes

$$\begin{pmatrix} 4 & 0 & 2 \\ 0 & 2 & 2 \\ 2 & 2 & 3 \end{pmatrix} \begin{pmatrix} x_1 \\ x_2 \\ x_3 \end{pmatrix} = \begin{pmatrix} 0 \\ 0 \\ 0 \end{pmatrix}.$$

This matrix equation represents the system of linear equations

$$\begin{cases} 4x_1 & + 2x_3 = 0 \\ 2x_2 + 2x_3 = 0 \\ 2x_1 + 2x_2 + 3x_3 = 0, \end{cases}$$

whereby $x_2 = 2x_1$ and $x_3 = -2x_1$. Hence the general form of the eigenvector associated with the eigenvalue -1 is $(t \quad 2t \quad -2t)^\mathsf{T}$, where t is any nonzero real number. For example, letting $t = 1$, we obtain the eigenvector $(1 \quad 2 \quad -2)^\mathsf{T}$ associated with the eigenvalue -1.

For $\lambda_2 = 2$, we have

$$\begin{pmatrix} 1 & 0 & 2 \\ 0 & -1 & 2 \\ 2 & 2 & 0 \end{pmatrix} \begin{pmatrix} x_1 \\ x_2 \\ x_3 \end{pmatrix} = \begin{pmatrix} 0 \\ 0 \\ 0 \end{pmatrix};$$

that is,

$$\begin{cases} x_1 & + 2x_3 = 0 \\ - x_2 + 2x_3 = 0 \\ 2x_1 + 2x_2 & = 0. \end{cases}$$

It follows that $x_1 = -2x_3$ and $x_2 = 2x_3$. The general form of the eigenvector associated with the eigenvalue 2 is $(-2t \quad 2t \quad t)^\mathsf{T}$, where t is any nonzero real number. In particular, letting $t = 1$, we obtain the eigenvector $(-2 \quad 2 \quad 1)^\mathsf{T}$ associated with the eigenvalue 2.

By a similar process, for $\lambda_3 = 5$ we obtain the system of linear equations

$$\begin{cases} -2x_1 & + 2x_3 = 0 \\ - 4x_2 + 2x_3 = 0 \\ 2x_1 + 2x_2 - 3x_3 = 0. \end{cases}$$

Therefore, $x_1 = 2x_2$ and $x_3 = 2x_2$, and $(2t \quad t \quad 2t)^\mathsf{T}$ is the general form of the eigenvector associated with the third eigenvalue. For $t = 1$, $(2 \quad 1 \quad 2)^\mathsf{T}$ is a particular eigenvector associated with the eigenvalue 5.

Several interesting and important properties of the eigenvalues and eigenvectors of matrices are stated here for reference purposes. Exercises 9 and 10 give the reader an opportunity to verify the following theorems.

Theorem 7.7. *If the eigenvalues of a matrix are distinct, then the associated eigenvectors are linearly independent.*

Theorem 7.8. *The eigenvalues of a symmetric matrix are real numbers.*

Theorem 7.9. *If A is a symmetric matrix, then the eigenvectors of A associated with distinct eigenvalues are mutually orthogonal vectors.*

Exercises

In Exercises 1–4 determine the characteristic equation, the eigenvalues, and a set of eigenvectors of each matrix.

1. $\begin{pmatrix} 3 & 1 \\ 2 & 2 \end{pmatrix}.$

3. $\begin{pmatrix} 9 & -12 \\ -12 & 16 \end{pmatrix}.$

2. $\begin{pmatrix} 1 & 0 & 0 \\ 0 & 4 & 0 \\ 0 & 0 & 2 \end{pmatrix}.$

4. $\begin{pmatrix} 4 & -1 & 1 \\ -1 & 4 & -1 \\ 1 & -1 & 4 \end{pmatrix}.$

5. Let A be any square matrix of order 3. Show that
    (a) $\lambda_1 + \lambda_2 + \lambda_3 = $ trace of A;   (b) $\lambda_1\lambda_2\lambda_3 = \det A$.

6. Use the matrix of Example 2 to verify the results of Exercise 5.

7. Prove that the trace of any square matrix of order n is equal to the sum of its eigenvalues.

8. Let t_1 be the trace of matrix A, t_2 the trace of A^2, and t_3 the trace of A^3. Use the matrix of Example 2 to verify the fact that the coefficients of the characteristic equation of a matrix of order 3 may be determined by using these formulas: $c_0 = 1$, $c_1 = -t_1$, $c_2 = -\frac{1}{2}(c_1 t_1 + t_2)$, and $c_3 = -\frac{1}{3}(c_2 t_1 + c_1 t_2 + t_3)$.

9. Verify Theorem 7.7 for the matrix

$$\begin{pmatrix} 1 & 1 & 2 \\ 3 & 1 & -2 \\ -1 & 1 & 3 \end{pmatrix}.$$

10. Verify Theorems 7.8 and 7.9 for the matrix

$$\begin{pmatrix} 3 & 0 & 0 \\ 0 & 2 & 5 \\ 0 & 5 & 4 \end{pmatrix}.$$

11. Take matrices $A = \begin{pmatrix} 2 & 0 \\ 0 & 2 \end{pmatrix}$ and $B = \begin{pmatrix} 2 & 1 \\ 0 & 2 \end{pmatrix}$ and show that if the eigenvalues of a matrix are not distinct, then the eigenvectors may or may not be linearly independent.

12. Consider the characteristic equation of the matrix A where $A = \begin{pmatrix} 2 & 3 \\ -1 & 1 \end{pmatrix}$. Replace λ by A, and each real number c_n by $\begin{pmatrix} c_n & 0 \\ 0 & c_n \end{pmatrix}$. Show that the resulting matrix equation is valid.

13. Repeat Exercise 12 for $A = \begin{pmatrix} a & b \\ c & d \end{pmatrix}$.

14. Prove that the eigenvalues of A and A^T are identical.

15. Prove that if A is a diagonal matrix, then the eigenvalues of A are the diagonal elements.

7.10 DIAGONALIZATION OF MATRICES

We have already seen that associated with each eigenvalue λ_i of a matrix A of order 3 is an eigenvector $(x_1 \quad x_2 \quad x_3)^\mathsf{T}$ such that

$$(A - \lambda_i I)(x_1 \quad x_2 \quad x_3)^\mathsf{T} = 0.$$

This relationship may be expressed in the form

$$A(x_1 \quad x_2 \quad x_3)^\mathsf{T} = \lambda_i(x_1 \quad x_2 \quad x_3)^\mathsf{T}. \tag{7.30}$$

For example, consider the matrix A of Example 2 of §7.9. Recall that the eigenvectors $(1 \quad 2 \quad -2)^\mathsf{T}$, $(-2 \quad 2 \quad 1)^\mathsf{T}$, and $(2 \quad 1 \quad 2)^\mathsf{T}$ were associated with the eigenvalues $\lambda_1 = -1$, $\lambda_2 = 2$, and $\lambda_3 = 5$ respectively. The following valid relationships for λ_1, λ_2, λ_3, and their associated eigenvectors are of the form (7.30):

$$\begin{pmatrix} 3 & 0 & 2 \\ 0 & 1 & 2 \\ 2 & 2 & 2 \end{pmatrix} \begin{pmatrix} 1 \\ 2 \\ -2 \end{pmatrix} = -1 \begin{pmatrix} 1 \\ 2 \\ -2 \end{pmatrix};$$

$$\begin{pmatrix} 3 & 0 & 2 \\ 0 & 1 & 2 \\ 2 & 2 & 2 \end{pmatrix} \begin{pmatrix} -2 \\ 2 \\ 1 \end{pmatrix} = 2 \begin{pmatrix} -2 \\ 2 \\ 1 \end{pmatrix};$$

$$\begin{pmatrix} 3 & 0 & 2 \\ 0 & 1 & 2 \\ 2 & 2 & 2 \end{pmatrix} \begin{pmatrix} 2 \\ 1 \\ 2 \end{pmatrix} = 5 \begin{pmatrix} 2 \\ 1 \\ 1 \end{pmatrix}.$$

These relationships can be expressed by the single matrix equation

$$\begin{pmatrix} 3 & 0 & 2 \\ 0 & 1 & 2 \\ 2 & 2 & 2 \end{pmatrix} \begin{pmatrix} 1 & -2 & 2 \\ 2 & 2 & 1 \\ -2 & 1 & 2 \end{pmatrix} = \begin{pmatrix} 1 & -2 & 2 \\ 2 & 2 & 1 \\ -2 & 1 & 2 \end{pmatrix} \begin{pmatrix} -1 & 0 & 0 \\ 0 & 2 & 0 \\ 0 & 0 & 5 \end{pmatrix}, \quad (7.31)$$

where $\begin{pmatrix} 1 & -2 & 2 \\ 2 & 2 & 1 \\ -2 & 1 & 2 \end{pmatrix}$ is a matrix whose columns are the eigenvectors of A,

and $\begin{pmatrix} -1 & 0 & 0 \\ 0 & 2 & 0 \\ 0 & 0 & 5 \end{pmatrix}$ is a diagonal matrix whose diagonal elements are the

eigenvalues of A. If both members of equation (7.31) are multiplied by the inverse of the matrix of eigenvectors, we obtain

$$\begin{pmatrix} 1 & -2 & 2 \\ 2 & 2 & 1 \\ -2 & 1 & 2 \end{pmatrix}^{-1} \begin{pmatrix} 3 & 0 & 2 \\ 0 & 1 & 2 \\ 2 & 2 & 2 \end{pmatrix} \begin{pmatrix} 1 & -2 & 2 \\ 2 & 2 & 1 \\ -2 & 1 & 2 \end{pmatrix} = \begin{pmatrix} -1 & 0 & 0 \\ 0 & 2 & 0 \\ 0 & 0 & 5 \end{pmatrix}.$$

Thus we are able to reduce the matrix A to a diagonal matrix whose diagonal elements are the eigenvalues of A by use of the matrix of eigenvectors and its inverse.

In general, if we construct a square matrix of order n, denoted by X, whose column vectors are eigenvectors of A, then

$$X^{-1}AX = \Lambda, \tag{7.32}$$

where Λ is a diagonal matrix whose diagonal elements are the distinct eigenvalues of A. The relationship expressed by (7.32) is referred to as the *diagonalization* of matrix A. By Theorem 7.7, we are guaranteed that for distinct eigenvalues of a matrix the inverse of the matrix of eigenvectors exists; thus the diagonalization of the matrix is possible. If the eigenvalues are not distinct, diagonalization of the matrix may not be possible. However, it can be shown as a direct consequence of Theorems 7.8 and 7.9 that *a diagonalization of every symmetric matrix is possible whether or not the eigenvalues are distinct.*

The diagonalization of a matrix is of fundamental importance in the study of the general equations of the conic sections (§§8.9–8.11) and of the quadric surfaces (Chapter 10).

In equation (7.32), matrices A and Λ are similar matrices. In general, two matrices M and N are *similar matrices* if there exists a matrix C such that $C^{-1}MC = N$. Note that if the matrix C is an orthogonal matrix, then $C^{\mathsf{T}}MC = N$.

Example. Show that

$$M = \begin{pmatrix} 2 & 0 \\ 1 & 1 \end{pmatrix} \quad \text{and} \quad N = \begin{pmatrix} 4 & 3 \\ -2 & -1 \end{pmatrix}$$

are similar matrices.

By definition, M and N are similar matrices if there exists a matrix C such that $C^{-1}MC = N$. This implies that $MC = CN$. Let $C = \begin{pmatrix} w & x \\ y & z \end{pmatrix}$ where $wz - xy \neq 0$. Then

$$\begin{pmatrix} 2 & 0 \\ 1 & 1 \end{pmatrix}\begin{pmatrix} w & x \\ y & z \end{pmatrix} = \begin{pmatrix} w & x \\ y & z \end{pmatrix}\begin{pmatrix} 4 & 3 \\ -2 & -1 \end{pmatrix},$$

$$\begin{pmatrix} 2w & 2x \\ w+y & x+z \end{pmatrix} = \begin{pmatrix} 4w-2x & 3w-x \\ 4y-2z & 3y-z \end{pmatrix}.$$

This matrix equation is equivalent to the system of linear homogeneous equations

$$\begin{cases} 2w - 2x & = 0 \\ 3w - 3x & = 0 \\ w - 3y + 2z & = 0 \\ x - 3y + 2z & = 0. \end{cases}$$

The solutions are of the form $w = 3s - 2t$, $x = 3s - 2t$, $y = s$, and $z = t$, where s and t are arbitrary real numbers. When $s = 1$ and $t = 0$, then $w = 3$, $x = 3$, $y = 1$, $z = 0$, and $wz - xy \neq 0$. Therefore,

$$C = \begin{pmatrix} 3 & 3 \\ 1 & 0 \end{pmatrix}, \quad C^{-1} = \begin{pmatrix} 0 & 1 \\ \frac{1}{3} & -1 \end{pmatrix},$$

$$C^{-1}MC = \begin{pmatrix} 0 & 1 \\ \frac{1}{3} & -1 \end{pmatrix}\begin{pmatrix} 2 & 0 \\ 1 & 1 \end{pmatrix}\begin{pmatrix} 3 & 3 \\ 1 & 0 \end{pmatrix} = \begin{pmatrix} 4 & 3 \\ -2 & -1 \end{pmatrix} = N.$$

Thus M and N are similar matrices.

Exercises

Perform the diagonalization of each matrix.

1. $\begin{pmatrix} 1 & 2 \\ 4 & 3 \end{pmatrix}.$

2. $\begin{pmatrix} 7 & 6 \\ 6 & 2 \end{pmatrix}.$

3. $\begin{pmatrix} 1 & 2 & 0 \\ 2 & 2 & 2 \\ 0 & 2 & 3 \end{pmatrix}.$

4. $\begin{pmatrix} 4 & -2 & 0 \\ -2 & 1 & 0 \\ 0 & 0 & 0 \end{pmatrix}.$

In Exercises 5 and 6 show that M and N are similar matrices.

5. $M = \begin{pmatrix} 1 & -3 \\ -3 & 1 \end{pmatrix}$ and $N = \begin{pmatrix} 1 & 0 \\ 0 & -2 \end{pmatrix}.$

6. $M = \begin{pmatrix} 0 & 0 & 3 \\ 1 & 0 & 4 \\ 0 & 2 & 0 \end{pmatrix}$ and $N = \begin{pmatrix} 3 & 2 & 0 \\ 4 & 4 & 1 \\ 0 & 5 & 0 \end{pmatrix}.$

7. Prove that similar matrices have equal determinants.

8. Verify the results of Exercise 7 for matrices M and N in the example of this section.

9. Prove that similar matrices have equal eigenvalues.

10. Verify the results of Exercise 9 for matrices M and N in the example of this section.

TRANSFORMATIONS

8.1 TRANSFORMATION OF COORDINATES

It is sometimes convenient to consider a change from one coordinate system to another coordinate system in order to simplify a problem. Such a change is called a *transformation of coordinates,* or *transformation of axes.* In this section and in subsequent sections of this chapter we shall study three types of transformations: translations, rotations, and reflections.

Any geometric property that is not altered by a particular transformation is called an *invariant* with respect to that transformation. The importance of the concept of invariance lies in the idea that geometry can be considered fundamentally to be a study of theorems concerning the invariants associated with the various classes of transformations.*

The study of Euclidean geometry of two-dimensional and three-dimensional space is the study of the geometry of rigid motions. A *rigid motion* is a transformation of coordinates under which the distance between two points is a scalar invariant. In this chapter we shall show that translations, rotations, and reflections are rigid motion transformations in the plane. Furthermore, we shall show that every rigid motion transformation in the plane can be represented by a product of, at most, a translation, a rotation, and a reflection. A *product of transformations* is a sequence of transformations; that is, one transformation followed by another transformation, and so forth.

It will be convenient for us to consider the use of homogeneous Cartesian coordinates. In a plane the *homogeneous Cartesian coordinates* of a point whose Cartesian coordinates are (x, y) are any three scalars (x_1, x_2, x_3)

---

* This approach to the classification of geometries according to types of transformations was outlined by Felix Klein in an address at the University of Erlangen in 1872 and came to be known as the "Erlanger Programm."

for which

$$x = \frac{x_1}{x_3} \quad \text{and} \quad y = \frac{x_2}{x_3},$$

provided that $x_3 \neq 0$. One set of homogeneous coordinates for the point (x, y) is always of the form $(x, y, 1)$. In an analogous fashion, a point in three-dimensional space whose Cartesian coordinates are (x, y, z) may be expressed in terms of a quadruple of homogeneous Cartesian coordinates (x_1, x_2, x_3, x_4) where

$$x = \frac{x_1}{x_4}, \quad y = \frac{x_2}{x_4}, \quad \text{and} \quad z = \frac{x_3}{x_4},$$

provided that $x_4 \neq 0$. The context of a discussion will generally indicate whether we are considering homogeneous Cartesian coordinates or Cartesian coordinates.

> **Example.** Determine several sets of homogeneous Cartesian coordinates of the point in the plane whose Cartesian coordinates are $(4, -2)$.
>
> $(4, -2, 1), (8, -4, 2), (-12, 6, -3), (4\sqrt{2}, -2\sqrt{2}, \sqrt{2})$, and, in general, $(4t, -2t, t)$ where t is any nonzero real number.

Exercises

Determine several sets of homogeneous Cartesian coordinates of the point whose Cartesian coordinates are given.

1. $(3, 4)$.
2. $(-5, 1)$.
3. $(8, 0)$.
4. $(1, -2)$.

5. $(3, 4, 2)$.
6. $(5, 0, 1)$.
7. $(6, 3, -5)$.
8. $(0, 0, 0)$.

Find the Cartesian coordinates of the point whose homogeneous Cartesian coordinates are given.

9. $(6, -2, 1)$.
10. $(5, 8, 2)$.
11. $(4, 3, -1)$.
12. $(0, 1, 2)$.

13. $(1, 3, -1, 1)$.
14. $(5, 0, 7, 1)$.
15. $(3, 9, -6, 3)$.
16. $(2, -1, 0, -1)$.

8.2   TRANSLATIONS IN THE PLANE AND IN SPACE

Consider any point P in a plane. The point P can be specified by two sets of number pairs (coordinates): (x, y) for the rectangular Cartesian coordinate system S and (x', y') for the rectangular Cartesian coordinate system S', as indicated in Figure 8.1. The x' axis and y' axis are parallel to the x axis

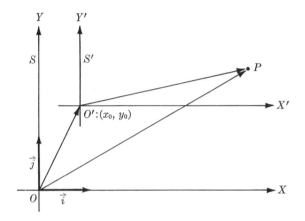

Figure 8.1

and y axis respectively, and have like orientation. If the origin of the S' reference system has coordinates (x_0, y_0) in the S reference system, then the relationship between the two sets of coordinates of P can be obtained by means of the vector equation

$$\vec{OP} = \vec{OO'} + \vec{O'P},$$

where $\vec{OP} = x\vec{i} + y\vec{j}$, $\vec{OO'} = x_0\vec{i} + y_0\vec{j}$, and $\vec{O'P} = x'\vec{i} + y'\vec{j}$. Thus

$$x\vec{i} + y\vec{j} = (x_0 + x')\vec{i} + (y_0 + y')\vec{j}.$$

By equating the coefficients of $\vec{i}$ and $\vec{j}$, we have

$$\begin{cases} x = x' + x_0 \\ y = y' + y_0, \end{cases} \tag{8.1}$$

whereby

$$\begin{cases} x' = x - x_0 \\ y' = y - y_0. \end{cases} \tag{8.2}$$

A change of reference system from S to S' described by either the set of equations (8.1) or the set of equations (8.2) is called a *translation of axes*.

We may consider that the relationship between the homogeneous Cartesian coordinates $(x', y', 1)$ of the point P with reference to the S' system and the homogeneous Cartesian coordinates $(x, y, 1)$ of P with reference to the S system is expressed by the matrix equation

$$\begin{pmatrix} x' \\ y' \\ 1 \end{pmatrix} = \begin{pmatrix} 1 & 0 & -x_0 \\ 0 & 1 & -y_0 \\ 0 & 0 & 1 \end{pmatrix} \begin{pmatrix} x \\ y \\ 1 \end{pmatrix}. \tag{8.3}$$

The matrix

$$\begin{pmatrix} 1 & 0 & -x_0 \\ 0 & 1 & -y_0 \\ 0 & 0 & 1 \end{pmatrix} \tag{8.4}$$

is called the *translation matrix* for the transformation of coordinate axes from S to S'. Every translation matrix for a plane is of the form (8.4). Note that the determinant of the translation matrix is equal to 1.

Example 1. A point P in the S system has Cartesian coordinates $(2, 5)$. Determine the new coordinates of P under a translation of the coordinate axes to the S' system whose origin has coordinates $(1, -3)$ in the S system.

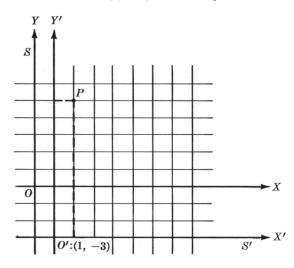

Figure 8.2

Since the origin of the S' system has coordinates $(1, -3)$ in the S system, as shown in Figure 8.2, the coordinates in the S' and S systems of any point in the plane are related by the equations

$$\begin{cases} x' = x - 1 \\ y' = y + 3. \end{cases}$$

The coordinates of P in the S' system are $(2 - 1, 5 + 3)$, that is, $(1, 8)$.

A point is called a *fixed point* if its coordinates remain unchanged under a transformation of axes. Note that there are no fixed points under translation when x_0 and y_0 are not both zero; that is, the coordinates of each point are changed. When $x_0 = y_0 = 0$, every point is a fixed point, and the translation is referred to as the *identity transformation*.

Example 2. Determine the equation of the graph of $x^2 + y^2 + 6x - 10y + 18 = 0$ under a translation of the coordinate axes represented by

$$\begin{pmatrix} 1 & 0 & 3 \\ 0 & 1 & -5 \\ 0 & 0 & 1 \end{pmatrix}.$$

Under a translation of the axes represented by the given matrix, the new coordinates of each point $(x, y, 1)$ in the plane become $(x', y', 1)$ where

$$\begin{pmatrix} x' \\ y' \\ 1 \end{pmatrix} = \begin{pmatrix} 1 & 0 & 3 \\ 0 & 1 & -5 \\ 0 & 0 & 1 \end{pmatrix}\begin{pmatrix} x \\ y \\ 1 \end{pmatrix}.$$

Hence

$$\begin{cases} x' = x + 3 \\ y' = y - 5 \end{cases} \quad \text{and} \quad \begin{cases} x = x' - 3 \\ y = y' + 5. \end{cases}$$

Therefore, the new equation of the graph of

$$x^2 + y^2 + 6x - 10y + 18 = 0$$

becomes

$$(x' - 3)^2 + (y' + 5)^2 + 6(x' - 3) - 10(y' + 5) + 18 = 0;$$

that is,

$$x'^2 + y'^2 = 16.$$

Note that this equation represents a circle with center at the origin and radius equal to 4 units. Furthermore, since the origin of the new coordinate system has coordinates $(-3, 5)$ in the S system, the graph of the equation

$$x^2 + y^2 + 6x - 10y + 18 = 0$$

is a circle with center at $(-3, 5)$ and radius equal to 4 units (Figure 8.3).

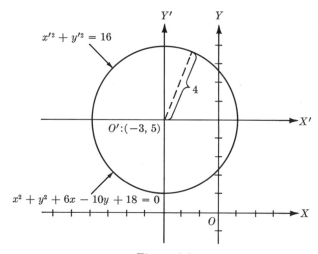

Figure 8.3

Consider any point P in space. The point can be specified by two sets of number triples (coordinates): (x, y, z) for the rectangular Cartesian coordinate system S and (x', y', z') for the rectangular Cartesian coordinate system S', as indicated in Figure 8.4. If the S' reference system is obtained from the S reference system by a translation of the coordinate axes such that the origin of the S' system has coordinates (x_0, y_0, z_0) in the S system, then the relationship between the two sets of coordinates of P can be

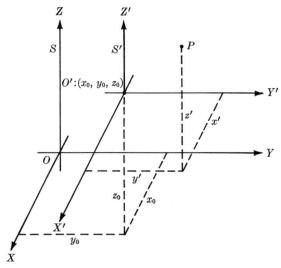

Figure 8.4

expressed by the equations

$$\begin{cases} x = x' + x_0 \\ y = y' + y_0 \\ z = z' + z_0 \end{cases}$$ (8.5)

or

$$\begin{cases} x' = x - x_0 \\ y' = y - y_0 \\ z' = z - z_0. \end{cases}$$ (8.6)

We may consider that the relationship between the homogeneous Cartesian coordinates of the point P in the S' system and the homogeneous Cartesian coordinates of P in the S system is represented by the matrix equation

$$\begin{pmatrix} x' \\ y' \\ z' \\ 1 \end{pmatrix} = \begin{pmatrix} 1 & 0 & 0 & -x_0 \\ 0 & 1 & 0 & -y_0 \\ 0 & 0 & 1 & -z_0 \\ 0 & 0 & 0 & 1 \end{pmatrix} \begin{pmatrix} x \\ y \\ z \\ 1 \end{pmatrix},$$ (8.7)

where

$$\begin{pmatrix} 1 & 0 & 0 & -x_0 \\ 0 & 1 & 0 & -y_0 \\ 0 & 0 & 1 & -z_0 \\ 0 & 0 & 0 & 1 \end{pmatrix}$$ (8.8)

is called the *translation matrix* for the transformation in space.

Exercises

Determine the new coordinates of the point $P:(x, y)$ under a translation of the coordinate axes of the plane such that $P_0:(-2, 4)$ is the origin.

1. $P:(5, 6)$.   3. $P:(-2, 4)$.

2. $P:(0, 0)$.   4. $P:(7, -1)$.

Determine the new coordinates of the point $P:(5, -2, 1)$ under a translation of the coordinate axes of space such that $P_0:(x_0, y_0, z_0)$ is the origin.

5. $P_0:(3, 4, -2)$.   7. $P_0:(0, 8, 3)$.

6. $P_0:(5, -2, 1)$.   8. $P_0:(6, 3, -7)$.

In Exercises 9 and 10 represent each translation of the coordinate axes by a matrix equation.

9. $\begin{cases} x' = x + 1 \\ y' = y - 2. \end{cases}$ 10. $\begin{cases} x' = x \\ y' = y - 3 \\ z' = z - 1. \end{cases}$

11. Prove that the product of any two translation matrices is a translation matrix. Interpret this result geometrically.

12. Prove that the multiplication of any two translation matrices is commutative. Interpret this result geometrically.

13. Determine the inverse of a translation matrix for the plane. Interpret this matrix geometrically.

14. Determine the equation of the graph of $x^2 + y^2 + 4x + 2y + 4 = 0$ under a translation of the coordinate axes represented by

$$\begin{pmatrix} 1 & 0 & 2 \\ 0 & 1 & 1 \\ 0 & 0 & 1 \end{pmatrix}.$$

Graph the equation.

15. Determine the equation of the graph of $3x^2 + y^2 - 6x + 8y + 10 = 0$ under a translation of the coordinate axes represented by

$$\begin{pmatrix} 1 & 0 & -1 \\ 0 & 1 & 4 \\ 0 & 0 & 1 \end{pmatrix}.$$

Graph the equation.

16. Determine the coordinates of the new origin under a translation of axes performed to eliminate the first degree terms of
(a) $x^2 - y^2 + 10x + 4y + 20 = 0$;
(b) $3x^2 + 2y^2 - 6x + 16y + 11 = 0$.

17. Prove that the distance between two points is a scalar invariant under a translation of the coordinate axes where the two points are (a) in a plane; (b) in space.

18. Verify that the distance between the points $A:(-2, 1)$ and $B:(5, 3)$ is a scalar invariant under a translation of the coordinate axes represented by

$$\begin{pmatrix} 1 & 0 & 4 \\ 0 & 1 & -1 \\ 0 & 0 & 1 \end{pmatrix}.$$

8.3   ROTATIONS IN THE PLANE

We shall now consider a transformation of the coordinate axes in a plane under which one and only one point, the origin, remains fixed. Let S and S' be two rectangular Cartesian coordinate systems with the same origin O, as

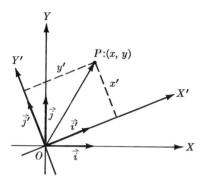

Figure 8.5

shown in Figure 8.5. The S' system may be obtained by rotating the axes of the S system counterclockwise through an angle θ. Let P be any point in the plane. Vector $\overrightarrow{OP}$ may be expressed as $x\vec{i} + y\vec{j}$ or $x'\vec{i'} + y'\vec{j'}$, where $\vec{i}, \vec{j}$, and $\vec{i'}, \vec{j'}$ are unit vectors along the coordinate axes in the S and S' systems respectively. Since

$$\vec{i'} = \cos\theta\,\vec{i} + \sin\theta\,\vec{j} \quad \text{and} \quad \vec{j'} = \cos\theta\,\vec{j} - \sin\theta\,\vec{i}$$

and

$$x\vec{i} + y\vec{j} = x'\vec{i'} + y'\vec{j'},$$

then

$$x\vec{i} + y\vec{j} = x'(\cos\theta\,\vec{i} + \sin\theta\,\vec{j}) + y'(\cos\theta\,\vec{j} - \sin\theta\,\vec{i})$$
$$= (x'\cos\theta - y'\sin\theta)\vec{i} + (x'\sin\theta + y'\cos\theta)\vec{j}.$$

By equating the coefficients of $\vec{i}$ and $\vec{j}$, we have

$$\begin{cases} x = x'\cos\theta - y'\sin\theta \\ y = x'\sin\theta + y'\cos\theta, \end{cases} \tag{8.9}$$

whereby

$$\begin{cases} x' = x\cos\theta + y\sin\theta \\ y' = -x\sin\theta + y\cos\theta. \end{cases} \tag{8.10}$$

A change of reference system from S to S' described by either the set of equations (8.9) or the set of equations (8.10) is called a *rotation of axes*.

The relationship between the coordinates of P in the S' and S systems may be expressed in matrix form as

$$\begin{pmatrix} x' \\ y' \\ 1 \end{pmatrix} = \begin{pmatrix} \cos\theta & \sin\theta & 0 \\ -\sin\theta & \cos\theta & 0 \\ 0 & 0 & 1 \end{pmatrix} \begin{pmatrix} x \\ y \\ 1 \end{pmatrix}. \tag{8.11}$$

The matrix

$$\begin{pmatrix} \cos\theta & \sin\theta & 0 \\ -\sin\theta & \cos\theta & 0 \\ 0 & 0 & 1 \end{pmatrix} \qquad (8.12)$$

is called the *rotation matrix* for the transformation from S to S'. The matrix (8.12) assigns new coordinates to each point $(x, y, 1)$ on the plane after a rotation of the coordinate axes counterclockwise about the origin through an angle θ. Every rotation of the axes about the origin can be represented by a matrix of the form (8.12). Note that every rotation matrix is a proper orthogonal matrix.

Example 1. Determine the new coordinates of the point $P:(2\sqrt{3}, 4)$ when the axes are rotated through an angle of $\pi/6$.

Since the measure of the angle of rotation θ is $\pi/6$, $\cos\theta = \sqrt{3}/2$ and $\sin\theta = 1/2$. Therefore, the rotation matrix for the transformation from S to S' (Figure 8.6) is given by

$$\begin{pmatrix} \dfrac{\sqrt{3}}{2} & \dfrac{1}{2} & 0 \\ -\dfrac{1}{2} & \dfrac{\sqrt{3}}{2} & 0 \\ 0 & 0 & 1 \end{pmatrix}.$$

Hence, by (8.11),

$$\begin{pmatrix} x' \\ y' \\ 1 \end{pmatrix} = \begin{pmatrix} \dfrac{\sqrt{3}}{2} & \dfrac{1}{2} & 0 \\ -\dfrac{1}{2} & \dfrac{\sqrt{3}}{2} & 0 \\ 0 & 0 & 1 \end{pmatrix} \begin{pmatrix} 2\sqrt{3} \\ 4 \\ 1 \end{pmatrix} = \begin{pmatrix} 5 \\ \sqrt{3} \\ 1 \end{pmatrix};$$

that is, the new coordinates of P are $(5, \sqrt{3})$.

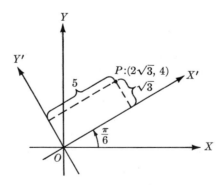

Figure 8.6

Example 2. Determine the equation of the graph of $x^2 - xy + y^2 = 6$ when the coordinate axes are rotated about the origin through an angle of $\pi/4$.

The coordinates (x, y) of each point of the graph are related to the new coordinates (x', y') by equations (8.9) where $\theta = \pi/4$. Therefore,

$$\begin{cases} x = \dfrac{\sqrt{2}}{2} x' - \dfrac{\sqrt{2}}{2} y' \\ y = \dfrac{\sqrt{2}}{2} x' + \dfrac{\sqrt{2}}{2} y'. \end{cases}$$

Substituting for x and y in the given equation $x^2 - xy + y^2 = 6$, we obtain

$$\left(\frac{\sqrt{2}}{2} x' - \frac{\sqrt{2}}{2} y' \right)^2$$

$$- \left(\frac{\sqrt{2}}{2} x' - \frac{\sqrt{2}}{2} y' \right) \left(\frac{\sqrt{2}}{2} x' + \frac{\sqrt{2}}{2} y' \right)$$

$$+ \left(\frac{\sqrt{2}}{2} x' + \frac{\sqrt{2}}{2} y' \right)^2 = 6,$$

$$\frac{1}{2} x'^2 + \frac{3}{2} y'^2 = 6,$$

$$x'^2 + 3y'^2 = 12.$$

Since $x'^2 + 3y'^2 = 12$ is the equation of an ellipse in standard form, its graph is readily obtained; that is, the graph of $x^2 - xy + y^2 = 6$ is an ellipse (Figure 8.7).

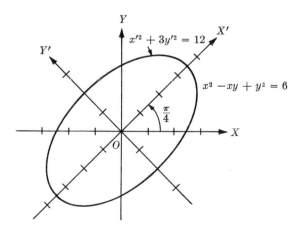

Figure 8.7

Exercises

Determine the new coordinates of the point P when the axes are rotated through an angle whose measure is θ.

1. $P:(3, 4); \theta = \pi/2.$

2. $P:(1, \sqrt{3}); \theta = \pi/6.$

3. $P:(5, 2); \theta = \pi.$

4. $P:(\sqrt{2}, -\sqrt{2}); \theta = \pi/4.$

Represent each rotation of the coordinate axes by a matrix equation. Determine the measure of the angle of rotation.

5.
$$\begin{cases} x' = \dfrac{3}{5}x - \dfrac{4}{5}y \\[2mm] y' = \dfrac{4}{5}x + \dfrac{3}{5}y. \end{cases}$$

6.
$$\begin{cases} x' = -\dfrac{7}{25}x + \dfrac{24}{25}y \\[2mm] y' = -\dfrac{24}{25}x - \dfrac{7}{25}y. \end{cases}$$

In Exercises 7 and 8 determine whether or not the matrix represents a rotation transformation.

7.
$$\begin{pmatrix} \dfrac{7}{25} & \dfrac{24}{25} & 0 \\[2mm] \dfrac{24}{25} & -\dfrac{7}{25} & 0 \\[2mm] 0 & 0 & 1 \end{pmatrix}.$$

8.
$$\begin{pmatrix} -\dfrac{5}{13} & -\dfrac{12}{13} & 0 \\[2mm] \dfrac{12}{13} & -\dfrac{5}{13} & 0 \\[2mm] 0 & 0 & 1 \end{pmatrix}.$$

9. Prove that the product of any two rotation matrices is a rotation matrix. Interpret this result geometrically.

10. Prove that the multiplication of any two rotation matrices is commutative. Interpret this result geometrically.

11. Find the product of the matrices

$$\begin{pmatrix} \cos\theta & \sin\theta & 0 \\ -\sin\theta & \cos\theta & 0 \\ 0 & 0 & 1 \end{pmatrix} \begin{pmatrix} \cos(-\theta) & \sin(-\theta) & 0 \\ -\sin(-\theta) & \cos(-\theta) & 0 \\ 0 & 0 & 1 \end{pmatrix}.$$

Interpret this result geometrically.

12. Determine the equation of the graph of $2x^2 - xy + 2y^2 = 25$ when the coordinate axes are rotated about the origin through an angle of $\pi/4$. Graph the equation.

13. Determine the equation of the graph of $x^2 + y^2 = r^2$ when the coordinate axes are rotated about the origin through an angle whose measure is θ.

14. Prove that the distance between two points in a plane is a scalar invariant under a rotation of the coordinate axes.

15. Verify that the distance between points $A:(-1, 0)$ and $B:(2, 4)$ is a scalar invariant under a rotation of the coordinate axes represented by

$$\begin{pmatrix} \dfrac{1}{2} & \dfrac{\sqrt{3}}{2} & 0 \\[2mm] -\dfrac{\sqrt{3}}{2} & \dfrac{1}{2} & 0 \\[2mm] 0 & 0 & 1 \end{pmatrix}.$$

16. Determine a matrix that represents a rotation of axes such that the new coordinates of $A:(1, 2)$ and $B:(5, 0)$ are $(2, 1)$ and $(4, -3)$ respectively.

17. Determine the measure of the angle of rotation under the rotation transformation performed to eliminate the cross product term xy in each equation.
    (a) $7x^2 - 48xy + 7y^2 + 200 = 0$;
    (b) $41x^2 + 24xy + 34y^2 + 15x - 10y - 60 = 0$.

18. Prove that the cross product term xy in the equation $Ax^2 + 2Bxy + Cy^2 + 2Dx + 2Ey + F = 0$ can be eliminated by a rotation of the coordinate axes through an angle equal to $\frac{1}{2} \arctan 2B/(A - C)$.

8.4   ROTATION OF AXES IN SPACE

Let P be any point in space. Let S and S' be two rectangular Cartesian coordinate systems with the same origin, as shown in Figure 8.8. Each system may be obtained from the other by a rotation of axes in space.

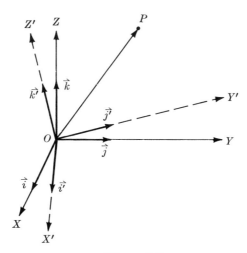

Figure 8.8

Vector $\overrightarrow{OP}$ may be expressed as $x\vec{i} + y\vec{j} + z\vec{k}$ or $x'\vec{i'} + y'\vec{j'} + z'\vec{k'}$, where $\vec{i}, \vec{j}, \vec{k}$ and $\vec{i'}, \vec{j'}, \vec{k'}$ are unit vectors along the coordinate axes in the S and S' systems respectively. Let $\vec{i'}, \vec{j'},$ and $\vec{k'}$ have direction cosines

$$(\cos\theta_{11} : \cos\theta_{12} : \cos\theta_{13}),$$
$$(\cos\theta_{21} : \cos\theta_{22} : \cos\theta_{23}),$$
$$(\cos\theta_{31} : \cos\theta_{32} : \cos\theta_{33})$$

respectively in the S system. Then

$$\begin{cases} \vec{i'} = \cos\theta_{11}\vec{i} + \cos\theta_{12}\vec{j} + \cos\theta_{13}\vec{k} \\ \vec{j'} = \cos\theta_{21}\vec{i} + \cos\theta_{22}\vec{j} + \cos\theta_{23}\vec{k} \\ \vec{k'} = \cos\theta_{31}\vec{i} + \cos\theta_{32}\vec{j} + \cos\theta_{33}\vec{k}, \end{cases} \qquad (8.13)$$

and

$$\begin{aligned} x\vec{i} + y\vec{j} + z\vec{k} = {} & x'(\cos\theta_{11}\vec{i} + \cos\theta_{12}\vec{j} + \cos\theta_{13}\vec{k}) \\ & + y'(\cos\theta_{21}\vec{i} + \cos\theta_{22}\vec{j} + \cos\theta_{23}\vec{k}) \\ & + z'(\cos\theta_{31}\vec{i} + \cos\theta_{32}\vec{j} + \cos\theta_{33}\vec{k}). \end{aligned}$$

Hence

$$\begin{cases} x = x'\cos\theta_{11} + y'\cos\theta_{21} + z'\cos\theta_{31} \\ y = x'\cos\theta_{12} + y'\cos\theta_{22} + z'\cos\theta_{32} \\ z = x'\cos\theta_{13} + y'\cos\theta_{23} + z'\cos\theta_{33}, \end{cases} \qquad (8.14)$$

which in matrix form may be expressed as

$$\begin{pmatrix} x \\ y \\ z \\ 1 \end{pmatrix} = \begin{pmatrix} \cos\theta_{11} & \cos\theta_{21} & \cos\theta_{31} & 0 \\ \cos\theta_{12} & \cos\theta_{22} & \cos\theta_{32} & 0 \\ \cos\theta_{13} & \cos\theta_{23} & \cos\theta_{33} & 0 \\ 0 & 0 & 0 & 1 \end{pmatrix} \begin{pmatrix} x' \\ y' \\ z' \\ 1 \end{pmatrix}. \qquad (8.15)$$

The matrix equation (8.15) represents the relationship between the rectangular Cartesian coordinates of a point in the two systems S and S'.

Since $\vec{i'}, \vec{j'},$ and $\vec{k'}$ of (8.13) are orthonormal vectors, then

$$\vec{i'} \cdot \vec{i'} = \vec{j'} \cdot \vec{j'} = \vec{k'} \cdot \vec{k'} = 1;$$

thus

$$\sum_{n=1}^{3} \cos^2\theta_{mn} = 1 \qquad \text{for} \quad m = 1, 2, 3. \qquad (8.16)$$

Furthermore, $\vec{i'} \cdot \vec{j'} = \vec{j'} \cdot \vec{k'} = \vec{k'} \cdot \vec{i'} = 0$; thus

$$\sum_{n=1}^{3} \cos\theta_{kn} \cos\theta_{mn} = 0 \qquad \text{for} \quad k \neq m. \qquad (8.17)$$

With the information in (8.16) and (8.17) it can be shown that

$$
\begin{pmatrix} x' \\ y' \\ z' \\ 1 \end{pmatrix} = \begin{pmatrix} \cos\theta_{11} & \cos\theta_{12} & \cos\theta_{13} & 0 \\ \cos\theta_{21} & \cos\theta_{22} & \cos\theta_{23} & 0 \\ \cos\theta_{31} & \cos\theta_{32} & \cos\theta_{33} & 0 \\ 0 & 0 & 0 & 1 \end{pmatrix} \begin{pmatrix} x \\ y \\ z \\ 1 \end{pmatrix}. \tag{8.18}
$$

Note that the inverse of the square matrix $((\cos\theta_{mn}))$ in equation (8.18) is equal to the square matrix $((\cos\theta_{mn}))^{\mathsf{T}}$ in equation (8.15). Each of these matrices represents a rotation of axes in space. Every matrix of rotation in space has the properties stated in (8.16) and (8.17), and thus is an orthogonal matrix. Indeed, every matrix of rotation in space is a proper orthogonal matrix. (See Exercise 3.)

Example. Given that the direction cosines of the positive halves of the x' axis, y' axis, and z' axis in terms of the xyz system are

$$
\left(\frac{1}{3} : \frac{2}{3} : \frac{2}{3} \right), \qquad \left(-\frac{2}{3} : -\frac{1}{3} : \frac{2}{3} \right), \qquad \text{and} \qquad \left(\frac{2}{3} : -\frac{2}{3} : \frac{1}{3} \right)
$$

respectively, find the equation of the plane $3x + 6y - 3z + 5 = 0$ in the $x'y'z'$ system.

The relationship between the xyz coordinates and $x'y'z'$ coordinates of any point in space is given by (8.15) as the matrix equation $(x \quad y \quad z \quad 1)^{\mathsf{T}} = R(x' \quad y' \quad z' \quad 1)^{\mathsf{T}}$ where

$$
R = \begin{pmatrix} \dfrac{1}{3} & -\dfrac{2}{3} & \dfrac{2}{3} & 0 \\ \dfrac{2}{3} & -\dfrac{1}{3} & -\dfrac{2}{3} & 0 \\ \dfrac{2}{3} & \dfrac{2}{3} & \dfrac{1}{3} & 0 \\ 0 & 0 & 0 & 1 \end{pmatrix}.
$$

That is, R is the matrix of rotation from the $x'y'z'$ system to the xyz system. Hence in the $x'y'z'$ system the equation of the plane $3x + 6y - 3z + 5 = 0$ becomes

$$
3(\tfrac{1}{3}x' - \tfrac{2}{3}y' + \tfrac{2}{3}z') + 6(\tfrac{2}{3}x' - \tfrac{1}{3}y' - \tfrac{2}{3}z')
$$
$$
- 3(\tfrac{2}{3}x' + \tfrac{2}{3}y' + \tfrac{1}{3}z') + 5 = 0,
$$
$$
3x' - 2y' - z' + 5 = 0.
$$

Exercises

In Exercises 1 and 2 determine the new coordinates of the point $P:(x, y, z)$ under a rotation of coordinate axes in space represented by

$$\begin{pmatrix} \frac{2}{7} & \frac{3}{7} & \frac{6}{7} & 0 \\ \frac{6}{7} & \frac{2}{7} & -\frac{3}{7} & 0 \\ \frac{3}{7} & -\frac{6}{7} & \frac{2}{7} & 0 \\ 0 & 0 & 0 & 1 \end{pmatrix}.$$

1. $P:(7, 0, -14)$.   **2.** $P:(\frac{3}{7}, \frac{2}{7}, -\frac{6}{7})$.

3.   Prove that the determinant of every matrix of rotation in space is equal to 1.

4.   Prove that the inverse of the square matrix $((\cos \theta_{mn}))$ in equation (8.18) is equal to $((\cos \theta_{mn}))^{\mathsf{T}}$.

In Exercises 5 and 6 determine whether or not the matrix represents a rotation transformation.

5. $$\begin{pmatrix} \dfrac{1}{\sqrt{2}} & 0 & -\dfrac{1}{\sqrt{2}} & 0 \\ -\dfrac{1}{\sqrt{2}} & 0 & \dfrac{1}{\sqrt{2}} & 0 \\ 0 & 1 & 0 & 0 \\ 0 & 0 & 0 & 1 \end{pmatrix}.$$

6. $$\begin{pmatrix} \dfrac{3}{13} & \dfrac{12}{13} & \dfrac{4}{13} & 0 \\ \dfrac{12}{13} & -\dfrac{4}{13} & \dfrac{3}{13} & 0 \\ \dfrac{4}{13} & \dfrac{3}{13} & -\dfrac{12}{13} & 0 \\ 0 & 0 & 0 & 1 \end{pmatrix}.$$

7.   Determine the elements a, b, c, and d of the rotation matrix

$$\begin{pmatrix} \frac{3}{5} & 0 & -\frac{4}{5} & 0 \\ \frac{4}{5} & 0 & a & 0 \\ b & c & d & 0 \\ 0 & 0 & 0 & 1 \end{pmatrix}.$$

8.   Determine a matrix that represents a rotation of axes such that the new coordinates of $A:(\frac{2}{3}, \frac{1}{3}, \frac{2}{3})$, $B:(\frac{1}{3}, \frac{2}{3}, -\frac{2}{3})$, and $C:(-\frac{2}{3}, \frac{2}{3}, \frac{1}{3})$ are $(1, 0, 0)$, $(0, 1, 0)$, and $(0, 0, 1)$ respectively.

9.   Determine a matrix that represents a rotation of axes from the xyz system to the $x'y'z'$ system such that the x' axis and z' axis are identical to the y axis and x axis respectively.

10.   Given that the direction cosines of the positive halves of the x' axis, y' axis, and z' axis in terms of the xyz system are

$$(\tfrac{1}{3}, -\tfrac{2}{3}, \tfrac{2}{3}), \ (\tfrac{2}{3}, -\tfrac{1}{3}, -\tfrac{2}{3}), \ \text{and} \ (\tfrac{2}{3}, \tfrac{2}{3}, \tfrac{1}{3})$$

respectively, find the equation of the plane $3x + 3y - 12z + 4 = 0$ in the $x'y'z'$ system.

8.5 INVARIANCE OF THE SCALAR PRODUCT UNDER ROTATION

It is important to note that the scalar product of two vectors is a scalar invariant under the rotation of a set of rectangular Cartesian coordinate axes in space.

Theorem 8.1. *If*

$$\vec{a} = a_1 \vec{i} + a_2 \vec{j} + a_3 \vec{k} = a_1' \vec{i}' + a_2' \vec{j}' + a_3' \vec{k}',$$

$$\vec{b} = b_1 \vec{i} + b_2 \vec{j} + b_3 \vec{k} = b_1' \vec{i}' + b_2' \vec{j}' + b_3' \vec{k}'$$

are two vectors expressed in terms of the sets of orthonormal vectors $\vec{i}$, $\vec{j}$, $\vec{k}$ and $\vec{i}'$, $\vec{j}'$, $\vec{k}'$ in the xyz and x'y'z' reference systems respectively, then

$$a_1' b_1' + a_2' b_2' + a_3' b_3' = a_1 b_1 + a_2 b_2 + a_3 b_3.$$

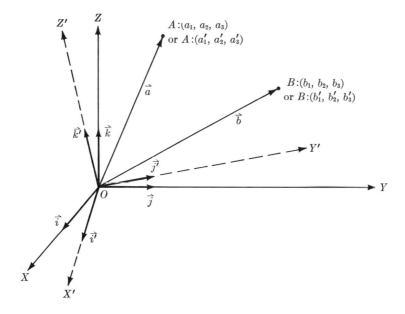

Figure 8.9

Proof: Let

$$((\cos \theta_{mn})) = \begin{pmatrix} \cos \theta_{11} & \cos \theta_{12} & \cos \theta_{13} & 0 \\ \cos \theta_{21} & \cos \theta_{22} & \cos \theta_{23} & 0 \\ \cos \theta_{31} & \cos \theta_{32} & \cos \theta_{33} & 0 \\ 0 & 0 & 0 & 1 \end{pmatrix}$$

be the matrix of rotation taking the xyz system into the $x'y'z'$ system. That is,

$$(\vec{i'} \quad \vec{j'} \quad \vec{k'} \quad 1)^\intercal = ((\cos \theta_{mn}))(\vec{i} \quad \vec{j} \quad \vec{k} \quad 1)^\intercal.$$

Note that the first three elements of each of the first three rows of the rotation matrix $((\cos \theta_{mn}))$ constitute sets of direction cosines for the unit vectors of the $x'y'z'$ system. It also follows that the first three elements of each of the first three columns represent sets of direction cosines since

$$(\vec{i} \quad \vec{j} \quad \vec{k} \quad 1)^\intercal = ((\cos \theta_{mn}))^\intercal(\vec{i'} \quad \vec{j'} \quad \vec{k'} \quad 1)^\intercal.$$

Hence

$$\cos^2 \theta_{11} + \cos^2 \theta_{12} + \cos^2 \theta_{13} = 1,$$

$$\cos^2 \theta_{21} + \cos^2 \theta_{22} + \cos^2 \theta_{23} = 1,$$

$$\cos^2 \theta_{31} + \cos^2 \theta_{32} + \cos^2 \theta_{33} = 1,$$

and

$$\cos^2 \theta_{11} + \cos^2 \theta_{21} + \cos^2 \theta_{31} = 1,$$

$$\cos^2 \theta_{12} + \cos^2 \theta_{22} + \cos^2 \theta_{32} = 1,$$

$$\cos^2 \theta_{13} + \cos^2 \theta_{23} + \cos^2 \theta_{33} = 1.$$

More briefly, as noted in part in (8.16),

$$\sum_{n=1}^{3} \cos^2 \theta_{mn} = 1 \quad \text{for} \quad m = 1, 2, 3,$$

and

$$\sum_{m=1}^{3} \cos^2 \theta_{mn} = 1 \quad \text{for} \quad n = 1, 2, 3.$$

Six other relationships are immediately evident since the unit vectors in each system are pairwise mutually orthogonal:

$$\cos \theta_{11} \cos \theta_{21} + \cos \theta_{12} \cos \theta_{22} + \cos \theta_{13} \cos \theta_{23} = 0,$$

$$\cos \theta_{21} \cos \theta_{31} + \cos \theta_{22} \cos \theta_{32} + \cos \theta_{23} \cos \theta_{33} = 0,$$

$$\cos \theta_{31} \cos \theta_{11} + \cos \theta_{32} \cos \theta_{12} + \cos \theta_{33} \cos \theta_{13} = 0$$

and

$$\cos \theta_{11} \cos \theta_{12} + \cos \theta_{21} \cos \theta_{22} + \cos \theta_{31} \cos \theta_{32} = 0,$$
$$\cos \theta_{12} \cos \theta_{13} + \cos \theta_{22} \cos \theta_{23} + \cos \theta_{32} \cos \theta_{33} = 0,$$
$$\cos \theta_{13} \cos \theta_{11} + \cos \theta_{23} \cos \theta_{21} + \cos \theta_{33} \cos \theta_{31} = 0.$$

Now,

$$\begin{aligned}
\vec{a} \cdot \vec{b} &= a_1' b_1' + a_2' b_2' + a_3' b_3' \\
&= (a_1 \cos \theta_{11} + a_2 \cos \theta_{12} + a_3 \cos \theta_{13}) \\
&\qquad (b_1 \cos \theta_{11} + b_2 \cos \theta_{12} + b_3 \cos \theta_{13}) \\
&\quad + (a_1 \cos \theta_{21} + a_2 \cos \theta_{22} + a_3 \cos \theta_{23}) \\
&\qquad (b_1 \cos \theta_{21} + b_2 \cos \theta_{22} + b_3 \cos \theta_{23}) \\
&\quad + (a_1 \cos \theta_{31} + a_2 \cos \theta_{32} + a_3 \cos \theta_{33}) \\
&\qquad (b_1 \cos \theta_{31} + b_2 \cos \theta_{32} + b_3 \cos \theta_{33}).
\end{aligned}$$

Multiplying and regrouping, we have

$$\begin{aligned}
\vec{a} \cdot \vec{b} &= a_1 b_1 (\cos^2 \theta_{11} + \cos^2 \theta_{21} + \cos^2 \theta_{31}) \\
&\quad + a_1 b_2 (\cos \theta_{11} \cos \theta_{12} + \cos \theta_{21} \cos \theta_{22} + \cos \theta_{31} \cos \theta_{32}) \\
&\quad + a_1 b_3 (\cos \theta_{11} \cos \theta_{13} + \cos \theta_{21} \cos \theta_{23} + \cos \theta_{31} \cos \theta_{33}) \\
&\quad + a_2 b_1 (\cos \theta_{12} \cos \theta_{11} + \cos \theta_{22} \cos \theta_{21} + \cos \theta_{32} \cos \theta_{31}) \\
&\quad + a_2 b_2 (\cos^2 \theta_{12} + \cos^2 \theta_{22} + \cos^2 \theta_{32}) \\
&\quad + a_2 b_3 (\cos \theta_{12} \cos \theta_{13} + \cos \theta_{22} \cos \theta_{23} + \cos \theta_{32} \cos \theta_{33}) \\
&\quad + a_3 b_1 (\cos \theta_{13} \cos \theta_{11} + \cos \theta_{23} \cos \theta_{21} + \cos \theta_{33} \cos \theta_{31}) \\
&\quad + a_3 b_2 (\cos \theta_{13} \cos \theta_{12} + \cos \theta_{23} \cos \theta_{22} + \cos \theta_{33} \cos \theta_{32}) \\
&\quad + a_3 b_3 (\cos^2 \theta_{13} + \cos^2 \theta_{23} + \cos^2 \theta_{33}).
\end{aligned}$$

Hence

$$\vec{a} \cdot \vec{b} = a_1 b_1 + a_2 b_2 + a_3 b_3,$$

and

$$a_1' b_1' + a_2' b_2' + a_3' b_3' = a_1 b_1 + a_2 b_2 + a_3 b_3.$$

Since the lengths of line segments (distances) and the measures of angles may be expressed in terms of the scalar product, it follows that these two properties are invariants under rotation.

Example. Verify that the distance between the points $A\!:\!(3, 2, 1)$ and $B\!:\!(2, 4, -1)$ is an invariant under a rotation of coordinate axes in space represented by

$$\begin{pmatrix} \frac{3}{13} & \frac{12}{13} & \frac{4}{13} & 0 \\ \frac{12}{13} & -\frac{4}{13} & \frac{3}{13} & 0 \\ \frac{4}{13} & \frac{3}{13} & -\frac{12}{13} & 0 \\ 0 & 0 & 0 & 1 \end{pmatrix}.$$

Under the given rotation, the new coordinates of points A and B are $\left(\frac{37}{13}, \frac{31}{13}, \frac{6}{13}\right)$ and $\left(\frac{50}{13}, \frac{5}{13}, \frac{32}{13}\right)$ respectively since

$$\begin{pmatrix} \frac{3}{13} & \frac{12}{13} & \frac{4}{13} & 0 \\ \frac{12}{13} & -\frac{4}{13} & \frac{3}{13} & 0 \\ \frac{4}{13} & \frac{3}{13} & -\frac{12}{13} & 0 \\ 0 & 0 & 0 & 1 \end{pmatrix} \begin{pmatrix} 3 \\ 2 \\ 1 \\ 1 \end{pmatrix} = \begin{pmatrix} \frac{37}{13} \\ \frac{31}{13} \\ \frac{6}{13} \\ 1 \end{pmatrix}$$

and

$$\begin{pmatrix} \frac{3}{13} & \frac{12}{13} & \frac{4}{13} & 0 \\ \frac{12}{13} & -\frac{4}{13} & \frac{3}{13} & 0 \\ \frac{4}{13} & \frac{3}{13} & -\frac{12}{13} & 0 \\ 0 & 0 & 0 & 1 \end{pmatrix} \begin{pmatrix} 2 \\ 4 \\ -1 \\ 1 \end{pmatrix} = \begin{pmatrix} \frac{50}{13} \\ \frac{5}{13} \\ \frac{32}{13} \\ 1 \end{pmatrix}.$$

The distance between the points A and B in terms of the original coordinates is given by

$$|AB| = \sqrt{(2-3)^2 + (4-2)^2 + (-1-1)^2}$$
$$= \sqrt{(-1)^2 + (2)^2 + (-2)^2} = 3;$$

the distance between the points A and B in terms of the new coordinates is given by

$$|AB| = \sqrt{\left(\frac{50}{13} - \frac{37}{13}\right)^2 + \left(\frac{5}{13} - \frac{31}{13}\right)^2 + \left(\frac{32}{13} - \frac{6}{13}\right)^2}$$
$$= \sqrt{(1)^2 + (-2)^2 + (2)^2} = 3.$$

Hence the distance between the points A and B is an invariant under the given rotation of coordinate axes.

Exercises

In Exercises 1–4 verify that the distance between the points $A:(5, 1, -3)$ and $B:(2, 7, 0)$ is an invariant under a rotation of coordinate axes in space represented by each matrix.

1. $\begin{pmatrix} \dfrac{1}{3} & -\dfrac{2}{3} & \dfrac{2}{3} & 0 \\[2mm] \dfrac{2}{3} & -\dfrac{1}{3} & -\dfrac{2}{3} & 0 \\[2mm] \dfrac{2}{3} & \dfrac{2}{3} & \dfrac{1}{3} & 0 \\[2mm] 0 & 0 & 0 & 1 \end{pmatrix}.$

3. $\begin{pmatrix} \dfrac{2}{7} & \dfrac{6}{7} & \dfrac{3}{7} & 0 \\[2mm] \dfrac{3}{7} & \dfrac{2}{7} & -\dfrac{6}{7} & 0 \\[2mm] \dfrac{6}{7} & -\dfrac{3}{7} & \dfrac{2}{7} & 0 \\[2mm] 0 & 0 & 0 & 1 \end{pmatrix}.$

2. $\begin{pmatrix} 1 & 0 & 0 & 0 \\ 0 & 0 & -1 & 0 \\ 0 & 1 & 0 & 0 \\ 0 & 0 & 0 & 1 \end{pmatrix}.$

4. $\begin{pmatrix} \dfrac{1}{\sqrt{3}} & -\dfrac{1}{\sqrt{3}} & \dfrac{1}{\sqrt{3}} & 0 \\[2mm] \dfrac{1}{\sqrt{2}} & \dfrac{1}{\sqrt{2}} & 0 & 0 \\[2mm] -\dfrac{1}{\sqrt{6}} & \dfrac{1}{\sqrt{6}} & \dfrac{2}{\sqrt{6}} & 0 \\[2mm] 0 & 0 & 0 & 1 \end{pmatrix}.$

5. Use the fact that a rotation matrix is an orthogonal matrix to present a concise proof that the scalar product of two vectors is an invariant under rotation.

8.6   **PRODUCT TRANSFORMATIONS**

One advantage of representing translations and rotations by means of matrices is that we are able to consider ordered products of these two types of transformations more easily. Consider a rotation of axes in the plane from the S system to the S' system, followed by a translation of axes from the S' system to the S'' system. If we denote the homogeneous coordinates of a point P in these three systems by $(x, y, 1)$, $(x', y', 1)$, and $(x'', y'', 1)$ respectively, we have the following general relationships:

$$\begin{pmatrix} x' \\ y' \\ 1 \end{pmatrix} = \begin{pmatrix} \cos\theta & \sin\theta & 0 \\ -\sin\theta & \cos\theta & 0 \\ 0 & 0 & 1 \end{pmatrix} \begin{pmatrix} x \\ y \\ 1 \end{pmatrix} \tag{8.19}$$

and

$$\begin{pmatrix} x'' \\ y'' \\ 1 \end{pmatrix} = \begin{pmatrix} 1 & 0 & -x_0 \\ 0 & 1 & -y_0 \\ 0 & 0 & 1 \end{pmatrix} \begin{pmatrix} x' \\ y' \\ 1 \end{pmatrix}. \tag{8.20}$$

Replacing $(x' \ y' \ 1)^\mathsf{T}$ in equation (8.20) by its equivalent expression in (8.19), we obtain

$$\begin{pmatrix} x'' \\ y'' \\ 1 \end{pmatrix} = \begin{pmatrix} 1 & 0 & -x_0 \\ 0 & 1 & -y_0 \\ 0 & 0 & 1 \end{pmatrix} \begin{pmatrix} \cos\theta & \sin\theta & 0 \\ -\sin\theta & \cos\theta & 0 \\ 0 & 0 & 1 \end{pmatrix} \begin{pmatrix} x \\ y \\ 1 \end{pmatrix}; \tag{8.21}$$

thus

$$\begin{pmatrix} x'' \\ y'' \\ 1 \end{pmatrix} = \begin{pmatrix} \cos\theta & \sin\theta & -x_0 \\ -\sin\theta & \cos\theta & -y_0 \\ 0 & 0 & 1 \end{pmatrix} \begin{pmatrix} x \\ y \\ 1 \end{pmatrix}. \tag{8.22}$$

Note that it is possible to accomplish both a rotation of coordinates and a translation of coordinates by means of a single transformation matrix of the form

$$\begin{pmatrix} \cos\theta & \sin\theta & -x_0 \\ -\sin\theta & \cos\theta & -y_0 \\ 0 & 0 & 1 \end{pmatrix}. \tag{8.23}$$

Order is of the utmost importance in considering the product of two transformations. In general, the effect of a translation followed by a rotation is different from that of a rotation followed by a translation. This should be evident since matrices are generally not commutative. For example, in the above general case, a translation preceding the rotation would have been represented by the single transformation matrix

$$\begin{pmatrix} \cos\theta & \sin\theta & -x_0\cos\theta - y_0\sin\theta \\ -\sin\theta & \cos\theta & x_0\sin\theta - y_0\cos\theta \\ 0 & 0 & 1 \end{pmatrix}. \tag{8.24}$$

Note that the determinants of the matrices (8.23) and (8.24) are equal to 1.

Example 1. Determine the equation of the graph of $x^2 + y^2 + 2xy - 3\sqrt{2}x - 5\sqrt{2}y - 10 = 0$ under a rotation of axes through an angle whose measure is $\pi/4$, followed by a translation of axes such that $(2, 1)$ is the origin.

The rotation matrix for the transformation from the xy system to the $x'y'$ system in Figure 8.10 is given by

$$\begin{pmatrix} \dfrac{\sqrt{2}}{2} & \dfrac{\sqrt{2}}{2} & 0 \\ -\dfrac{\sqrt{2}}{2} & \dfrac{\sqrt{2}}{2} & 0 \\ 0 & 0 & 1 \end{pmatrix};$$

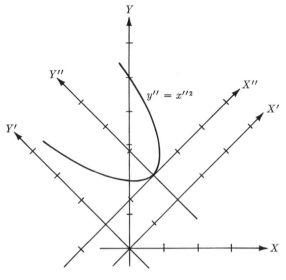

Figure 8.10

the translation matrix for the transformation from the $x'y'$ system to $x''y''$ system is given by

$$\begin{pmatrix} 1 & 0 & -2 \\ 0 & 1 & -1 \\ 0 & 0 & 1 \end{pmatrix}.$$

Therefore, the matrix representing the rotation followed by the translation is given by

$$\begin{pmatrix} 1 & 0 & -2 \\ 0 & 1 & -1 \\ 0 & 0 & 1 \end{pmatrix} \begin{pmatrix} \dfrac{\sqrt{2}}{2} & \dfrac{\sqrt{2}}{2} & 0 \\ -\dfrac{\sqrt{2}}{2} & \dfrac{\sqrt{2}}{2} & 0 \\ 0 & 0 & 1 \end{pmatrix};$$

that is,

$$\begin{pmatrix} x'' \\ y'' \\ 1 \end{pmatrix} = \begin{pmatrix} 1 & 0 & -2 \\ 0 & 1 & -1 \\ 0 & 0 & 1 \end{pmatrix} \begin{pmatrix} \dfrac{\sqrt{2}}{2} & \dfrac{\sqrt{2}}{2} & 0 \\ -\dfrac{\sqrt{2}}{2} & \dfrac{\sqrt{2}}{2} & 0 \\ 0 & 0 & 1 \end{pmatrix} \begin{pmatrix} x \\ y \\ 1 \end{pmatrix},$$

$$\begin{pmatrix} x'' \\ y'' \\ 1 \end{pmatrix} = \begin{pmatrix} \dfrac{\sqrt{2}}{2} & \dfrac{\sqrt{2}}{2} & -2 \\ -\dfrac{\sqrt{2}}{2} & \dfrac{\sqrt{2}}{2} & -1 \\ 0 & 0 & 1 \end{pmatrix} \begin{pmatrix} x \\ y \\ 1 \end{pmatrix}.$$

Since the inverse of

$$\begin{pmatrix} \dfrac{\sqrt{2}}{2} & \dfrac{\sqrt{2}}{2} & -2 \\ -\dfrac{\sqrt{2}}{2} & \dfrac{\sqrt{2}}{2} & -1 \\ 0 & 0 & 1 \end{pmatrix}$$

is

$$\begin{pmatrix} \dfrac{\sqrt{2}}{2} & -\dfrac{\sqrt{2}}{2} & \dfrac{\sqrt{2}}{2} \\ \dfrac{\sqrt{2}}{2} & \dfrac{\sqrt{2}}{2} & \dfrac{3\sqrt{2}}{2} \\ 0 & 0 & 1 \end{pmatrix},$$

then

$$\begin{pmatrix} x \\ y \\ 1 \end{pmatrix} = \begin{pmatrix} \dfrac{\sqrt{2}}{2} & -\dfrac{\sqrt{2}}{2} & \dfrac{\sqrt{2}}{2} \\ \dfrac{\sqrt{2}}{2} & \dfrac{\sqrt{2}}{2} & \dfrac{3\sqrt{2}}{2} \\ 0 & 0 & 1 \end{pmatrix} \begin{pmatrix} x'' \\ y'' \\ 1 \end{pmatrix}$$

and

$$\begin{cases} x = \dfrac{\sqrt{2}}{2} x'' - \dfrac{\sqrt{2}}{2} y'' + \dfrac{\sqrt{2}}{2} \\ y = \dfrac{\sqrt{2}}{2} x'' + \dfrac{\sqrt{2}}{2} y'' + \dfrac{3\sqrt{2}}{2}. \end{cases}$$

Substituting for x and y in $x^2 + y^2 + 2xy - 3\sqrt{2}x - 5\sqrt{2}y + 10 = 0$, we obtain $y'' = x''^2$ as the desired equation.

Analogously, we can represent the product of two transformations in space by a single transformation matrix. Denote the homogeneous Cartesian coordinates of a point P in space by $(x, y, z, 1)$, $(x', y', z', 1)$, and $(x'', y'', z'', 1)$ in the three systems S, S', and S'' respectively. If a transformation of axes from S to S' is denoted by the matrix T_1, and a transformation of axes from S' to S'' is denoted by the matrix T_2, then

$$(x' \quad y' \quad z' \quad 1)^{\mathsf{T}} = T_1(x \quad y \quad z \quad 1)^{\mathsf{T}}$$

and

$$(x'' \quad y'' \quad z'' \quad 1)^{\mathsf{T}} = T_2(x' \quad y' \quad z' \quad 1)^{\mathsf{T}},$$

whereby

$$\begin{aligned} (x'' \quad y'' \quad z'' \quad 1)^{\mathsf{T}} &= T_2[T_1(x \quad y \quad z \quad 1)^{\mathsf{T}}] \\ &= (T_2 T_1)(x \quad y \quad z \quad 1)^{\mathsf{T}}. \end{aligned}$$

For example, if T_1 represents a rotation of axes and T_2 represents a translation of axes, then

$$\begin{pmatrix} x'' \\ y'' \\ z'' \\ 1 \end{pmatrix} = \begin{pmatrix} \cos\theta_{11} & \cos\theta_{12} & \cos\theta_{13} & -x_0 \\ \cos\theta_{21} & \cos\theta_{22} & \cos\theta_{23} & -y_0 \\ \cos\theta_{31} & \cos\theta_{32} & \cos\theta_{33} & -z_0 \\ 0 & 0 & 0 & 1 \end{pmatrix} \begin{pmatrix} x \\ y \\ z \\ 1 \end{pmatrix}.$$

Example 2. Find new coordinates of point $P:(2, -3, 4)$ under a rotation of the coordinate axes represented by the matrix

$$\begin{pmatrix} \dfrac{3}{5} & 0 & \dfrac{4}{5} & 0 \\ -\dfrac{4}{5} & 0 & \dfrac{3}{5} & 0 \\ 0 & -1 & 0 & 0 \\ 0 & 0 & 0 & 1 \end{pmatrix},$$

followed by a translation of the new coordinate axes represented by the matrix

$$\begin{pmatrix} 1 & 0 & 0 & 2 \\ 0 & 1 & 0 & 1 \\ 0 & 0 & 1 & -2 \\ 0 & 0 & 0 & 1 \end{pmatrix}.$$

The matrix representing the product of the rotation of axes followed by the translation of axes is given by the equation

$$\begin{pmatrix} 1 & 0 & 0 & 2 \\ 0 & 1 & 0 & 1 \\ 0 & 0 & 1 & -2 \\ 0 & 0 & 0 & 1 \end{pmatrix} \begin{pmatrix} \dfrac{3}{5} & 0 & \dfrac{4}{5} & 0 \\ -\dfrac{4}{5} & 0 & \dfrac{3}{5} & 0 \\ 0 & -1 & 0 & 0 \\ 0 & 0 & 0 & 1 \end{pmatrix}$$

$$= \begin{pmatrix} \dfrac{3}{5} & 0 & \dfrac{4}{5} & 2 \\ -\dfrac{4}{5} & 0 & \dfrac{3}{5} & 1 \\ 0 & -1 & 0 & -2 \\ 0 & 0 & 0 & 1 \end{pmatrix}.$$

Therefore, the new coordinates of the point P are given by the matrix equation

$$\begin{pmatrix} x'' \\ y'' \\ z'' \\ 1 \end{pmatrix} = \begin{pmatrix} \frac{3}{5} & 0 & \frac{4}{5} & 2 \\ -\frac{4}{5} & 0 & \frac{3}{5} & 1 \\ 0 & -1 & 0 & -2 \\ 0 & 0 & 0 & 1 \end{pmatrix} \begin{pmatrix} 2 \\ -3 \\ 4 \\ 1 \end{pmatrix} = \begin{pmatrix} \frac{32}{25} \\ \frac{9}{5} \\ 1 \\ 1 \end{pmatrix};$$

that is, the new coordinates of P are $\left(\dfrac{32}{5}, \dfrac{9}{5}, 1\right)$.

Example 3. Find new coordinates of point P in Example 2 if the translation is followed by the rotation.

The matrix representing the product transformation is given by the equation

$$\begin{pmatrix} \frac{3}{5} & 0 & \frac{4}{5} & 0 \\ -\frac{4}{5} & 0 & \frac{3}{5} & 0 \\ 0 & -1 & 0 & 0 \\ 0 & 0 & 0 & 1 \end{pmatrix} \begin{pmatrix} 1 & 0 & 0 & 2 \\ 0 & 1 & 0 & 1 \\ 0 & 0 & 1 & -2 \\ 0 & 0 & 0 & 1 \end{pmatrix}$$

$$= \begin{pmatrix} \frac{3}{5} & 0 & \frac{4}{5} & -\frac{2}{5} \\ -\frac{4}{5} & 0 & \frac{3}{5} & -\frac{14}{5} \\ 0 & -1 & 0 & -1 \\ 0 & 0 & 0 & 1 \end{pmatrix}.$$

Therefore,

$$\begin{pmatrix} x'' \\ y'' \\ z'' \\ 1 \end{pmatrix} = \begin{pmatrix} \frac{3}{5} & 0 & \frac{4}{5} & -\frac{2}{5} \\ -\frac{4}{5} & 0 & \frac{3}{5} & -\frac{14}{5} \\ 0 & -1 & 0 & -1 \\ 0 & 0 & 0 & 1 \end{pmatrix} \begin{pmatrix} 2 \\ -3 \\ 4 \\ 1 \end{pmatrix} = \begin{pmatrix} 4 \\ -2 \\ 2 \\ 1 \end{pmatrix}.$$

Hence the new coordinates of P are $(4, -2, 2)$ if the translation of the coordinate axes is followed by the rotation of the coordinate axes.

Exercises

1. Find the new coordinates of the point $P:(3, 4)$ in the plane under a translation of axes such that $(2, -3)$ is the origin, followed by a rotation of axes about the origin through an angle whose measure is $\pi/3$.

2. Change the order of the transformations in Exercise 1, and determine the new coordinates of the point P.

Determine the equation of the graph of each given equation under a rotation of axes through an angle whose measure is θ, followed by a translation of axes such that P_0 is the new origin. Graph each equation.

3. $2x^2 - 4xy + 2y^2 - 5\sqrt{2}x + 3\sqrt{2}y + 10 = 0$; $\theta = \pi/4$; $P_0:(3, -1)$.

4. $2x^2 + 72xy + 23y^2 - 80x - 190y + 175 = 0$; $\theta = \arctan\frac{4}{3}$; $P_0:(2, -1)$.

In Exercises 5 and 6 determine the equation of the graph of each given equation under a translation of axes such that P_0 is the new origin, followed by a rotation of axes through an angle whose measure is θ. Graph each equation.

5. $x^2 + xy + y^2 - 4x + 10y + 50 = 0$; $P_0:(6, -8)$; $\theta = \pi/4$.

6. $2x^2 + 4\sqrt{3}xy - 2y^2 - 4x + 12\sqrt{3}y - 30 = 0$; $P_0:(-2, \sqrt{3})$; $\theta = \pi/6$.

7. Find the new coordinates of the point $P:(1, 2, 0)$ if the coordinate axes are translated and then rotated, where the translation matrix and the rotation matrix are respectively

$$\begin{pmatrix} 1 & 0 & 0 & -1 \\ 0 & 1 & 0 & -2 \\ 0 & 0 & 1 & 0 \\ 0 & 0 & 0 & 1 \end{pmatrix} \quad \text{and} \quad \begin{pmatrix} -1 & 0 & 0 & 0 \\ 0 & 1 & 0 & 0 \\ 0 & 0 & -1 & 0 \\ 0 & 0 & 0 & 1 \end{pmatrix}.$$

8. Find the new coordinates of the point P in Exercise 7 if the rotation transformation precedes the translation transformation.

9. Determine the equation of the graph of $3x^2 + y^2 + 3z^2 + 2x + 2y - 6z + 4 = 0$ under a translation of coordinate axes represented by the matrix

$$\begin{pmatrix} 1 & 0 & 0 & 0 \\ 0 & 1 & 0 & 1 \\ 0 & 0 & 1 & -1 \\ 0 & 0 & 0 & 1 \end{pmatrix},$$

followed by a rotation of the new coordinate axes represented by the matrix

$$\begin{pmatrix} 0 & \dfrac{1}{\sqrt{2}} & \dfrac{1}{\sqrt{2}} & 0 \\ -1 & 0 & 0 & 0 \\ 0 & -\dfrac{1}{\sqrt{2}} & \dfrac{1}{\sqrt{2}} & 0 \\ 0 & 0 & 0 & 1 \end{pmatrix}.$$

10. Determine the equation of the graph of $3x + 2y + z = 6$ under a transformation of coordinate axes represented by

$$\begin{pmatrix} 3 & 0 & 0 & 0 \\ 0 & 2 & 0 & 0 \\ 0 & 0 & 1 & 0 \\ 0 & 0 & 0 & 1 \end{pmatrix}.$$

Describe the transformation of the coordinate axes.

8.7 REFLECTIONS IN THE PLANE AND IN SPACE

Consider a change in orientation on a coordinate axis in the plane. Such a transformation of coordinate axes may be represented by each of the following sets of equations:

$$\begin{cases} x' = -x \\ y' = y \end{cases} \tag{8.25}$$

and

$$\begin{cases} x' = x \\ y' = -y. \end{cases} \tag{8.26}$$

These sets of equations assign to each point $P:(x, y)$ in a plane a new set of coordinates $(-x, y)$ and $(x, -y)$ respectively. The new coordinates of each point are the coordinates of its "mirror image" with respect to the y axis and the x axis respectively. The set of equations (8.25) describes a change of orientation on the x axis; the set of equations (8.26) describes a change of orientation on the y axis. A change of reference system from S to S' described by either the set of equations (8.25) or the set of equations (8.26) is called a *reflection of axes* in the plane.

A reflection of axes in the plane may be represented by one of the following two matrices, called *reflection matrices:*

$$\begin{pmatrix} -1 & 0 & 0 \\ 0 & 1 & 0 \\ 0 & 0 & 1 \end{pmatrix} \quad \text{and} \quad \begin{pmatrix} 1 & 0 & 0 \\ 0 & -1 & 0 \\ 0 & 0 & 1 \end{pmatrix}. \tag{8.27}$$

These matrices assign to each point P with homogeneous Cartesian coordinates $(x, y, 1)$ a new set of coordinates $(-x, y, 1)$ and $(x, -y, 1)$ respectively.

It is interesting to note that the product of any two reflection matrices is a rotation matrix:

$$\begin{pmatrix} -1 & 0 & 0 \\ 0 & 1 & 0 \\ 0 & 0 & 1 \end{pmatrix}\begin{pmatrix} -1 & 0 & 0 \\ 0 & 1 & 0 \\ 0 & 0 & 1 \end{pmatrix} = \begin{pmatrix} 1 & 0 & 0 \\ 0 & 1 & 0 \\ 0 & 0 & 1 \end{pmatrix}, \qquad \text{a rotation of } 0;$$

$$\begin{pmatrix} 1 & 0 & 0 \\ 0 & -1 & 0 \\ 0 & 0 & 1 \end{pmatrix}\begin{pmatrix} 1 & 0 & 0 \\ 0 & -1 & 0 \\ 0 & 0 & 1 \end{pmatrix} = \begin{pmatrix} 1 & 0 & 0 \\ 0 & 1 & 0 \\ 0 & 0 & 1 \end{pmatrix}, \qquad \text{a rotation of } 0;$$

$$\begin{pmatrix} -1 & 0 & 0 \\ 0 & 1 & 0 \\ 0 & 0 & 1 \end{pmatrix}\begin{pmatrix} 1 & 0 & 0 \\ 0 & -1 & 0 \\ 0 & 0 & 1 \end{pmatrix} = \begin{pmatrix} -1 & 0 & 0 \\ 0 & -1 & 0 \\ 0 & 0 & 1 \end{pmatrix}, \qquad \text{a rotation of } \pi;$$

$$\begin{pmatrix} 1 & 0 & 0 \\ 0 & -1 & 0 \\ 0 & 0 & 1 \end{pmatrix}\begin{pmatrix} -1 & 0 & 0 \\ 0 & 1 & 0 \\ 0 & 0 & 1 \end{pmatrix} = \begin{pmatrix} -1 & 0 & 0 \\ 0 & -1 & 0 \\ 0 & 0 & 1 \end{pmatrix}, \qquad \text{a rotation of } \pi.$$

Example. Prove that the distance between two points in a plane is invariant under the reflection of axes described by the sets of equations:

$$\textbf{(a)} \quad \begin{cases} x' = -x \\ y' = y; \end{cases} \qquad\qquad \textbf{(b)} \quad \begin{cases} x' = x \\ y' = -y. \end{cases}$$

Let $A:(x_1, y_1)$ and $B:(x_2, y_2)$ be any two points in a coordinate plane. The distance $|AB|$ between the two points A and B is given by $\sqrt{(x_2 - x_1)^2 + (y_2 - y_1)^2}$.

(a) Under the reflection of axes described by

$$\begin{cases} x' = -x \\ y' = y \end{cases}$$

the new coordinates of A and B become $(-x_1, y_1)$ and $(-x_2, y_2)$ respectively. In terms of the new coordinates, the distance $|AB|$ is given by

$$\sqrt{(-x_2 - (-x_1))^2 + (y_2 - y_1)^2}$$
$$= \sqrt{(x_1 - x_2)^2 + (y_2 - y_1)^2}$$
$$= \sqrt{(x_2 - x_1)^2 + (y_2 - y_1)^2}.$$

(b) Under the reflection of axes described by

$$\begin{cases} x' = x \\ y' = -y \end{cases}$$

the new coordinates of A and B become $(x_1, -y_1)$ and $(x_2, -y_2)$ respectively. In terms of the new coordinates, the distance $|AB|$ is given by

$$\sqrt{(x_2 - x_1)^2 + (-y_2 - (-y_1))^2}$$
$$= \sqrt{(x_2 - x_1)^2 + (y_1 - y_2)^2}$$
$$= \sqrt{(x_2 - x_1)^2 + (y_2 - y_1)^2}.$$

In an analogous fashion a change of orientation on a coordinate axis in three-dimensional space may be represented by one of the following three sets of equations:

$$\begin{cases} x' = -x \\ y' = y \\ z' = z, \end{cases} \tag{8.28}$$

$$\begin{cases} x' = x \\ y' = -y \\ z' = z, \end{cases} \tag{8.29}$$

$$\begin{cases} x' = x \\ y' = y \\ z' = -z. \end{cases} \tag{8.30}$$

These sets of equations assign to each point $P:(x, y, z)$ in space a new set of coordinates $(-x, y, z)$, $(x, -y, z)$, and $(x, y, -z)$ respectively; that is, they represent a change of orientation on the x axis, the y axis, and the z axis respectively. Note that the new coordinates of each point are the coordinates of its "mirror image" with respect to the yz plane, the zx plane, and the xy plane respectively.

In an analogous fashion a change of orientation on a coordinate axis in three-dimensional space may be represented by one of the following three reflection matrices:

$$\begin{pmatrix} -1 & 0 & 0 & 0 \\ 0 & 1 & 0 & 0 \\ 0 & 0 & 1 & 0 \\ 0 & 0 & 0 & 1 \end{pmatrix}, \quad \begin{pmatrix} 1 & 0 & 0 & 0 \\ 0 & -1 & 0 & 0 \\ 0 & 0 & 1 & 0 \\ 0 & 0 & 0 & 1 \end{pmatrix}, \quad \begin{pmatrix} 1 & 0 & 0 & 0 \\ 0 & 1 & 0 & 0 \\ 0 & 0 & -1 & 0 \\ 0 & 0 & 0 & 1 \end{pmatrix}. \tag{8.31}$$

These matrices assign to each point P with homogeneous Cartesian coordinates $(x, y, z, 1)$ a new set of coordinates $(-x, y, z, 1)$, $(x, -y, z, 1)$, and $(x, y, -z, 1)$ respectively.

Once again it is interesting to note that the product of any two reflection matrices for space is a rotation matrix. (See Exercise 3.) Furthermore, the transformations effected by a product of two reflection matrices for space is a rotation of axes in a plane through an angle whose measure is π. For example,

$$\begin{pmatrix} -1 & 0 & 0 & 0 \\ 0 & 1 & 0 & 0 \\ 0 & 0 & 1 & 0 \\ 0 & 0 & 0 & 1 \end{pmatrix} \begin{pmatrix} 1 & 0 & 0 & 0 \\ 0 & -1 & 0 & 0 \\ 0 & 0 & 1 & 0 \\ 0 & 0 & 0 & 1 \end{pmatrix} = \begin{pmatrix} -1 & 0 & 0 & 0 \\ 0 & -1 & 0 & 0 \\ 0 & 0 & 1 & 0 \\ 0 & 0 & 0 & 1 \end{pmatrix},$$

where

$$\begin{pmatrix} -1 & 0 & 0 & 0 \\ 0 & -1 & 0 & 0 \\ 0 & 0 & 1 & 0 \\ 0 & 0 & 0 & 1 \end{pmatrix}$$

represents a rotation of the axes in the xy plane through an angle whose measure is π, keeping the z axis fixed.

Exercises

1. Describe geometrically the effect of a rotation of axes in the plane represented by the matrix $\begin{pmatrix} 0 & 1 & 0 \\ -1 & 0 & 0 \\ 0 & 0 & 1 \end{pmatrix}$, followed by a reflection of axes represented by the matrix $\begin{pmatrix} -1 & 0 & 0 \\ 0 & 1 & 0 \\ 0 & 0 & 1 \end{pmatrix}$.

2. Describe geometrically the effect of a rotation of axes in the plane represented by the matrix $\begin{pmatrix} 0 & -1 & 0 \\ 1 & 0 & 0 \\ 0 & 0 & 1 \end{pmatrix}$, followed by a reflection of axes represented by the matrix $\begin{pmatrix} -1 & 0 & 0 \\ 0 & 1 & 0 \\ 0 & 0 & 1 \end{pmatrix}$.

3. Prove that the product of any two matrices representing a reflection of axes in space is a rotation matrix.

4. Write the transformation for space that represents a rotation of axes (a) in the yz plane through an angle whose measure is π, keeping the x axis fixed; (b) in the zx plane through an angle whose measure is π, keeping the y axis fixed.

5. Prove that every matrix of reflection in a plane or in space is an improper orthogonal matrix.

8.8 RIGID MOTION TRANSFORMATIONS

In this section we shall restrict our attention to transformations in the plane. However, the results of this section can be extended to and generalized for three-dimensional space.

In §8.1 we defined the set of transformations of coordinates under which the distance between two points is a scalar invariant to be the rigid motion transformations. By means of the examples and exercises of the previous sections of this chapter, we have shown that translations, rotations, and reflections are rigid motion transformations. Indeed, the set of ordered products of translations, rotations, and reflections is the set of rigid motion transformations.

By an examination of the matrices which represent translations, rotations, and reflections of coordinate axes, note that each matrix is of the form

$$\begin{pmatrix} a & b & e \\ c & d & f \\ 0 & 0 & 1 \end{pmatrix}, \tag{8.32}$$

where

$$a^2 + c^2 = 1, \tag{8.33}$$

$$b^2 + d^2 = 1, \tag{8.34}$$

$$ab + cd = 0. \tag{8.35}$$

Theorems 8.2 and 8.3 state that a necessary and sufficient condition for a transformation of axes to be a rigid motion transformation is that the transformation be represented by a matrix of the form (8.32) with the properties (8.33), (8.34), and (8.35).

Theorem 8.2. *Let*

$$T = \begin{pmatrix} a & b & e \\ c & d & f \\ 0 & 0 & 1 \end{pmatrix}$$

represent a rigid motion transformation. Then $a^2 + c^2 = 1$, $b^2 + d^2 = 1$, and $ab + cd = 0$.

Proof: Consider the points O and P whose homogeneous Cartesian coordinates are $(0, 0, 1)$ and $(1, 0, 1)$ respectively.

Under the transformation represented by T, the new coordinates of O and P are $(e, f, 1)$ and $(a + e, c + f, 1)$ respectively. Since T represents a rigid motion transformation, the distance between two points is a scalar invariant. Thus

$$\sqrt{[(a + e) - e]^2 + [(c + f) - f]^2} = \sqrt{(1 - 0)^2 + (0 - 0)^2},$$
$$\sqrt{a^2 + c^2} = \sqrt{1^2},$$
$$a^2 + c^2 = 1.$$

Considering, in a similar manner, the points O and M whose homogeneous Cartesian coordinates are $(0, 0, 1)$ and $(0, 1, 1)$ respectively, it can be shown that

$$b^2 + d^2 = 1.$$

Finally, consider the points O and N whose homogeneous Cartesian coordinates are $(0, 0, 1)$ and $(1, 1, 1)$ respectively. Under the transformation represented by T, the new coordinates of O and N are respectively $(e, f, 1)$ and $(a + b + e, c + d + f, 1)$. Again, since T represents a rigid motion transformation, the distance between two points is a scalar invariant:

$$\sqrt{[(a + b + e) - e]^2 + [(c + d + f) - f]^2}$$
$$= \sqrt{(1 - 0)^2 + (1 - 0)^2},$$
$$\sqrt{(a + b)^2 + (c + d)^2} = \sqrt{1^2 + 1^2},$$
$$(a + b)^2 + (c + d)^2 = 2,$$
$$(a^2 + c^2) + (b^2 + d^2) + 2(ab + cd) = 2,$$
$$1 + 1 + 2(ab + cd) = 2,$$
$$2(ab + cd) = 0,$$
$$ab + cd = 0.$$

Theorem 8.3. *Let*

$$T = \begin{pmatrix} a & b & e \\ c & d & f \\ 0 & 0 & 1 \end{pmatrix}$$

represent a transformation of coordinates so that $a^2 + c^2 = 1$, $b^2 + d^2 = 1$, and $ab + cd = 0$. Then the transformation represented by T is a rigid motion transformation.

Proof: Consider any points $P_1:(x_1, y_1, 1)$ and $P_2:(x_2, y_2, 1)$ in the plane. Under the transformation represented by T, the new coordinates of the points P_1 and P_2 are

$$(ax_1 + by_1 + e, cx_1 + dy_1 + f, 1)$$

and

$$(ax_2 + by_2 + e, cx_2 + dy_2 + f, 1)$$

respectively. Now, the distance $|P_1P_2|$ between the two points in terms of the new coordinates is given by

$$
\begin{aligned}
|P_1P_2|^2 &= [(ax_2 + by_2 + e) - (ax_1 + by_1 + e)]^2 \\
&\quad + [(cx_2 + dy_2 + f) - (cx_1 + dy_1 + f)]^2 \\
&= [a(x_2 - x_1) + b(y_2 - y_1)]^2 \\
&\quad + [c(x_2 - x_1) + d(y_2 - y_1)]^2 \\
&= (a^2 + c^2)(x_2 - x_1)^2 \\
&\quad + 2(ab + cd)(x_2 - x_1)(y_2 - y_1) \\
&\quad + (b^2 + d^2)(y_2 - y_1)^2.
\end{aligned}
$$

Since $a^2 + c^2 = 1$, $b^2 + d^2 = 1$, and $ab + cd = 0$, then

$$|P_1P_2|^2 = (x_2 - x_1)^2 + (y_2 - y_1)^2,$$

$$|P_1P_2| = \sqrt{(x_2 - x_1)^2 + (y_2 - y_1)^2}.$$

Hence the distance between two points is a scalar invariant under the transformation of coordinates represented by T; that is, the transformation represented by T is a rigid motion transformation.

As a preliminary to Theorem 8.5, we prove an additional property of the matrices that represent rigid motion transformations.

Theorem 8.4. *Let*

$$
\begin{pmatrix}
a & b & e \\
c & d & f \\
0 & 0 & 1
\end{pmatrix}
$$

be a matrix such that $a^2 + c^2 = 1$, $b^2 + d^2 = 1$, *and* $ab + cd = 0$. *Then*

$$ad - bc = \pm 1. \tag{8.36}$$

Proof: Since $a^2 + c^2 = 1$ and $b^2 + d^2 = 1$, then

$$(a^2 + c^2)(b^2 + d^2) = 1,$$

$$a^2b^2 + a^2d^2 + b^2c^2 + c^2d^2 = 1.$$

Since $ab + cd = 0$, then

$$(ab + cd)^2 = 0,$$

$$a^2b^2 + 2abcd + c^2d^2 = 0.$$

Subtracting equals from equals, we obtain

$$(a^2b^2 + a^2d^2 + b^2c^2 + c^2d^2) - (a^2b^2 + 2abcd + c^2d^2) = 1,$$
$$a^2d^2 - 2abcd + b^2c^2 = 1,$$
$$(ad - bc)^2 = 1,$$
$$ad - bc = \pm 1.$$

The next theorem characterizes the types of rigid motion transformations that exist.

Theorem 8.5. *Every rigid motion transformation can be expressed as a product of translations, rotations, and reflections.*

Proof: Let

$$T = \begin{pmatrix} a & b & e \\ c & d & f \\ 0 & 0 & 1 \end{pmatrix}$$

represent a rigid motion transformation. It is possible to express T as the product of two matrices:

$$\begin{pmatrix} 1 & 0 & e \\ 0 & 1 & f \\ 0 & 0 & 1 \end{pmatrix} \begin{pmatrix} a & b & 0 \\ c & d & 0 \\ 0 & 0 & 1 \end{pmatrix},$$

where the first matrix represents a translation. It remains for us to analyze the second matrix.

If $ad - bc = 1$, then

$$a(ad - bc) = a, \qquad \text{(by (8.36))}$$
$$c(ab + cd) = 0. \qquad \text{(by (8.35))}$$

Adding equals to equals, we obtain

$$a^2d + c^2d = a,$$
$$d(a^2 + c^2) = a,$$
$$d = a.$$

When $d = a$, then (8.35) becomes

$$a(b + c) = 0,$$

whereby either $a = 0$ or $b = -c$.

(i) If $a = d = 0$, then $c = \pm 1$ by (8.33) and $b = \mp 1$ by

(8.36). Therefore, the second matrix is of the form

$$\begin{pmatrix} 0 & -1 & 0 \\ 1 & 0 & 0 \\ 0 & 0 & 1 \end{pmatrix} \quad \text{or} \quad \begin{pmatrix} 0 & 1 & 0 \\ -1 & 0 & 0 \\ 0 & 0 & 1 \end{pmatrix}.$$

Each of these matrices represents a rotation of axes. (Describe each rotation.)

(ii) If $b = -c$, then the second matrix is of the form

$$\begin{pmatrix} a & -c & 0 \\ c & a & 0 \\ 0 & 0 & 1 \end{pmatrix}.$$

Since $a^2 + c^2 = 1$, an angle θ exists such that $\cos \theta = a$ and $-\sin \theta = c$, and the matrix represents a rotation of axes.

If $ad - bc = -1$, then

$$a(ad - bc) = -a, \qquad \text{(by (8.36))}$$
$$c(ab + cd) = 0. \qquad \text{(by (8.35))}$$

Adding equals to equals, we obtain

$$a^2 d + c^2 d = -a,$$
$$d(a^2 + c^2) = -a,$$
$$d = -a.$$

When $d = -a$, then (8.35) becomes

$$a(b - c) = 0,$$

whereby either $a = 0$ or $b = c$.

(iii) If $a = 0$, then $c = \pm 1$ by (8.33) and $b = \pm 1$ by (8.36). Therefore, the second matrix is of the form

$$\begin{pmatrix} 0 & 1 & 0 \\ 1 & 0 & 0 \\ 0 & 0 & 1 \end{pmatrix} \quad \text{or} \quad \begin{pmatrix} 0 & -1 & 0 \\ -1 & 0 & 0 \\ 0 & 0 & 1 \end{pmatrix}.$$

Each of these matrices represents a product of rotations and reflections. (See Exercises 1 and 2 of §8.7.)

(iv) If $b = c$, the second matrix is of the form

$$\begin{pmatrix} a & c & 0 \\ c & -a & 0 \\ 0 & 0 & 1 \end{pmatrix}.$$

This is equal to

$$\begin{pmatrix} a & -c & 0 \\ c & a & 0 \\ 0 & 0 & 1 \end{pmatrix} \begin{pmatrix} 1 & 0 & 0 \\ 0 & -1 & 0 \\ 0 & 0 & 1 \end{pmatrix},$$

a product of a reflection followed by a rotation.

Hence, if the matrix T represents a rigid motion transformation, it can be expressed as the product of matrices representing translations, rotations, and reflections.

8.9 REPRESENTATION OF THE CONIC SECTIONS IN MATRIX FORM

In §6.2 the conic sections were defined as the graphs of the general equation of the second degree in two variables:

$$f(x, y) = ax^2 + 2bxy + cy^2 + 2dx + 2ey + f = 0,$$

where a, b, c, d, e, and f are real numbers. The process of transforming the equation of a conic section to one of the canonical forms (6.2) or (6.3) can be accomplished by means of a rotation of coordinate axes, a translation of coordinate axes, or a product of both.

Note that the equation of a conic section can be written in the matrix form

$$(x \quad y \quad 1) \begin{pmatrix} a & b & d \\ b & c & e \\ d & e & f \end{pmatrix} \begin{pmatrix} x \\ y \\ 1 \end{pmatrix} = 0. \tag{8.37}$$

The matrix

$$\mathfrak{F} = \begin{pmatrix} a & b & d \\ b & c & e \\ d & e & f \end{pmatrix} \tag{8.38}$$

is called the *matrix of the conic section*. The matrix

$$F = \begin{pmatrix} a & b \\ b & c \end{pmatrix} \tag{8.39}$$

is of prime importance in the study of the conic section since it represents that portion of $f(x, y)$ in *quadratic form;* that is, it represents those terms which are of degree 2:

$$(x \quad y) \begin{pmatrix} a & b \\ b & c \end{pmatrix} \begin{pmatrix} x \\ y \end{pmatrix} = ax^2 + 2bxy + y^2.$$

Since F is a symmetric matrix, we know that it is possible to reduce F to a diagonal matrix whose diagonal elements are the eigenvalues λ_1 and λ_2 of F:

$$R^{-1}FR = \begin{pmatrix} \lambda_1 & 0 \\ 0 & \lambda_2 \end{pmatrix}. \tag{8.40}$$

Furthermore, the matrix R is a matrix whose columns are the eigenvectors associated with the eigenvalues λ_1 and λ_2 of F. If the eigenvectors are normalized by the use of an appropriate constant, then the matrix R can be made a proper orthogonal matrix, whereby $R^{-1} = R^{\mathsf{T}}$. Every proper orthogonal matrix of order 2 is a rotation matrix. (See Exercise 9 of §7.6.) Therefore, a rotation of axes represented by the equation

$$\begin{pmatrix} x \\ y \\ 1 \end{pmatrix} = \mathcal{R} \begin{pmatrix} x' \\ y' \\ 1 \end{pmatrix},$$

where $\mathcal{R}$ has the form

$$\begin{pmatrix} \cos\theta & -\sin\theta & 0 \\ \sin\theta & \cos\theta & 0 \\ 0 & 0 & 1 \end{pmatrix},$$

will transform the equation of the conic to a form void of the cross product term $x'y'$. For example,

$$(x' \quad y' \quad 1)\mathcal{R}^{\mathsf{T}} \begin{pmatrix} a & b & d \\ b & c & e \\ d & e & f \end{pmatrix} \mathcal{R} \begin{pmatrix} x' \\ y' \\ 1 \end{pmatrix} = 0,$$

$$(x' \quad y' \quad 1) \begin{pmatrix} \lambda_1 & 0 & d' \\ 0 & \lambda_2 & e' \\ d' & e' & f \end{pmatrix} \begin{pmatrix} x' \\ y' \\ 1 \end{pmatrix} = 0; \tag{8.41}$$

that is,

$$\lambda_1 x'^2 + \lambda_2 y'^2 + 2d'x' + 2e'y' + f = 0. \tag{8.42}$$

If neither λ_1 nor λ_2 is zero, then a translation of axes to the $x''y''$ system with origin at $\left(-\dfrac{d'}{\lambda_1}, -\dfrac{e'}{\lambda_2}\right)$ in the $x'y'$ system will transform the equation of the conic section to a canonical form. The translation may be represented in matrix form as

$$\begin{pmatrix} x' \\ y' \\ 1 \end{pmatrix} = \begin{pmatrix} 1 & 0 & -\dfrac{d'}{\lambda_1} \\ 0 & 1 & -\dfrac{e'}{\lambda_2} \\ 0 & 0 & 1 \end{pmatrix} \begin{pmatrix} x'' \\ y'' \\ 1 \end{pmatrix}.$$

Thus after the translation of axes, equation (8.41) of the conic section becomes

$$(x'' \ y'' \ 1) \begin{pmatrix} 1 & 0 & 0 \\ 0 & 1 & 0 \\ -\dfrac{d'}{\lambda_1} & -\dfrac{e'}{\lambda_2} & 1 \end{pmatrix} \begin{pmatrix} \lambda_1 & 0 & d' \\ 0 & \lambda_2 & e' \\ d' & e' & f \end{pmatrix} \begin{pmatrix} 1 & 0 & -\dfrac{d'}{\lambda_1} \\ 0 & 1 & -\dfrac{e'}{\lambda_2} \\ 0 & 0 & 1 \end{pmatrix} \begin{pmatrix} x'' \\ y'' \\ 1 \end{pmatrix} = 0,$$

$$(x'' \ y'' \ 1) \begin{pmatrix} \lambda_1 & 0 & 0 \\ 0 & \lambda_2 & 0 \\ 0 & 0 & f' \end{pmatrix} \begin{pmatrix} x'' \\ y'' \\ 1 \end{pmatrix} = 0; \tag{8.43}$$

that is,

$$\lambda_1 x''^2 + \lambda_2 y''^2 + f' = 0. \tag{8.44}$$

This equation is in the canonical form (6.2).

If one of the eigenvalues λ_1 and λ_2 equals zero, then a translation of axes which would remove both linear terms of the variables in the equation of the conic does not exist. Consider $\lambda_2 = 0$. If $e' \neq 0$, then a translation of axes to the $x''y''$ system with origin at $\left(-\dfrac{d'}{\lambda_1}, \dfrac{d'^2}{2e'\lambda_1} - \dfrac{f}{2e'}\right)$ in the $x'y'$ system will transform (8.41) or (8.42) to a canonical form:

$$(x'' \ y'' \ 1) \begin{pmatrix} 1 & 0 & 0 \\ 0 & 1 & 0 \\ -\dfrac{d'}{\lambda_1} & \dfrac{d'^2}{2e'\lambda_1} - \dfrac{f}{2e'} & 1 \end{pmatrix} \begin{pmatrix} \lambda_1 & 0 & d' \\ 0 & 0 & e' \\ d' & e' & f \end{pmatrix}$$

$$\begin{pmatrix} 1 & 0 & -\dfrac{d'}{\lambda_1} \\ 0 & 1 & \dfrac{d'^2}{2e'\lambda_1} - \dfrac{f}{2e'} \\ 0 & 0 & 1 \end{pmatrix} \begin{pmatrix} x'' \\ y'' \\ 1 \end{pmatrix} = 0,$$

$$(x'' \ y'' \ 1) \begin{pmatrix} \lambda_1 & 0 & 0 \\ 0 & 0 & e' \\ 0 & e' & 0 \end{pmatrix} \begin{pmatrix} x'' \\ y'' \\ 1 \end{pmatrix} = 0; \tag{8.45}$$

that is,

$$\lambda_1 x''^2 + 2e' y'' = 0. \tag{8.46}$$

This equation is in the canonical form (6.3). If $\lambda_2 = 0$ and $e' = 0$, then equation (8.41) or (8.42) obviously represents a degenerate conic since it is a quadratic equation in x.

This completes the argument demonstrating that the general equation of a conic section can be transformed to one of two standard, or canonical, forms.

Example 1. Transform the equation of the conic $2x^2 + \sqrt{3}xy + 3y^2 - 4 = 0$ to a canonical form.

The equation of the conic section can be written in the matrix form

$$
(x \quad y \quad 1)
\begin{pmatrix}
2 & \dfrac{\sqrt{3}}{2} & 0 \\
\dfrac{\sqrt{3}}{2} & 3 & 0 \\
0 & 0 & -4
\end{pmatrix}
\begin{pmatrix}
x \\ y \\ 1
\end{pmatrix}.
$$

The characteristic equation of the matrix

$$
\begin{pmatrix}
2 & \dfrac{\sqrt{3}}{2} \\
\dfrac{\sqrt{3}}{2} & 3
\end{pmatrix}
$$

is $4\lambda^2 - 20\lambda + 21 = 0$. The eigenvalues are $3/2$ and $7/2$, and a pair of associated normalized eigenvectors are $\left(\dfrac{\sqrt{3}}{2}, -\dfrac{1}{2}\right)^{\mathsf{T}}$ and $\left(\dfrac{1}{2}, \dfrac{\sqrt{3}}{2}\right)^{\mathsf{T}}$ respectively. Therefore, a rotation of axes represented by the equation

$$
\begin{pmatrix}
x \\ y \\ 1
\end{pmatrix}
=
\begin{pmatrix}
\dfrac{\sqrt{3}}{2} & \dfrac{1}{2} & 0 \\
-\dfrac{1}{2} & \dfrac{\sqrt{3}}{2} & 0 \\
0 & 0 & 1
\end{pmatrix}
\begin{pmatrix}
x' \\ y' \\ 1
\end{pmatrix}
$$

will transform the equation of the conic to a form void of the cross product term $x'y'$:

$$
(x' \quad y' \quad 1)
\begin{pmatrix}
\dfrac{\sqrt{3}}{2} & -\dfrac{1}{2} & 0 \\
\dfrac{1}{2} & \dfrac{\sqrt{3}}{2} & 0 \\
0 & 0 & 1
\end{pmatrix}
\begin{pmatrix}
2 & \dfrac{\sqrt{3}}{2} & 0 \\
\dfrac{\sqrt{3}}{2} & 3 & 0 \\
0 & 0 & -4
\end{pmatrix}
$$

$$
\begin{pmatrix}
\dfrac{\sqrt{3}}{2} & \dfrac{1}{2} & 0 \\
-\dfrac{1}{2} & \dfrac{\sqrt{3}}{2} & 0 \\
0 & 0 & 1
\end{pmatrix}
\begin{pmatrix}
x' \\ y' \\ 1
\end{pmatrix}
= 0,
$$

$$(x' \quad y' \quad 1) \begin{pmatrix} \frac{3}{2} & 0 & 0 \\ 0 & \frac{7}{2} & 0 \\ 0 & 0 & -4 \end{pmatrix} \begin{pmatrix} x' \\ y' \\ 1 \end{pmatrix} = 0;$$

that is,

$$3x'^2 + 7y'^2 - 8 = 0.$$

This last equation represents the ellipse shown in Figure 8.11.

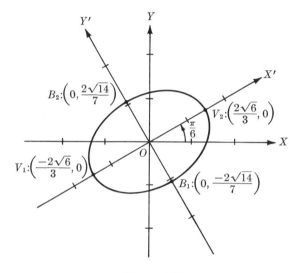

Figure 8.11

Example 2. Transform the equation of the conic $9x^2 + 24xy + 16y^2 - 20x + 30y = 0$ to a canonical form.

The matrix of the conic section is

$$\begin{pmatrix} 9 & 12 & -10 \\ 12 & 16 & 15 \\ -10 & 15 & 0 \end{pmatrix}.$$

The characteristic equation of $\begin{pmatrix} 9 & 12 \\ 12 & 16 \end{pmatrix}$ is $\lambda^2 - 25\lambda = 0$.

The eigenvalues are 25 and 0, and a pair of associated normalized eigenvectors are $\left(\dfrac{3}{5} \quad \dfrac{4}{5}\right)^{\mathsf{T}}$ and $\left(-\dfrac{4}{5} \quad \dfrac{3}{5}\right)^{\mathsf{T}}$ respectively. Therefore, the transformed equation of the conic section after a rotation of axes becomes

$$(x' \quad y' \quad 1) \begin{pmatrix} \frac{3}{5} & \frac{4}{5} & 0 \\ -\frac{4}{5} & \frac{3}{5} & 0 \\ 0 & 0 & 1 \end{pmatrix} \begin{pmatrix} 9 & 12 & -10 \\ 12 & 16 & 15 \\ -10 & 15 & 0 \end{pmatrix}$$

$$\begin{pmatrix} \frac{3}{5} & -\frac{4}{5} & 0 \\ \frac{4}{5} & \frac{3}{5} & 0 \\ 0 & 0 & 1 \end{pmatrix} \begin{pmatrix} x' \\ y' \\ 1 \end{pmatrix} = 0,$$

$$(x' \quad y' \quad 1) \begin{pmatrix} 25 & 0 & 6 \\ 0 & 0 & 17 \\ 6 & 17 & 0 \end{pmatrix} \begin{pmatrix} x' \\ y' \\ 1 \end{pmatrix} = 0.$$

Since $\lambda_1 = 25$, $\lambda_2 = 0$, $d' = 6$, $e' = 17$, and $f = 0$, then a translation of axes to the $x''y''$ system with origin at $(-\frac{6}{25}, \frac{18}{425})$ in the $x'y'$ system will transform the equation of the conic section to a canonical form:

$$(x'' \quad y'' \quad 1) \begin{pmatrix} 1 & 0 & 0 \\ 0 & 1 & 0 \\ -\frac{6}{25} & \frac{18}{425} & 1 \end{pmatrix} \begin{pmatrix} 25 & 0 & 6 \\ 0 & 0 & 17 \\ 6 & 17 & 0 \end{pmatrix}$$

$$\begin{pmatrix} 1 & 0 & -\frac{6}{25} \\ 0 & 1 & \frac{18}{425} \\ 0 & 0 & 1 \end{pmatrix} \begin{pmatrix} x'' \\ y'' \\ 1 \end{pmatrix} = 0,$$

$$(x'' \quad y'' \quad 1) \begin{pmatrix} 25 & 0 & 0 \\ 0 & 0 & 17 \\ 0 & 17 & 0 \end{pmatrix} \begin{pmatrix} x'' \\ y'' \\ 1 \end{pmatrix} = 0;$$

that is,

$$25x''^2 + 34y'' = 0.$$

This equation represents a parabola in canonical form.

Exercises

In Exercises 1–4 transform the equation of each conic to a canonical form. Graph each conic.

1. $2x^2 + 4xy + 5y^2 - 2 = 0$.

2. $17x^2 - 12xy + 8y^2 - 20 = 0$.

3. $x^2 - 2xy + y^2 + 10x + 10y - 25 = 0$.

4. $5x^2 + 6xy + 5y^2 - 4x + 4y - 4 = 0$.

5. In equation (8.41), show that $d' = d \cos \theta - e \sin \theta$ and $e' = d \sin \theta + e \cos \theta$, where θ is the angle of rotation in matrix $\mathcal{R}$.

6. Show that the geometric center $C:(x, y)$ of the conic $8x^2 + 8xy - 2y^2 + x - 3y + 8 = 0$ satisfies the system of equations

$$\begin{cases} ax + by + d = 0 \\ bx + cy + e = 0. \end{cases}$$

8.10 CLASSIFICATION OF THE CONIC SECTIONS

The results in the previous section indicate that the type of conic section represented by the general equation of the second degree in two variables can be determined by an investigation of the values and the algebraic signs of the eigenvalues of matrix F.

If the eigenvalues λ_1 and λ_2 are nonzero and have like algebraic signs, then a rotation of axes followed by a translation of axes transforms the general equation of the conic to the form of equation (8.44). This equation represents a real ellipse, an imaginary ellipse, or a point depending upon whether f' differs in sign from the eigenvalues, agrees in sign, or is zero respectively. Furthermore, if $\lambda_1 = \lambda_2$ in the case of a real ellipse, then the conic section is a circle.

If the eigenvalues are nonzero, but differ in algebraic sign, then equation (8.44) represents a hyperbola or a pair of intersecting lines depending upon whether f' is nonzero or zero respectively. Furthermore, if $|\lambda_1| = |\lambda_2|$ in the case of a hyperbola, then the conic is an equilateral hyperbola.

Consider the case where one of the eigenvalues λ_i is zero, say λ_2. A rotation of axes transforms the general equation of the conic to the form of equation (8.42). If $e' \neq 0$, then a translation of axes further transforms the equation of the conic to the form of equation (8.46), which represents a parabola. If $e' = 0$, then (8.42) becomes $\lambda_1 x'^2 + 2d'x' + f = 0$. This equation represents a pair of real parallel lines, a pair of coincident lines, or a pair of imaginary parallel lines depending upon whether $d'^2 - f\lambda_1$ is greater than zero, equal to zero, or less than zero respectively.

8.11 RANK OF THE CONICS

The rank of $\mathfrak{F}$, the matrix of the conic section, is called the *rank of the conic*. Since the rank of a matrix is not changed by an elementary row operation, and since every rigid motion transformation can be expressed as the product of a set of elementary row operation matrices (Exercise 22 of §7.7), then it follows that the rank of a conic is an invariant under such transformations.

Note that in §8.9 the matrix of the conic section

$$\mathfrak{F} = \begin{pmatrix} a & b & d \\ b & c & e \\ d & e & f \end{pmatrix}$$

is transformed under the rigid motion transformations to

$$\mathfrak{F}_1 = \begin{pmatrix} \lambda_1 & 0 & 0 \\ 0 & \lambda_2 & 0 \\ 0 & 0 & f' \end{pmatrix} \tag{8.47}$$

in equation (8.43);

$$\mathfrak{F}_2 = \begin{pmatrix} \lambda_1 & 0 & 0 \\ 0 & 0 & e' \\ 0 & e' & 0 \end{pmatrix} \tag{8.48}$$

in equation (8.45); or

$$\mathfrak{F}_3 = \begin{pmatrix} \lambda_1 & 0 & d' \\ 0 & 0 & 0 \\ d' & 0 & f \end{pmatrix} \tag{8.49}$$

in equation (8.41), with $\lambda_2 = 0$ and $e' = 0$.

If $f' \neq 0$, matrix $\mathfrak{F}_1$ is of rank 3. Hence from the discussion of the classification of the conic sections, real and imaginary ellipses and hyperbolas are conics of rank 3.

If $f' = 0$, matrix $\mathfrak{F}_1$ is of rank 2; thus points and pairs of intersecting lines are conics of rank 2.

The matrix $\mathfrak{F}_2$ is of rank 3. Hence parabolas are conics of rank 3.

If $d'^2 - f\lambda_1 \neq 0$, matrix $\mathfrak{F}_3$ is of rank 2. Hence pairs of real parallel lines and pairs of imaginary parallel lines are conics of rank 2.

If $d'^2 - f\lambda_1 = 0$, matrix $\mathfrak{F}_3$ is of rank 1; thus pairs of coincident lines are conics of rank 1.

Note that the real proper conics are the real conics of rank 3. Conics whose ranks are less than 3 are degenerate conic sections. Furthermore, the real conics whose ranks are 3 and for which $\det F \neq 0$ are the *real proper central conics;* that is, conics with a geometric center.

The rank of a conic is not the only scalar invariant associated with a conic under a rigid motion transformation. Since similar matrices have equal eigenvalues (Exercise 9 of §7.10), similar matrices have the same characteristic function. Equation (8.40) states that

$$\begin{pmatrix} a & b \\ b & c \end{pmatrix} \quad \text{and} \quad \begin{pmatrix} \lambda_1 & 0 \\ 0 & \lambda_2 \end{pmatrix}$$

are similar matrices. Therefore, their characteristic functions

$$\lambda^2 - (a + c)\lambda + (ac - b^2) \quad \text{and} \quad \lambda^2 - (\lambda_1 + \lambda_2)\lambda + \lambda_1\lambda_2$$

are identical. Thus

$$a + c = \lambda_1 + \lambda_2 \tag{8.50}$$

and

$$ac - b^2 = \lambda_1\lambda_2 ; \tag{8.51}$$

that is, $a + c$ and $ac - b^2$ are scalar invariants under the rotation transformation. In addition, since

$$\begin{pmatrix} 1 & 0 & 0 \\ 0 & 1 & 0 \\ x_0 & y_0 & 1 \end{pmatrix}\begin{pmatrix} a & b & - \\ b & c & - \\ - & - & - \end{pmatrix}\begin{pmatrix} 1 & 0 & x_0 \\ 0 & 1 & y_0 \\ 0 & 0 & 1 \end{pmatrix} = \begin{pmatrix} a & b & - \\ b & c & - \\ - & - & - \end{pmatrix}$$

for any values of x_0 and y_0, the quantities $a + c$ and $ac - b^2$ are scalar invariants under the translation transformation.

Theorem 8.6. *A proper conic* $ax^2 + 2bxy + cy^2 + 2dx + 2ey + f = 0$ *is:*
  (i) *an ellipse if* $ac - b^2 > 0$;
  (ii) *a hyperbola if* $ac - b^2 < 0$;
  (iii) *a parabola if* $ac - b^2 = 0$.

Proof: If the equation of a conic represents a proper conic, it can be reduced by means of the rigid motion transformations to one of the two following forms:

$$\lambda_1 x''^2 + \lambda_2 y''^2 + f' = 0, \tag{8.52}$$

where $f' \neq 0$ and f' differs in sign from at least one λ_i; or

$$\lambda_1 x''^2 + 2e'y'' = 0, \tag{8.53}$$

where $e' \neq 0$.

  (i) If $ac - b^2 > 0$, then λ_1 and λ_2 have like algebraic signs since $ac - b^2 = \lambda_1\lambda_2$. If λ_1 and λ_2 have like algebraic signs, then the form (8.52) represents an ellipse.
  (ii) If $ac - b^2 < 0$, then λ_1 and λ_2 have unlike algebraic signs, and the form (8.52) represents a hyperbola.
  (iii) If $ac - b^2 = 0$, then λ_1 or λ_2 is zero. Consider $\lambda_2 = 0$. Then the equation of the proper conic can be reduced to the form (8.53), which represents a parabola.

Exercises

In Exercises 1–4 find the rank of each conic.

1. $x^2 - 4xy + 4y^2 - 4 = 0$.

2. $3x^2 - 4xy + 4x + 8y = 0$.

3. $3x^2 + 2xy + 3y^2 + 16x - 16y + 52 = 0$.

4. $5x^2 - 4xy + 8y^2 + 18x - 36y + 9 = 0$.

In Exercises 5 and 6 verify for each conic that (a) $a + c$; (b) $ac - b^2$ are scalar invariants.

5. $16x^2 + 24xy + 9y^2 + x + 2y - 1 = 0$.

6. $9x^2 + 4xy + 6y^2 + 12x + 36y + 44 = 0$.

7. Prove that $a + c + f$ is a scalar invariant for any conic under a rotation of axes.

8. Prove that $d^2 + e^2$ is a scalar invariant for any conic under a rotation of axes.

QUADRIC SURFACES

9.1 INTRODUCTION

Surfaces may be defined by purely geometric conditions. However, we shall define surfaces by means of their equations; that is, we shall define surfaces as sets of points whose coordinates satisfy an equation of the form

$$f(x, y, z) = 0.$$

Note that a surface may or may not consist of a set of real points depending upon whether or not its equation is satisfied by a set of real number triples. If no real points lie on a given surface, it is called *imaginary*. If $f(x, y, z)$ in the above equation is a real polynomial expression in three variables x, y, and z, then the surface defined by the equation is called an *algebraic surface*. The graph of the most general polynomial equation of the second degree in x, y, and z is called a *quadric surface*. The equation of a quadric surface can be written in the form

$$ax^2 + by^2 + cz^2 + 2fyz + 2gzx + 2hxy + 2rx + 2sy + 2tz + d = 0, \quad (9.1)$$

where the coefficients a, b, c, f, g, h, r, s, t, and d are real numbers.

There are seventeen basic quadric surfaces, of which three are imaginary. For later reference we shall list the quadric surfaces as follows:

    (1)   Real ellipsoid
    (2)   Imaginary ellipsoid
    (3)   Hyperboloid of one sheet
    (4)   Hyperboloid of two sheets
    (5)   Elliptic paraboloid
    (6)   Hyperbolic paraboloid
    (7)   Quadric cone

    (8)   Point
    (9)   Real elliptic cylinder
  (10)   Imaginary elliptic cylinder
  (11)   Hyperbolic cylinder
  (12)   Parabolic cylinder
  (13)   Intersecting planes
  (14)   Line
  (15)   Real parallel planes
  (16)   Imaginary parallel planes
  (17)   Coincident planes

By an appropriate rotation or translation of axes, or both, the general equation of the quadric surface may be transformed into one of two *standard*, or *canonical, forms:*

$$Ax^2 + By^2 + Cz^2 = D; \tag{9.2}$$

$$Ax^2 + By^2 + Cz = 0. \tag{9.3}$$

In this chapter, we shall discuss the properties of the quadric surfaces in these simple canonical forms. It should be understood that in the discussion of these equations, an interchange of variables is possible which does not affect the fundamental characteristics to be examined. For example, equation (9.3) could have been written in the form

$$Ax^2 + Bz^2 + Cy = 0,$$

in which case the roles of the variables y and z would be interchanged. Furthermore, replacing a variable by its negative is a transformation which does not affect our discussion since we may think of this operation as merely a relabeling of the coordinate axes.

    An analysis of a given equation of a quadric surface in order to determine the nature of its graph may be made by determining the type of curves of intersection obtained by intersecting planes. Such curves of intersection will be called *sections* of the surface. If the plane is a coordinate plane, the section will be called a *trace* of the surface in that coordinate plane.

    If none of the constants in equation (9.2) is zero, the equation can be written in the form

$$\frac{x^2}{a^2} \pm \frac{y^2}{b^2} \pm \frac{z^2}{c^2} \pm 1 = 0.$$

With an appropriate choice of algebraic signs this equation may represent one of the first four quadric surfaces, the ellipsoids and hyperboloids. In the remainder of this chapter it shall be convenient to treat a, b, and c as positive real numbers.

9.2 THE ELLIPSOIDS

The set of points whose coordinates satisfy the equation

$$\frac{x^2}{a^2} + \frac{y^2}{b^2} + \frac{z^2}{c^2} = 1 \tag{9.4}$$

is a *real ellipsoid* (Figure 9.1). Since only even powers of x, y, and z occur in the equation, the surface is symmetric with respect to all three coordinate planes and axes. Therefore, the surface is symmetric with respect to the origin, its *geometric center*. A plane of symmetry of a quadric surface is frequently called a *principal plane* of the quadric surface. The coordinate planes are principal planes of the real ellipsoid.

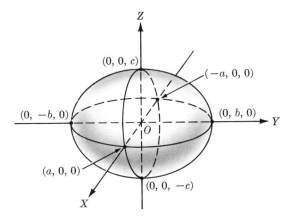

Figure 9.1

Plane sections of the ellipsoid parallel to the coordinate planes are ellipses. For example, the intersection of the ellipsoid with the plane $z = k$, provided that $|k| < c$, is the ellipse

$$\frac{x^2}{a^2} + \frac{y^2}{b^2} = 1 - \frac{k^2}{c^2}, \qquad z = k.$$

If $|k| = c$, the section is a point ellipse, that is, a point. If $k = 0$, the section is the trace of the ellipsoid in the xy plane, the ellipse

$$\frac{x^2}{a^2} + \frac{y^2}{b^2} = 1, \qquad z = 0.$$

The sections of the ellipsoid in planes parallel to the yz plane and zx plane are defined in an analogous fashion.

The segments of length $2a$, $2b$, and $2c$, that are cut off on the coordinate axes are called the *axes* of the ellipsoid. If only two semi-axes are equal, the ellipsoid is an *ellipsoid of revolution:* a *prolate spheroid* if the equal axes are less than the third axis; an *oblate spheroid* if the equal axes are greater than the third axis.* If the three semi-axes are equal, the surface is a *sphere*, which is a special case of the real ellipsoid.

The equation

$$\frac{x^2}{a^2} + \frac{y^2}{b^2} + \frac{z^2}{c^2} = -1 \qquad (9.5)$$

represents an *imaginary ellipsoid* since no real points lie on the surface.

Exercises

1. Discuss and sketch the surface defined by

$$\frac{x^2}{9} + \frac{y^2}{25} + \frac{z^2}{16} = 1.$$

2. Where does the ellipsoid $4x^2 + 9y^2 + 4z^2 = 36$ intersect the coordinate axes? What type of ellipsoid is it?

3. Determine the smallest values of a, b, and c such that the surface in Exercise 2 lies entirely in the region

$$\begin{cases} |x| \le a \\ |y| \le b \\ |z| \le c. \end{cases}$$

4. Determine the values of k for which the plane $y = k$ intersects the ellipsoid $4x^2 + y^2 + 16z^2 + 16 = 0$.

5. Find the equation of an ellipsoid whose geometric center is the origin and whose semi-axes are 4, 2, and 1.

6. Determine the equation and type of ellipsoid generated by revolving the ellipse $x^2 + 3y^2 = 6$ about its **(a)** major axis; **(b)** minor axis.

7. By completing the squares in x, y, and z respectively, show that the equation $2x^2 + 3y^2 + z^2 - 4x - 6y + 8z + 9 = 0$ represents an ellipsoid. Sketch the ellipsoid. Locate the geometric center, and determine the semi-axes.

---

* The surface generated by revolving a plane curve about a line in the same plane is called a *surface of revolution*. The line is called the *axis of revolution*. For example, if $f(x, y) = 0$ is the equation of a curve in the xy plane, the surface formed by revolving the curve about one of the axes in the plane, say the y axis, has the equation $f(\sqrt{x^2 + z^2}, y) = 0$.

8. Show that the set of points P in space for which the sum of the distances of P from the points $A:(-a, 0, 0)$ and $B:(a, 0, 0)$ equals a constant is an ellipsoid.

9. Discuss the eccentricity of the elliptical sections of the ellipsoid

$$\frac{x^2}{a^2} + \frac{y^2}{b^2} + \frac{z^2}{c^2} = 1$$

formed by planes parallel to the (a) xy plane; (b) yz plane; (c) zx plane. (The ellipses in each case are called *similar ellipses*.)

10. Express the area of the section of the ellipsoid

$$\frac{x^2}{a^2} + \frac{y^2}{b^2} + \frac{z^2}{c^2} = 1$$

formed by the plane $x = k$ as a function of k. (The area of an ellipse whose equation is $x^2/A^2 + y^2/B^2 = 1$ is πAB.)

11. Find the equation of the ellipsoid that contains points $A:(-2, 2, -4)$, $B:(0, 0, 6)$, and $C:(2, 2, 4)$ and whose geometric center is at the origin.

9.3 THE HYPERBOLOID OF ONE SHEET

The connected surface represented by the equation

$$\frac{x^2}{a^2} + \frac{y^2}{b^2} - \frac{z^2}{c^2} = 1 \tag{9.6}$$

is called a *hyperboloid of one sheet* (Figure 9.2). The surface has all three coordinate planes as its principal planes. As a result, this surface is also symmetric with respect to the three coordinate axes and the origin.

Sections of the hyperboloid of one sheet in planes parallel to the xy plane are ellipses, while sections in planes parallel to the yz plane or the zx plane are hyperbolas. If $a = b$, sections in planes parallel to the xy plane are circles, and the surface is then called a *hyperboloid of revolution of one sheet*.

By analogy to the situation in plane analytic geometry, we define a and b as the *transverse semi-axes* and c as the *conjugate semi-axis* of the hyperboloid of one sheet.

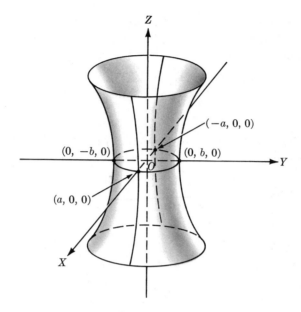

Figure 9.2

Exercises

1. Discuss and sketch the surface defined by

$$\frac{x^2}{4} + \frac{y^2}{16} - \frac{z^2}{9} = 1.$$

2. Find the equations of the traces of $a^2x^2 + b^2y^2 - a^2z^2 = a^2b^2$.

3. Determine the area of the smallest elliptical section of the hyperboloid

$$\frac{x^2}{a^2} + \frac{y^2}{b^2} - \frac{z^2}{c^2} = 1.$$

4. Find the equation of the surface obtained by revolving the hyperbola $x^2 - y^2 = k^2$ about the y axis.

5. Find the equation of a plane curve which generates the hyperboloid of revolution $9x^2 - 4y^2 + 9z^2 = 36$. What is the axis of revolution?

6. Does a hyperboloid of revolution of one sheet necessarily have equal transverse axes?

7. What is the axis of revolution for all hyperboloids of revolution of one sheet?

8. Determine the equations of the principal planes of the hyperboloid of one sheet

$$3x^2 + 4y^2 - 2z^2 + 6x - 16y + 8z = 13.$$

9. Show that sections of the hyperboloid of one sheet

$$\frac{x^2}{a^2} + \frac{y^2}{b^2} - \frac{z^2}{c^2} = 1$$

   in planes parallel to the xy plane are similar ellipses.

9.4 THE HYPERBOLOID OF TWO SHEETS

The equation

$$\frac{x^2}{a^2} + \frac{y^2}{b^2} - \frac{z^2}{c^2} = -1 \tag{9.7}$$

represents two disconnected surfaces called a *hyperboloid of two sheets* (Figure 9.3).

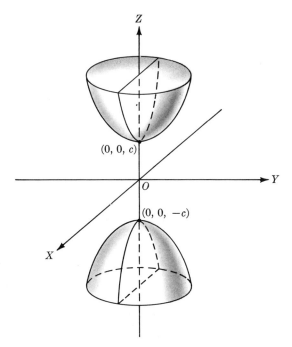

Figure 9.3

The surface has properties similar to those of the hyperboloid of one sheet. Its principal planes are the coordinate planes, and its geometric center is the origin. Sections of the hyperboloid of two sheets in a plane parallel to the xy plane, $z = k$, do not exist if $|k| < c$. If $|k| = c$, the section is a point ellipse; if $|k| > c$, the section is an ellipse. Sections made by planes parallel to the other coordinate planes are hyperbolas.

In the case of the hyperboloid of two sheets, only one transverse semi-axis c exists, while a and b are the conjugate semi-axes.

If $a = b$, the quadric surface is a *hyperboloid of revolution of two sheets.*

Exercises

1. Discuss and sketch the surface defined by

$$\frac{x^2}{9} - \frac{y^2}{16} - \frac{z^2}{4} = 1.$$

2. Discuss the trace of the hyperboloid of two sheets

$$\frac{x^2}{a^2} - \frac{y^2}{b^2} - \frac{z^2}{c^2} = 1$$

   in the   (a) xy plane;   (b) yz plane;   (c) zx plane.

3. For what values of k does the plane $z = k$ intersect the surface

$$\frac{z^2}{c^2} - \frac{x^2}{a^2} - \frac{y^2}{b^2} = 1?$$

4. State the transverse and conjugate semi-axes of the surface defined by the equation $x^2 + y^2 - 2z^2 = 1$.

5. Find the equation of the set of points P in space for which the difference of the distances of P from the points $A:(2, 4, 1)$ and $B:(2, -4, 1)$ is 6.

6. Determine the equation of a plane curve whose surface of revolution is $4x^2 - 9y^2 - 9z^2 = 36$. What is the axis of revolution?

7. Find the equation of the surface generated by revolving the hyperbola $y^2 - z^2 = a^2$ about its   (a) transverse axis;   (b) conjugate axis.

8. Determine the principal planes of the hyperboloid of two sheets

$$2x^2 - 3y^2 - 2z^2 - 8x + 6y - 12z = 21.$$

9. Show that the elliptical sections of the hyperboloid of two sheets are similar ellipses.

9.5 THE QUADRIC CONES

Closely associated with the hyperboloids is the quadric surface called a *quadric cone* (Figure 9.4), which is defined by the equation

$$\frac{x^2}{a^2} + \frac{y^2}{b^2} = z^2. \tag{9.8}$$

This equation is of the form (9.2) where $D = 0$, and A and B differ in algebraic sign from C. This surface is symmetric with respect to the three coordinate planes, the three coordinate axes, and the origin, as are the ellipsoids and the hyperboloids.

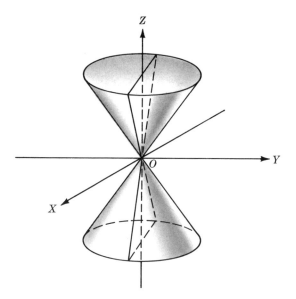

Figure 9.4

Sections of the cone in planes parallel to the xy plane are ellipses. That is, if $z = k \neq 0$, the section of the quadric cone has the equation

$$\frac{x^2}{(ka)^2} + \frac{y^2}{(kb)^2} = 1, \qquad z = k.$$

In the xy plane the trace is a point ellipse, the origin. A section of the quadric cone in any plane parallel to the yz plane or zx plane is a hyperbola. Its trace in either of these coordinate planes is a pair of lines intersecting at the origin. The equations of the pairs of intersecting lines are respectively

$$y = \pm bz, \qquad x = 0$$

and

$$x = \pm az, \qquad y = 0.$$

If $a = b$, sections in planes parallel to the xy plane are circles or a point ellipse. Furthermore, the quadric surface is called a *circular cone*, or *cone of revolution*.

The quadric cone defined by

$$\frac{x^2}{a^2} + \frac{y^2}{b^2} - \frac{z^2}{c^2} = 0$$

is frequently called the *asymptotic cone* of the two types of hyperboloids defined by

$$\frac{x^2}{a^2} + \frac{y^2}{b^2} - \frac{z^2}{c^2} = \pm 1.$$

In general, the definition of a *conical surface* is a surface which can be generated by a line that contains a fixed point, called the *vertex*, and intersects a fixed curve, called the *directrix*. That the surface represented by equation (9.8) is in fact a conical surface with vertex at the origin can easily be shown. Let $P:(x_0, y_0, z_0)$ be any point other than the origin O on the locus of equation (9.8). Then the line OP has the parametric equations

$$\begin{cases} x = x_0 t \\ y = y_0 t \\ z = z_0 t. \end{cases}$$

Each point on line OP is on the locus of equation (9.8) since

$$\frac{(x_0 t)^2}{a^2} + \frac{(y_0 t)^2}{b^2} = (z_0 t)^2$$

is implied by the equation

$$\frac{x_0^2}{a^2} + \frac{y_0^2}{b^2} = z_0^2.$$

The set of points defined by the equation

$$\frac{x^2}{a^2} + \frac{y^2}{b^2} = -z^2 \tag{9.9}$$

consists of a single *point*, the origin. The form of this equation may be obtained from equation (9.2) if $D = 0$ and A, B, and C have like algebraic signs. Since the graph of this equation is the origin, the origin is its geometric center. Although this statement appears to be trivial, its importance lies in the fact that the quadric surfaces discussed thus far have the common property that they have a unique geometric center, the origin. For this reason such quadric surfaces are sometimes called the *central quadrics*.

Exercises

1. Discuss and sketch the surface defined by
$$\frac{x^2}{25} + \frac{y^2}{16} = z^2.$$

2. Find the equation of the asymptotic cone of the hyperboloid of two sheets
$$\frac{x^2}{16} - \frac{y^2}{25} - \frac{z^2}{100} = -1.$$

3. Determine the section of the quadric cone $4x^2 + 2y^2 - 3z^2 = 0$ formed by the plane $x = 3$.

4. Determine the equation of the quadric cone generated by revolving the line $y = 3x$ about the **(a)** x axis; **(b)** y axis. What type of quadric cone is generated in each case?

5. By completing the squares in x, y, and z respectively, show that the equation $x^2 - 9y^2 + z^2 - 2x + 54y - 80 = 0$ represents a quadric cone. Find the equation of a plane curve which generates the cone by a revolution. What is the axis of revolution?

6. Find the equation of the set of points $P:(x, y, z)$ in space for which the distance of P from the x axis is twice its distance from the z axis.

7. Find the vertex of the quadric cone $3x^2 - 12y^2 + 4z^2 + 96y = 192$.

8. Prove that sections of the quadric cone defined by equation (9.8) in planes parallel to the xy plane are similar ellipses.

9. Show that the traces of
$$\frac{x^2}{a^2} + \frac{y^2}{b^2} - \frac{z^2}{c^2} = 0$$

in the yz plane and zx plane are asymptotes to the traces of the hyperboloids with equations (9.6) and (9.7) respectively.

9.6 THE PARABOLOIDS

If none of the constants in equation (9.3) is zero, the equation may be written either in the form
$$\frac{x^2}{a^2} + \frac{y^2}{b^2} = cz \tag{9.10}$$

or in the form

$$\frac{x^2}{a^2} - \frac{y^2}{b^2} = cz. \tag{9.11}$$

The set of points defined by the equation (9.10) is called an *elliptic paraboloid* (Figure 9.5), while the set of points defined by equation (9.11) is called a *hyperbolic paraboloid* (Figure 9.6). Properties common to both paraboloids include the fact that sections made by planes parallel to the zx plane or yz plane are parabolas. Both surfaces are symmetric with respect to the yz plane and zx plane respectively. Both have one line of symmetry, the z axis, called the *axis* of the surface. The axis intersects each surface in a single point, the origin, which is called the *vertex* of the surface.

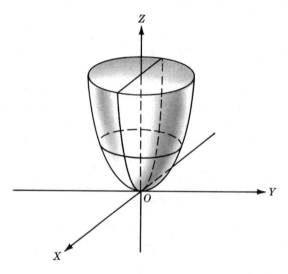

Figure 9.5

The elliptic paraboloid is distinguished from the hyperbolic paraboloid in terms of the sections made by the plane $z = k$, which are ellipses for the former (if $k > 0$) and hyperbolas for the latter. The elliptical sections of the elliptic paraboloid increase in size as k increases. If $k > 0$, the transverse and conjugate axes of sections of the hyperbolic paraboloid are parallel to the x axis and y axis respectively; if $k < 0$, the transverse and conjugate axes are parallel to the y axis and x axis respectively.

If $a = b$ in equation (9.10), then the surface is called a *paraboloid of revolution*, a special form of the elliptic paraboloid. It may be obtained by revolving the parabola $x^2 = a^2cz$ about the z axis.

The trace of the hyperbolic paraboloid in the xy plane consists of a pair of intersecting lines

$$y = \pm \frac{b}{a} x.$$

Furthermore, note that the vertex of the surface is a minimum point for its trace in the xz plane and a maximum point for its trace in the yz plane. Such a point is called a *minimax*, or *saddle point*, of the surface. A surface containing a saddle point is frequently called a *saddle surface*.

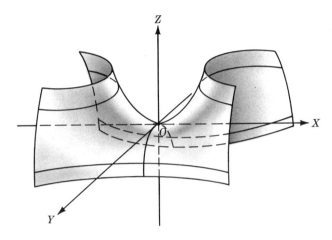

Figure 9.6

Exercises

1. Discuss and sketch the surface defined by the equation $y^2 + 4z^2 = 16x$.

2. Find an equation of a plane curve which generates the elliptic paraboloid $x^2 + y^2 = z$ by means of a revolution. What is the axis of revolution?

3. Prove that plane sections parallel to the zx plane or yz plane are parabolas in the case of the surfaces defined by equations (9.10) and (9.11).

4. Discuss the surface defined by the equation $16x^2 - 9y^2 = 144z$. Sketch the surface.

5. Find the equation of the set of points P in space for which the square of the distance of P from the z axis is twice its distance from the xy plane. Discuss the surface.

6. Determine the equation of the surface of revolution obtained by revolving the parabola $4 - y^2 = kx$ about the x axis. Discuss the properties of this surface of revolution.

7. Determine the vertex of the elliptic paraboloid $3x^2 + 2y^2 - 12x - 12z + 36 = 0$.

8. Find the equation of a paraboloid with vertex at the origin, the y axis as a line of symmetry, and containing the points $(2, 2, 3)$ and $(0, 1, -3)$.

9. Discuss the surface defined by equations (9.10) and (9.11) respectively if c is negative.

10. Determine and discuss the trace of the hyperbolic paraboloid $25x^2 - 4y^2 - 100z = 0$ in the **(a)** xy plane; **(b)** yz plane; **(c)** zx plane.

11. Find the vertex and focus of the parabolic section determined by the surface $x^2/a^2 - y^2/b^2 = z$ and the plane $x = k$.

12. Find the equation of the elliptic paraboloid with vertex at the origin and one of whose sections is the ellipse $x^2 + 9y^2 = 144$, $z = 2$.

9.7 THE QUADRIC CYLINDERS

The surface generated by a straight line, called the *generator*, moving always parallel to its original position and intersecting a given plane curve, called the *directrix*, is defined as a *cylindrical surface*, or *cylinder* (Figure 9.7). The directrix must lie in a plane that is not parallel to the generator. Every fixed position of the generator is called a *ruling*, or *element of the cylinder*. Note that a cylindrical surface is not necessarily closed since the directrix need not be a closed curve. For example, if the directrix is a straight line, the cylinder is simply a plane.

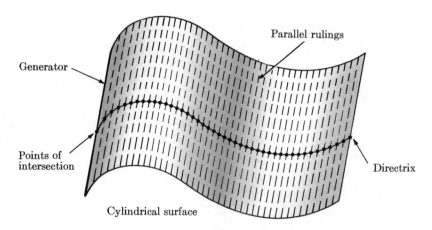

Figure 9.7

A section made by any plane perpendicular to the rulings of the cylinder is called a *right section*. It is obvious that all right sections are identical. A line through the center of any right section, if the center exists, and parallel to the rulings of the cylinder is called the *axis of the cylinder*. The axis of a cylinder is an axis of symmetry.

The equation of a cylindrical surface whose rulings are perpendicular to one of the coordinate planes is the equation of the trace of the cylinder in that plane. This equation is in two variables only. We will limit our study to such cylindrical surfaces. Furthermore, if the directrix is a conic section, the cylindrical surface belongs to the class of quadric surfaces called *quadric cylinders*. Thus the locus of any real quadratic equation $f(x, y, z) = 0$ lacking one variable, say z, is a cylinder having a conic section in the xy plane as the directrix and with rulings parallel to the z axis. In three-dimensional space its equation is $f(x, y) = 0$ and $z = z$, or simply $f(x, y) = 0$, which is identical to the equation of the conic directrix. Furthermore, note that every right section is a conic.

We are now in a position to prove a fundamental fact which may by now have become apparent. If $f(x, y, z) = 0$ is any real quadratic equation and $ax + by + cz + d = 0$ represents any real plane, then it is obvious that a rotation in space exists such that the equation of the plane becomes $z = k$. The equation of the quadric surface becomes $g(x, y, z) = 0$. The intersection of the plane and the quadric surface lies on the cylinder $g(x, y, k) = 0$. Now, $g(x, y, k) = 0$ is a cylinder with rulings parallel to the z axis. The plane $z = k$ is perpendicular to the z axis and is therefore a right section of the surface. Since all right sections are conics, *any plane section of a quadric surface is a conic section*.

We may now proceed to consider the various types of equations representing cylindrical surfaces obtained from the canonical forms (9.2) and (9.3) by allowing A, B, or C to vanish.

The *real elliptic cylinder* is defined as the set of points in space whose coordinates satisfy the equation

$$\frac{x^2}{a^2} + \frac{y^2}{b^2} = 1 \tag{9.12}$$

(Figure 9.8). If $a = b$, the surface is called a *right circular cylinder*, or *cylinder of revolution*.

The completely imaginary surface defined by the equation

$$\frac{x^2}{a^2} + \frac{y^2}{b^2} = -1 \tag{9.13}$$

is called an *imaginary elliptic cylinder*. Its properties in complex space are analogous to the properties of the real elliptic cylinder in real space.

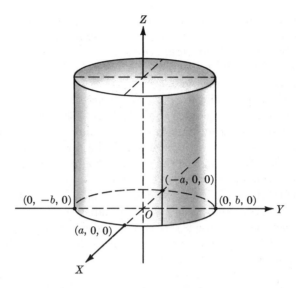

Figure 9.8

The *hyperbolic cylinder*, the set of points in space defined by the equation

$$\frac{x^2}{a^2} - \frac{y^2}{b^2} = 1, \tag{9.14}$$

is symmetric with respect to all three coordinate planes and axes (Figure 9.9). The z axis is the axis of the hyperbolic cylinder since the variable z is missing in the equation (9.14). The properties of symmetry of the hyperbolic cylinder are identical to the properties of symmetry of the real elliptic cylinder.

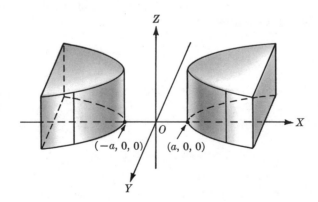

Figure 9.9

The quadric cylinder defined by the equation

$$x^2 = cz \qquad (9.15)$$

is called a *parabolic cylinder* (Figure 9.10). Since the parabola does not contain a geometric center, the parabolic cylinder has no axis. It is, however, symmetric with respect to the yz plane and zx plane respectively. The y axis contains the vertices of all the right sections and is sometimes referred to as the *line of vertices*.

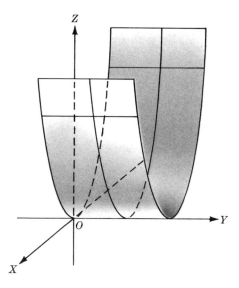

Figure 9.10

Exercises

1. Discuss and sketch the surface defined by $9y^2 + 9z^2 = 25$.

2. Sketch and discuss the surface in three-dimensional space represented by the equation $y^2 = 8x$.

3. Find the equation of a cylinder whose directrix is a hyperbola in the yz plane with transverse axis 5 units in length along the y axis and conjugate axis 3 units in length.

4. Find the equation of a quadric cylinder whose directrix is an ellipse with semi-axes 4 units and 3 units in length along a pair of coordinate axes, the origin as geometric center, and whose rulings are parallel to the (**a**) x axis; (**b**) y axis; (**c**) z axis.

5. Find the equation of the cylinder of revolution whose radius is k and whose rulings are parallel to the y axis.

6. Find the equation of the set of points P equidistant from the y axis and the plane $z = 2$.

7. Discuss and sketch the surface defined by the equation $9x^2 - 4y^2 - 36x - 8y = 4$.

8. Find the equation of a parabolic cylinder that contains the point $(2, -4, 12)$ and has the z axis as the line of vertices.

9. Determine the equations of the planes asymptotic to the hyperbolic cylinder defined by equation (9.14).

9.8 DEGENERATE CYLINDERS

The equation

$$\frac{x^2}{a^2} - \frac{y^2}{b^2} = 0 \tag{9.16}$$

represents a pair of *real intersecting planes*

$$bx + ay = 0 \qquad \text{and} \qquad bx - ay = 0$$

(Figure 9.11). The intersection of the two planes is the z axis, the axis of symmetry for the surface. The intersecting planes contain all sets of asymptotes to the right sections of the hyperbolic cylinder

$$\frac{x^2}{a^2} - \frac{y^2}{b^2} = 1.$$

The set of points whose coordinates satisfy the equation

$$\frac{x^2}{a^2} + \frac{y^2}{b^2} = 0 \tag{9.17}$$

in space is a *line*, the z axis. Hence the surface is sometimes called a *line cylinder*. Equation (9.17) is reducible to a pair of *imaginary intersecting planes*

$$bx + iay = 0 \qquad \text{and} \qquad bx - iay = 0.$$

The remaining quadric surfaces consist of the sets of points whose coordinates satisfy the real quadratic equation $f(x, y, z) = 0$ in which two

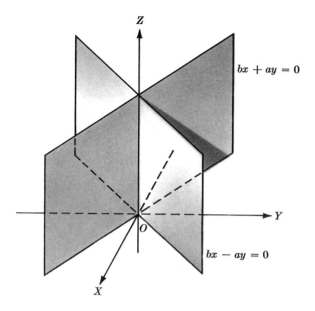

$bx + ay = 0$

$bx - ay = 0$

Figure 9.11

variables are absent, say y and z. They are also degenerate forms of the cylindrical surfaces, along with the real intersecting planes and the real line. Their equations may be obtained by letting B and C vanish in equations (9.2) and (9.3).

If A and D have like algebraic signs in equation (9.2), the equation can be written in the form

$$x^2 = a^2, \tag{9.18}$$

and represents two distinct *real parallel planes*

$$x = a \quad \text{and} \quad x = -a$$

(Figure 9.12). If A and D differ in algebraic sign, the quadric surface consists of two distinct *imaginary parallel planes*

$$x^2 + a^2 = 0, \tag{9.19}$$

that is,

$$x + ia = 0 \quad \text{and} \quad x - ia = 0.$$

From equation (9.3) we can obtain the equation of two *coincident planes*,

$$x^2 = 0. \tag{9.20}$$

This pair of coincident planes represents the yz plane.

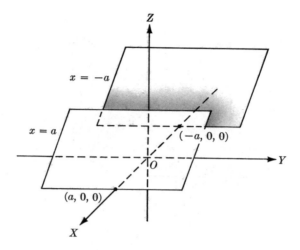

Figure 9.12

9.9 COMMENTS

Note that only three quadric surfaces are *imaginary surfaces:* the imaginary
ellipsoid, the imaginary elliptic cylinder, and the imaginary parallel planes.
The *real proper quadrics,* or *conicoids,* are composed of the real ellipsoid,
the hyperboloids of one and two sheets, and the elliptic and hyperbolic
paraboloids. The remaining quadrics are sometimes called the *degenerate
forms* of the quadric surfaces. Furthermore, we might note that only the real
ellipsoid and the hyperboloids are *real proper central quadrics.*

Exercises

Determine, sketch, and discuss the surfaces represented by each equation.

1. $4x^2 + 36y^2 + 9z^2 = 72.$ 5. $4x^2 + 8y + z^2 = 0.$

2. $x^2 + y^2 - 6z^2 = 0.$ 6. $x^2 + y^2 + z^2 + 2x + 2y + 2z = 1.$

3. $2x^2 + y^2 + 4 = 0.$ 7. $x^2 - 16y^2 - 9z^2 = 144.$

4. $x^2 + z^2 = 9.$ 8. $x^2 + y^2 + 3z^2 = 27.$

9. $x^2 + 4y^2 = 4z$.

10. $9x = 9z^2 - y^2$.

11. $3x^2 - 12y^2 + 3z^2 = 12$.

12. $y^2 = z^2$.

13. $xy = 1$.

14. $x^2 + y^2 = k$.

15. $x^2 + y^2 + z^2 = 16$.

16. $9x^2 + 9y^2 = 144 - 16z^2$.

17. $4(x^2 + y^2) + z^2 = 4$.

18. $9x^2 - y^2 + 9z^2 = 0$.

19. $16x^2 + 16y^2 - 25z^2 = 400$.

20. $x^2 + y^2 = (z - 3)^2$.

21. $y = e^x$.

In Exercises 22–27 classify and describe the surface generated by revolving each plane curve about the x axis.

22. $x^2 + 4y^2 = 16$.

23. $x^2 - y^2 = 9$.

24. $y = 3$.

25. $y^2 - x^2 = 16$.

26. $x = 4z^2$.

27. $3x^2 + z^2 = 9$.

28. Find the equation of the set of points $P:(x, y, z)$ in space for which the distance of P from the plane $z = 4$ is equal to the distance of P from the point $(0, 0, -4)$.

29. Find the equation of the set of points $P:(x, y, z)$ in space for which the distances of P from $A:(1, -1, 1)$ and $B:(-4, 4, -4)$ are in the ratio 3 to 4.

30. What is the directrix of the line cylinder $\dfrac{x^2}{a^2} + \dfrac{y^2}{b^2} = 0$?

In Exercises 31–36 determine the nature of the surface defined by each equation by completing the squares in x, y, and z respectively.

31. $9x^2 - 4y^2 - 9z^2 - 18x + 24y = 28$.

32. $3x^2 + 2z^2 - 6x - 12y + 8z - 13 = 0$.

33. $4x^2 - 9y^2 + 16z^2 - 24x - 36y - 64z = 80$.

34. $4x^2 - z^2 - 2x + 12y + 6z - 6 = 0$.

35. $3x^2 - 12y^2 + 4z^2 + 96y = 192$.

36. $x^2 + y^2 + 4z^2 + 2x + 2y - 8z = 10$.

37. Consider the set of points $P:(x, y, z)$ in space for which the ratio of the distances of P from two fixed points is a constant k. Discuss the type of quadric surface generated where (a) $k < 1$; (b) $k = 1$; (c) $k > 1$.

$$f(x,y,z) = a_1x + b_1y + g_1z + rx$$
$$+ h_1x + b_1y + f_1z + sy$$
$$+ g_3x + f_3y + c_3z + tz$$
$$+ rx + sy + tz + d$$

THE GENERAL QUADRIC

10.1 INTRODUCTION

In Chapter 9 it was stated that the most general equation of the second degree in the three variables x, y, and z could be written in the form

$$ax^2 + by^2 + cz^2 + 2fyz + 2gzx + 2hxy + 2rx + 2sy + 2tz + d = 0, \quad (10.1)$$

where the coefficients a, b, c, f, g, h, r, s, t, and d are real numbers. The set of points whose coordinates satisfy equation (10.1) is a quadric surface. However, these surfaces were studied in their canonical forms. In this chapter we shall discuss the appropriate rotations and translations of coordinates necessary to transform the general equation to canonical form, and we will approach the problem from the point of view of matrix algebra.

10.2 TRANSFORMATION TO CANONICAL FORM

If we write the general quadratic function $f(x, y, z)$ in the form

$$\begin{aligned}
f(x, y, z) = {} & axx + hxy + gxz + rx \\
& + hyx + byy + fyz + sy \\
& + gzx + fzy + czz + tz \\
& + rx + sy + tz + d,
\end{aligned} \quad (10.2)$$

a valuable form is suggested. The function can be expressed as the product of three matrices:

$$
(x \quad y \quad z \quad 1)
\begin{pmatrix}
a & h & g & r \\
h & b & f & s \\
g & f & c & t \\
r & s & t & d
\end{pmatrix}
\begin{pmatrix}
x \\
y \\
z \\
1
\end{pmatrix}.
\tag{10.3}
$$

Note that the matrix of central importance

$$
\Delta =
\begin{pmatrix}
a & h & g & r \\
h & b & f & s \\
g & f & c & t \\
r & s & t & d
\end{pmatrix},
\tag{10.4}
$$

which defines the particular quadric being studied, is a real symmetric matrix. The matrix Δ is sometimes called the *matrix of the quadric surface*. The symmetric matrix

$$
D =
\begin{pmatrix}
a & h & g \\
h & b & f \\
g & f & c
\end{pmatrix}
\tag{10.5}
$$

is also important in the analysis of $f(x, y, z)$. When the matrix D is premultiplied by the row vector $(x \quad y \quad z)$ and postmultiplied by $(x \quad y \quad z)^\mathsf{T}$, the expression represents the quadratic form of the general quadratic; that is,

$$
(x \quad y \quad z)
\begin{pmatrix}
a & h & g \\
h & b & f \\
g & f & c
\end{pmatrix}
\begin{pmatrix}
x \\
y \\
z
\end{pmatrix}
= ax^2 + by^2 + cz^2 + 2fyz + 2gzx + 2hxy.
\tag{10.6}
$$

As an example of the process of reducing a general quadratic equation to its canonical form by means of a rotation and translation of coordinates, consider the case of the quadric surface

$$
f(x, y, z) = 3x^2 + y^2 + 3z^2 + 2zx + 2x - 2y + 6z + 3 = 0.
$$

We can write the equation in the matrix form

$$
(x \quad y \quad z \quad 1)
\begin{pmatrix}
3 & 0 & 1 & 1 \\
0 & 1 & 0 & -1 \\
1 & 0 & 3 & 3 \\
1 & -1 & 3 & 3
\end{pmatrix}
\begin{pmatrix}
x \\
y \\
z \\
1
\end{pmatrix}
= 0.
$$

Now, the characteristic equation associated with D is

$$
\begin{vmatrix}
3 - \lambda & 0 & 1 \\
0 & 1 - \lambda & 0 \\
1 & 0 & 3 - \lambda
\end{vmatrix}
= 0;
$$

that is,
$$(3 - \lambda)^2(1 - \lambda) - (1 - \lambda) = 0,$$
$$(1 - \lambda)(9 - 6\lambda + \lambda^2 - 1) = 0,$$
$$(1 - \lambda)(2 - \lambda)(4 - \lambda) = 0.$$

Hence the eigenvalues of D are
$$\lambda_1 = 1, \qquad \lambda_2 = 2, \qquad \lambda_3 = 4.$$

If we consider $(l_1 \quad m_1 \quad n_1)^\mathsf{T}$, $(l_2 \quad m_2 \quad n_2)^\mathsf{T}$, and $(l_3 \quad m_3 \quad n_3)^\mathsf{T}$ to represent the eigenvectors associated with λ_1, λ_2, and λ_3 respectively, the following sets of equations are obtained:

$$\begin{cases} 2l_1 + n_1 = 0 \\ l_1 + 2n_1 = 0; \end{cases} \qquad \begin{cases} l_2 + n_2 = 0 \\ - m_2 = 0 \\ l_2 + n_2 = 0; \end{cases} \qquad \begin{cases} -l_3 + n_3 = 0 \\ - 3m_3 = 0 \\ l_3 - n_3 = 0. \end{cases}$$

Then three normalized eigenvectors associated with the eigenvalues 1, 2, and 4 are $(0 \quad -1 \quad 0)^\mathsf{T}$, $\left(\dfrac{1}{\sqrt{2}} \quad 0 \quad -\dfrac{1}{\sqrt{2}}\right)^\mathsf{T}$, and $\left(\dfrac{1}{\sqrt{2}} \quad 0 \quad \dfrac{1}{\sqrt{2}}\right)^\mathsf{T}$ respectively. Therefore, a rotation of axes represented by the equation

$$\begin{pmatrix} x \\ y \\ z \\ 1 \end{pmatrix} = \begin{pmatrix} 0 & \dfrac{1}{\sqrt{2}} & \dfrac{1}{\sqrt{2}} & 0 \\ -1 & 0 & 0 & 0 \\ 0 & -\dfrac{1}{\sqrt{2}} & \dfrac{1}{\sqrt{2}} & 0 \\ 0 & 0 & 0 & 1 \end{pmatrix} \begin{pmatrix} x' \\ y' \\ z' \\ 1 \end{pmatrix}$$

will transform the equation $f(x, y, z) = 0$ to a form void of the cross product terms $x'y'$, $y'z'$, and $z'x'$. Thus

$$(x' \; y' \; z' \; 1) \begin{pmatrix} 0 & -1 & 0 & 0 \\ \dfrac{1}{\sqrt{2}} & 0 & -\dfrac{1}{\sqrt{2}} & 0 \\ \dfrac{1}{\sqrt{2}} & 0 & \dfrac{1}{\sqrt{2}} & 0 \\ 0 & 0 & 0 & 1 \end{pmatrix} \begin{pmatrix} 3 & 0 & 1 & 1 \\ 0 & 1 & 0 & -1 \\ 1 & 0 & 3 & 3 \\ 1 & -1 & 3 & 3 \end{pmatrix}$$

$$\begin{pmatrix} 0 & \dfrac{1}{\sqrt{2}} & \dfrac{1}{\sqrt{2}} & 0 \\ -1 & 0 & 0 & 0 \\ 0 & -\dfrac{1}{\sqrt{2}} & \dfrac{1}{\sqrt{2}} & 0 \\ 0 & 0 & 0 & 1 \end{pmatrix} \begin{pmatrix} x' \\ y' \\ z' \\ 1 \end{pmatrix} = 0,$$

$$(x' \; y' \; z' \; 1) \begin{pmatrix} 1 & 0 & 0 & -1 \\ 0 & 2 & 0 & -\sqrt{2} \\ 0 & 0 & 4 & 2\sqrt{2} \\ -1 & -\sqrt{2} & 2\sqrt{2} & 3 \end{pmatrix} \begin{pmatrix} x' \\ y' \\ z' \\ 1 \end{pmatrix} = 0,$$

$$x'^2 - 2x' + 2y'^2 - 2\sqrt{2}y' + 4z'^2 + 4\sqrt{2}z' + 3 = 0.$$

By a translation of axes to an $x''\, y''\, z''$ system with origin at

$$\left(1, \frac{\sqrt{2}}{2}, -\frac{\sqrt{2}}{2}\right)$$

in the $x'\, y'\, z'$ system, which can be expressed in matrix form as

$$\begin{pmatrix} x' \\ y' \\ z' \\ 1 \end{pmatrix} = \begin{pmatrix} 1 & 0 & 0 & 1 \\ 0 & 1 & 0 & \dfrac{\sqrt{2}}{2} \\ 0 & 0 & 1 & -\dfrac{\sqrt{2}}{2} \\ 0 & 0 & 0 & 1 \end{pmatrix} \begin{pmatrix} x'' \\ y'' \\ z'' \\ 1 \end{pmatrix},$$

we obtain

$$(x''\ y''\ z''\ 1) \begin{pmatrix} 1 & 0 & 0 & 0 \\ 0 & 1 & 0 & 0 \\ 0 & 0 & 1 & 0 \\ 1 & \dfrac{\sqrt{2}}{2} & -\dfrac{\sqrt{2}}{2} & 1 \end{pmatrix}$$

$$\begin{pmatrix} 1 & 0 & 0 & -1 \\ 0 & 2 & 0 & -\sqrt{2} \\ 0 & 0 & 4 & 2\sqrt{2} \\ -1 & -\sqrt{2} & 2\sqrt{2} & 3 \end{pmatrix} \begin{pmatrix} 1 & 0 & 0 & 1 \\ 0 & 1 & 0 & \dfrac{\sqrt{2}}{2} \\ 0 & 0 & 1 & -\dfrac{\sqrt{2}}{2} \\ 0 & 0 & 0 & 1 \end{pmatrix} \begin{pmatrix} x'' \\ y'' \\ z'' \\ 1 \end{pmatrix};$$

that is,

$$(x''\ y''\ z''\ 1) \begin{pmatrix} 1 & 0 & 0 & 0 \\ 0 & 2 & 0 & 0 \\ 0 & 0 & 4 & 0 \\ 0 & 0 & 0 & -1 \end{pmatrix} \begin{pmatrix} x'' \\ y'' \\ z'' \\ 1 \end{pmatrix}.$$

Hence a canonical form of the quadratic equation is

$$x''^2 + 2y''^2 + 4z''^2 = 1.$$

The surface is a real ellipsoid with principal axes along the x'' axis, y'' axis, and z'' axis respectively.

It should be noted that the eigenvectors determined earlier lie along the principal axes of the quadric surface. Furthermore, the eigenvalues are inversely proportional to the squares of the semi-axes.

Note that after the rotation of coordinate axes, the equation of the quadric surface has the form

$$\lambda_1 x'^2 + \lambda_2 y'^2 + \lambda_3 z'^2 + 2\alpha x' + 2\beta y' + 2\gamma z' + d = 0; \qquad (10.7)$$

that is,

$$(x'\ y'\ z'\ 1)\begin{pmatrix} \lambda_1 & 0 & 0 & \alpha \\ 0 & \lambda_2 & 0 & \beta \\ 0 & 0 & \lambda_3 & \gamma \\ \alpha & \beta & \gamma & d \end{pmatrix}\begin{pmatrix} x' \\ y' \\ z' \\ 1 \end{pmatrix},\qquad (10.8)$$

where the λ_i are the eigenvalues of the matrix D, and

$$\begin{aligned} \alpha &= rl_1 + sm_1 + tn_1, \\ \beta &= rl_2 + sm_2 + tn_2, \\ \gamma &= rl_3 + sm_3 + tn_3. \end{aligned}\qquad (10.9)$$

The translation transformation relating the new coordinates axes x'', y'', and z'' to the x' axis, y' axis, and z' axis is given by the equations

$$\begin{cases} x'' = x' + \dfrac{\alpha}{\lambda_1} \\[2mm] y'' = y' + \dfrac{\beta}{\lambda_2} \\[2mm] z'' = z' + \dfrac{\gamma}{\lambda_3}. \end{cases}\qquad (10.10)$$

If at least one λ_i equals zero, a translation does not exist which would remove all the linear terms of the variables in the equation. Hence the surface is a noncentral quadric. If some λ_i equals zero, matrix D is necessarily singular.

When D is a nonsingular matrix, we may first perform a translation of coordinate axes to the center of the quadric surface in order that the coefficients of the linear terms may vanish.

The coordinates of the center (x_0, y_0, z_0) of the quadric surface in terms of the original coefficients of $f(x, y, z)$ can be shown to satisfy the equations

$$\begin{cases} ax_0 + hy_0 + gz_0 + r = 0 \\ hx_0 + by_0 + fz_0 + s = 0 \\ gx_0 + fy_0 + cz_0 + t = 0. \end{cases}\qquad (10.11)$$

Having performed a transformation to parallel coordinate axes, we can next perform a rotation of axes so as to eliminate the cross product terms and reduce the equation to the form

$$\lambda_1 x''^2 + \lambda_2 y''^2 + \lambda_3 z''^2 + d' = 0\qquad (10.12)$$

where

$$d' = d - \frac{\alpha^2}{\lambda_1} - \frac{\beta^2}{\lambda_2} - \frac{\gamma^2}{\lambda_3}.$$

Recall that in Chapter 9 it was mentioned that the quadric surfaces defined by equation (10.12) are called central quadrics.

Exercises

In Exercises 1–6 determine the surface represented by each equation.

1. $x^2 - 3y^2 + z^2 - 8x + 12y + 6z + 13 = 0.$

2. $3y^2 + 4z^2 + 4x - 6y + 16z + 27 = 0.$

3. $2x^2 - 5y^2 + 3z^2 + 20y + 6z - 47 = 0.$

4. $2x^2 - y^2 - z^2 - 2yz - 4x + 6y + 2z + 2 = 0.$

5. $x^2 + 4y^2 - 8z^2 + 4xy - 4yz + 8zx = 0.$

6. $xy + yz + zx = 0.$

7. Find the matrix of rotation which transforms the equations of the planes $2x + y - 2z = 0$, $2x - 2y - z = 0$, and $x + 2y + 2z = 0$ into $z' = 0$, $x' = 0$, and $y' = 0$ respectively.

8. Transform the equation of $y^2 - z^2 = x$ by a rotation of the y axis and z axis through an angle whose measure is $\pi/4$.

9. Find the equation of the surface $x^2 + y^2 + 7z^2 + 16xy + 8yz - 8zx - 81 = 0$ after a rotation to a new rectangular Cartesian coordinate system whose axes are the lines containing the origin and the points $(1, 2, 2)$, $(2, 1, -2)$, and $(2, -2, 1)$ respectively.

10. Show that in general nine points determine one and only one quadric surface.

10.3   CLASSIFICATION OF THE QUADRIC SURFACES

It is evident from the discussion of the previous section that the type of quadric surface which $f(x, y, z) = 0$ represents can be determined by an investigation of the values and the algebraic signs of the eigenvalues of matrix D.

If every λ_i is distinct from zero and all have like signs, equation (10.12) represents an imaginary ellipsoid, a real ellipsoid, or an imaginary quadric cone (containing the real point $(0, 0, 0)$) depending upon whether d' agrees in sign with the λ_i, differs in sign from them, or is zero respectively. Further, if any two λ_i are equal, then the quadric is a surface of revolution. If all three λ_i are equal in the case of the real ellipsoid, the surface is a sphere.

Consider the case where the λ_i are distinct from zero but differ in sign. If d' agrees in sign with two of the λ_i, then equation (10.12) represents a hyperboloid of two sheets. If d' agrees in sign with only one of the λ_i, then the quadric surface is a hyperboloid of one sheet. If d' is zero, then the set of points whose coordinates satisfy equation (10.12) is a real quadric cone.

In the case where one and only one λ_i is zero, a translation transformation reducing equation (10.7) to equation (10.12) is not possible. Consider $\lambda_3 = 0$. Then the translation

$$\begin{cases} x'' = x' + \dfrac{\alpha}{\lambda_1} \\ y'' = y' + \dfrac{\beta}{\lambda_2} \\ z'' = z' \end{cases}$$

transforms equation (10.7) to the form

$$\lambda_1 x''^2 + \lambda_2 y''^2 + 2\gamma z'' + d' = 0. \tag{10.13}$$

If $\gamma \neq 0$, equation (10.13) can be transformed further to the form

$$\lambda_1 x''^2 + \lambda_2 y''^2 + 2\gamma z'' = 0. \tag{10.14}$$

If $\gamma = 0$, equation (10.13) becomes

$$\lambda_1 x''^2 + \lambda_2 y''^2 + d' = 0. \tag{10.15}$$

Now, equation (10.14) represents an elliptic paraboloid or hyperbolic paraboloid depending upon whether λ_1 and λ_2 have like or opposite signs respectively.

If $d' \neq 0$, then equation (10.15) represents a cylinder. When λ_1 and λ_2 have like signs, the surface is an imaginary elliptic cylinder or a real elliptic cylinder depending upon whether or not d' agrees in sign with the λ_i respectively. If the λ_i differ in sign, the surface is a hyperbolic cylinder.

If $d' = 0$, then the quadric surface defined by equation (10.15) is two distinct imaginary planes (containing a real line of intersection) or two distinct real intersecting planes depending upon whether or not the λ_i agree in sign respectively.

In the case where exactly two of the λ_i are zero, say λ_2 and λ_3, equation (10.7) may be transformed to

$$\lambda_1 x''^2 + 2\beta y'' + 2\gamma z'' + d' = 0 \tag{10.16}$$

by the translation

$$\begin{cases} x'' = x' + \dfrac{\alpha}{\lambda_1} \\ y'' = y' \\ z'' = z'. \end{cases}$$

If β and γ are different from zero, one of the linear terms and the constant can be made to vanish by an additional rotation about the x axis followed by a translation. In this case, the surface represented by equation (10.16) is a parabolic cylinder.

If $\beta = \gamma = 0$, equation (10.16) is of the form

$$\lambda_1 x''^2 + d' = 0. \tag{10.17}$$

If $d' \neq 0$, the surface defined by equation (10.17) consists of two distinct imaginary parallel planes or two distinct real parallel planes depending upon whether or not λ_1 and d' have like signs respectively. If $d' = 0$, the equation represents two real coincident planes.

10.4   RANK OF THE QUADRICS

The rank of Δ, the matrix of the quadric surface, is called the *rank of the quadric*. Since the rank of a matrix is an invariant under the elementary row operations, and since every rotation and translation matrix is the product of elementary row operations, the rank of Δ is an invariant under the rigid motion transformations of space.

The transformed matrix of the quadric surface is represented in equation (10.12) by

$$\Delta_1 = \begin{pmatrix} \lambda_1 & 0 & 0 & 0 \\ 0 & \lambda_2 & 0 & 0 \\ 0 & 0 & \lambda_3 & 0 \\ 0 & 0 & 0 & d' \end{pmatrix}. \tag{10.18}$$

If $d' \neq 0$, then Δ_1 is of rank 4. Hence from our previous discussion of the classification of the quadric surfaces, real and imaginary ellipsoids and the hyperboloids of one and two sheets are quadrics of rank 4. If $d' = 0$, then Δ_1 is of rank 3. Hence the real and imaginary quadric cones are of rank 3.

The transformed Δ is represented in equation (10.13) by

$$\Delta_2 = \begin{pmatrix} \lambda_1 & 0 & 0 & 0 \\ 0 & \lambda_2 & 0 & 0 \\ 0 & 0 & 0 & \gamma \\ 0 & 0 & \gamma & d' \end{pmatrix}. \tag{10.19}$$

If $\gamma \neq 0$, then Δ_2 is of rank 4. Hence the elliptic and hyperbolic paraboloids are quadrics of rank 4. If $\gamma = 0$ but $d' \neq 0$, then Δ_2 is of rank 3. Therefore, the real and imaginary elliptic cylinders and the hyperbolic cylinders are quadrics of rank 3. If $\gamma = 0$ and $d' = 0$, then Δ_2 is of rank 2. It follows that two distinct real or imaginary intersecting planes are quadric surfaces of rank 2.

The transformed Δ is represented in equation (10.16) by

$$\Delta_3 = \begin{pmatrix} \lambda_1 & 0 & 0 & 0 \\ 0 & 0 & 0 & \beta \\ 0 & 0 & 0 & \gamma \\ 0 & \beta & \gamma & d' \end{pmatrix}. \tag{10.20}$$

If $\beta \neq 0$ and $\gamma \neq 0$, it was mentioned that by an additional transformation either β or γ, as well as d', can be made to vanish. Therefore, the rank of Δ_3 is 3. Hence a parabolic cylinder is a quadric of rank 3. If $\beta = \gamma = 0$, the rank of Δ_3 is 1 or 2 depending upon whether or not $d' = 0$ respectively. It follows that the rank of two distinct real or imaginary parallel planes is 2, while two coincident planes is a quadric of rank 1.

It should be noted that the real proper quadrics are quadrics of rank 4; that is, the matrix of a real proper quadric is nonsingular. Quadrics whose ranks are less than 4 are degenerate quadric surfaces. The real quadrics whose ranks are 4 and for which $\det D \neq 0$ are the real proper central quadrics.

Exercises

In Exercises 1–6 find the rank of each quadric.

1. $x^2 + 2y^2 + 6z^2 + 4yz - 2zx = 0$.

2. $x^2 + 4y^2 + 4xy + 4x + 4y - 6z + 6 = 0$.

3. $2x^2 + 3y^2 + 7z^2 + 8yz + 6zx - 2xy + 4x + 6y + 14z + 6 = 0$.

4. $2y^2 - 2yz - 2zx + 2xy - 4x - 3y + 2z - 1 = 0$.

5. $x^2 + 2zx + 2xy - 2x + 2y + 2z - 2 = 0$.

6. $x^2 + y^2 - 3z^2 - 4xy = 1$.

10.5   QUADRIC INVARIANTS

We have already seen that the rank of D is a quadric invariant. In order to study some of the other important invariants associated with the general quadric surfaces, recall that similar matrices have the same characteristic functions and eigenvalues. Since a rotation of coordinate axes transforms D into a similar matrix, the characteristic function of D is an invariant under the rotation transformation. In addition, since the elements of D are the coefficients of the second degree terms in x, y, and z, and since these coefficients are unchanged by a translation of coordinate axes, the characteristic function of D is an invariant under the translation transformation. The characteristic function of D is

$$\lambda^3 - (a + b + c)\lambda^2 + (ab + bc + ca - f^2 - g^2 - h^2)\lambda$$
$$- (abc + 2fgh - af^2 - bg^2 - ch^2). \quad (10.21)$$

Hence the following quantities are quadric invariants under the rigid motion transformations:

$$a + b + c, \quad (10.22)$$

$$ab + bc + ca - f^2 - g^2 - h^2, \quad (10.23)$$

$$abc + 2fgh - af^2 - bg^2 - ch^2. \quad (10.24)$$

Note that

$$a + b + c = \lambda_1 + \lambda_2 + \lambda_3,$$

$$ab + bc + ca - f^2 - g^2 - h^2 = \lambda_1\lambda_2 + \lambda_2\lambda_3 + \lambda_3\lambda_1,$$

$$\det D = abc + 2fgh - af^2 - bg^2 - ch^2 = \lambda_1\lambda_2\lambda_3.$$

Since Δ is a real symmetric matrix, the following quantities are invariants under the rotation transformation:

$$a + b + c + d, \quad (10.25)$$

$$ab + ac + ad + bc + bd + cd - f^2 - g^2 - h^2 - r^2 - s^2 - t^2, \quad (10.26)$$

$$\begin{vmatrix} a & h & g \\ h & b & f \\ g & f & c \end{vmatrix} + \begin{vmatrix} a & g & r \\ g & c & t \\ r & t & d \end{vmatrix} + \begin{vmatrix} a & h & r \\ h & b & s \\ r & s & d \end{vmatrix} + \begin{vmatrix} b & f & s \\ f & c & t \\ s & t & d \end{vmatrix}, \quad (10.27)$$

$$\det \Delta. \quad (10.28)$$

If R is a translation matrix, it is of the form

$$\begin{pmatrix} 1 & 0 & 0 & l \\ 0 & 1 & 0 & m \\ 0 & 0 & 1 & n \\ 0 & 0 & 0 & 1 \end{pmatrix}.$$

The translation of the general quadratic function is given by

$$(x' \quad y' \quad z' \quad 1)R^\mathsf{T}\Delta R(x' \quad y' \quad z' \quad 1)^\mathsf{T}. \quad (10.29)$$

Now, since $\det R^{\mathsf{T}} = \det R = 1$, it follows that

$$\det (R^{\mathsf{T}} \Delta R) = \det R^{\mathsf{T}} \cdot \det \Delta \cdot \det R = \det \Delta. \qquad (10.30)$$

Hence $\det \Delta$ is an invariant under the translation transformation as well as under the rotation of axes.

Exercises

1. Prove that $r^2 + s^2 + t^2$, where r, s, t are defined in equation (10.1), is invariant under the rotation transformation.

Determine a set of necessary and sufficient conditions in terms of the quadric invariants $\det \Delta$, $\det D$, $ab + bc + ca - f^2 - g^2 - h^2$, and $a + b + c$ for equation (10.1) to represent each surface.

2. Real ellipsoid.

3. Imaginary ellipsoid.

4. Hyperbolic paraboloid.

5. Elliptic paraboloid.

6. Hyperboloid of one sheet.

7. Hyperboloid of two sheets.

ANSWERS TO SELECTED EXERCISES

§1.1 **2.** Distance function.
3. Not a distance function; property (iv) is not satisfied.
4. Distance function. **5.** Distance function.
6. Not a distance function; property (ii) is not satisfied.

§1.3 **1.** (a) 8; (b) 3; (c) 3; (d) 5; (e) 8; (f) 2.
2. (a) Possible; (b) not possible; (c) possible;
(d) possible; (e) not possible.

§1.4 **1.** (a) $|PS| = 2\sqrt{19}$ and $|P'S'| = 2\sqrt{43}$.
(b) Choose the same unit distances.
2. (a) $|AB| = |BC| = |CD| = |DA| = 1$. The quadrilateral is a parallelogram but not a rhombus.
(b) $B{:}(\frac{3}{2}, 1)$, $C{:}(\frac{3}{2}, -1)$, $D{:}(1, -1)$; $|AB| = \frac{1}{2}$, $|BC| = 2$, $|CD| = \frac{1}{2}$, $|DA| = 2$.
(c) $|AB| = 1$, $|BC| = 2$, $|CD| = 1$, $|DA| = 2$. The quadrilateral is a parallelogram.

§1.5 **1.** $4\sqrt{2 - \sqrt{2}}$. **2.** $2\sqrt{37}$. **3.** $4\sqrt{3}$. **4.** $2\sqrt{10 - 3\sqrt{2}}$.
5. (a) $A{:}(1, \sqrt{3})$; (b) $B{:}(0, \frac{3}{2})$; (c) $C{:}(5, 0)$; (d) $D{:}(-2, 2\sqrt{3})$.
9. (b) If $3r^2 = s^2$. **10.** $D{:}(5, 4)$, $D{:}(1, -2)$, or $D{:}(-3, 6)$.
11. Distance function. **12.** Distance function. **13.** Distance function.

§1.6 **1.** (a) $2\sqrt{5}$; (b) $4\sqrt{2}$; (c) choose the same unit distances.
2. $|PR| = \sqrt{43}$. **3.** $|PR| = 2\sqrt{5}$.
6. (a) $\sqrt{y^2 + z^2}$; (b) $\sqrt{x^2 + z^2}$; (c) $\sqrt{x^2 + y^2}$;
(d) $|x|$; (e) $|y|$; (f) $|z|$.
9. (a) 3; (b) 5.

§2.1 **1.** $\overrightarrow{SR} = [7]$; $\overrightarrow{RS} = [-7]$. **2.** $\overrightarrow{SR} = [-5, 4]$; $\overrightarrow{RS} = [5, -4]$.
3. $\overrightarrow{SR} = [-1, -1, -8]$; $\overrightarrow{RS} = [1, 1, 8]$. **4.** $\overrightarrow{SR} = [5]$; $\overrightarrow{RS} = [-5]$.
5. $\overrightarrow{SR} = [-3, -4]$; $\overrightarrow{RS} = [3, 4]$. **6.** $\overrightarrow{SR} = [1, -1, 1]$; $\overrightarrow{RS} = [-1, 1, -1]$.

§2.2 **1.** Opposite directions; $|AB| = |CD|$.
2. Same direction; $|AB| = |CD|$.

3. Opposite directions; $|AB| = 3|CD|$.

4. Opposite directions; $2|AB| = |CD|$.

5. Same direction; $2|AB| = |CD|$.

6. Same direction; $2|AB| = |CD|$.

7. Neither; $|AB| \neq t|CD|$ where t is any positive real number.

8. Opposite directions; $|AB| = 8|CD|$.

9. *In the answers, t is any positive real number.*

(**a**) $(2t)$; (**b**) $(-t)$; (**c**) $(3t : t)$;

(**d**) $(-t : 0)$; (**e**) $(2t : 2t : t)$; (**f**) $(3t : 7t : -2t)$.

10. (**a**) (1); (**b**) (-1); (**c**) $\left(-\dfrac{1}{\sqrt{2}} : \dfrac{1}{\sqrt{2}}\right)$;

(**d**) $(\tfrac{3}{5} : \tfrac{4}{5})$; (**e**) $(\tfrac{1}{3} : \tfrac{2}{3} : \tfrac{2}{3})$; (**f**) $(\tfrac{6}{11} : \tfrac{6}{11} : \tfrac{7}{11})$.

12. (**a**) $\cos \alpha = \dfrac{x}{\sqrt{x^2 + y^2 + z^2}}$; $\cos \beta = \dfrac{y}{\sqrt{x^2 + y^2 + z^2}}$;

$\cos \gamma = \dfrac{z}{\sqrt{x^2 + y^2 + z^2}}$;

(**b**) $\cos^2 \alpha + \cos^2 \beta + \cos^2 \gamma = 1$.

13. $P:(12, 12\sqrt{2}, 12)$. **14.** $A:\left(\dfrac{1}{\sqrt{3}}, \dfrac{1}{\sqrt{3}}, \dfrac{1}{\sqrt{3}}\right)$.

15. (**b**) $\left(\dfrac{1}{\sqrt{2}} : -\dfrac{1}{\sqrt{2}}\right)$ and $\left(-\dfrac{1}{\sqrt{2}} : \dfrac{1}{\sqrt{2}}\right)$;

(**c**) $(\tfrac{3}{13} : \tfrac{4}{13} : \tfrac{12}{13})$ and $(-\tfrac{3}{13} : -\tfrac{4}{13} : -\tfrac{12}{13})$.

§2.3   **1.** Equal.   **2.** Equal.   **3.** Equal.

4. Not equal.   **5.** Not equal.   **6.** Not equal.

7. $x = 12; y = 5$.   **8.** $D:(3, 8, 6)$, $D:(-3, 2, 0)$, or $D:(9, -2, 8)$.

9. $\overrightarrow{CA}$, $\overrightarrow{CD}$, and $\overrightarrow{CB}$.   **10.** $P:(-4, -4, 0)$.

§2.4   **1.** $[4, 5, 4]$.   **2.** $[6, 2]$.

3. (**a**) 11; (**b**) 1; (**c**) opposite to the direction of $\vec{m}$ and $\vec{n}$.

4. (**a**) $\overrightarrow{AE}$; (**b**) $\vec{0}$; (**c**) $\overrightarrow{BC}$; (**d**) $2\overrightarrow{AB}$.

10. $[\tfrac{6}{11}, -\tfrac{6}{11}, \tfrac{7}{11}]$.   **11.** $\vec{a} = [\cos \theta, \sin \theta]$.   **12.** $[4, -6, 8]$.

13. (**a**) $[15, 4, -1]$; (**b**) $[0, 12, 12]$.   **14.** (**a**) 2; (**b**) 0.

15. (**a**) $r = 2$ and $s = -2$; (**b**) $r = 0$ and $s = 0$.

§2.5   **1.** $\vec{c} = 3\vec{a} + \tfrac{1}{2}\vec{b}$.   **2.** No.

3. $\vec{a} = [1, 0], \vec{b} = [0, 1], r = 1, s = 1$; $\vec{a} = [1, 1], \vec{b} = [1, -1], r = 1, s = 0$;

$\vec{a} = [2, 1], \vec{b} = [0, 1], r = \tfrac{1}{2}, s = \tfrac{1}{2}$.

(Infinitely many other base vectors exist.)

4. (**a**) $\overrightarrow{OP} = 2\vec{a} + \tfrac{1}{3}\vec{b} - 2\vec{c}$; (**b**) $\overrightarrow{AB} = \tfrac{1}{2}\vec{a} + \vec{b} - 3\vec{c}$.

5. (**a**) $\overrightarrow{OP} = 4\vec{i} + \vec{j} - 2\vec{k}$; (**b**) $\overrightarrow{AB} = \vec{i} + 3\vec{j} - 3\vec{k}$.

6. Linearly independent.   **7.** Linearly dependent.

8. Linearly dependent.   **9.** Linearly independent.

§2.6 **1. (a)** Collinear; **(b)** noncollinear; **(c)** noncollinear; **(d)** noncollinear.
2. $(-1, -2, 4)$.
5. (a) $(\frac{10}{3}, \frac{7}{3}, -2)$; **(b)** $(\frac{14}{5}, \frac{11}{5}, -\frac{8}{5})$;
(c) $(-10, -1, 8)$; **(d)** $(-6, 0, 5)$.
6. $\left(\dfrac{x_1 + x_2 + x_3}{3}, \dfrac{y_1 + y_2 + y_3}{3}, \dfrac{z_1 + z_2 + z_3}{3} \right)$.

§2.7 **1.** 9. **3.** $|\vec{a}| = 6$; $\vec{a}/|\vec{a}| = \left[\dfrac{5}{6}, \dfrac{1}{6}, -\dfrac{\sqrt{10}}{6} \right]$.
4. $\pi/3$. **5.** $\pi/4$. **6.** 0. **7.** π.
8. (a) Orthogonal; **(b)** orthogonal; **(c)** orthogonal; **(d)** nonorthogonal.
13. 1. **14.** $7/\sqrt{2}$.
15. (a) 1; **(b)** 0; **(c)** 0; **(d)** 1. **16.** 2.
17. $\cos \alpha = \dfrac{a_1}{\sqrt{a_1{}^2 + a_2{}^2 + a_3{}^2}}$; $\cos \beta = \dfrac{a_2}{\sqrt{a_1{}^2 + a_2{}^2 + a_3{}^2}}$;

$\cos \gamma = \dfrac{a_3}{\sqrt{a_1{}^2 + a_2{}^2 + a_3{}^2}}$.

21. $[\frac{4}{13}, \frac{3}{13}, -\frac{12}{13}]$.

§2.8 **1.** 0, 1, or -2. **2.** Orthogonal basis. **3.** Orthogonal basis.
4. Not an orthogonal basis. **5.** Not an orthogonal basis.
6. Not an orthogonal basis. **7.** Orthogonal basis.
8. Orthogonal basis. **9.** Not an orthogonal basis.

10. $\left[\dfrac{1}{\sqrt{2}}, -\dfrac{1}{\sqrt{2}} \right]$ and $\left[\dfrac{1}{\sqrt{2}}, \dfrac{1}{\sqrt{2}} \right]$ or

$\left[\dfrac{1}{\sqrt{2}}, -\dfrac{1}{\sqrt{2}} \right]$ and $\left[-\dfrac{1}{\sqrt{2}}, -\dfrac{1}{\sqrt{2}} \right]$.

11. $\left[-\dfrac{1}{\sqrt{5}}, \dfrac{2}{\sqrt{5}} \right]$ and $\left[\dfrac{2}{\sqrt{5}}, \dfrac{1}{\sqrt{5}} \right]$ or

$\left[-\dfrac{1}{\sqrt{5}}, \dfrac{2}{\sqrt{5}} \right]$ and $\left[-\dfrac{2}{\sqrt{5}}, -\dfrac{1}{\sqrt{5}} \right]$.

12. $[-1, 0]$ and $[0, 1]$ or $[-1, 0]$ and $[0, -1]$.
13. $[\frac{3}{5}, \frac{4}{5}]$ and $[\frac{4}{5}, -\frac{3}{5}]$ or $[\frac{3}{5}, \frac{4}{5}]$ and $[-\frac{4}{5}, \frac{3}{5}]$.

14. $\left[\dfrac{1}{\sqrt{2}}, -\dfrac{1}{\sqrt{2}}, 0 \right], \left[\dfrac{1}{\sqrt{2}}, \dfrac{1}{\sqrt{2}}, 0 \right]$, and $[0, 0, 1]$ or

$\left[\dfrac{1}{\sqrt{2}}, -\dfrac{1}{\sqrt{2}}, 0 \right], \left[\dfrac{1}{\sqrt{2}}, \dfrac{1}{\sqrt{2}}, 0 \right]$, and $[0, 0, -1]$.

15. $\left[\dfrac{2}{3}, \dfrac{1}{3}, \dfrac{2}{3} \right], \left[\dfrac{1}{3\sqrt{2}}, -\dfrac{4}{3\sqrt{2}}, \dfrac{1}{3\sqrt{2}} \right]$ and $\left[\dfrac{1}{\sqrt{2}}, 0, -\dfrac{1}{\sqrt{2}} \right]$ or

$\left[\dfrac{2}{3}, \dfrac{1}{3}, \dfrac{2}{3} \right], \left[\dfrac{1}{3\sqrt{2}}, -\dfrac{4}{3\sqrt{2}}, \dfrac{1}{3\sqrt{2}} \right]$ and $\left[-\dfrac{1}{\sqrt{2}}, 0, \dfrac{1}{\sqrt{2}} \right]$.

17. $[1, 0, 1]$ and $[\frac{1}{2}, -\frac{1}{2}, -\frac{1}{2}]$. (Other orthogonal bases exist.)

§2.9 **1.** 9. **2.** 24. **3.** 27. **4.** 4. **5.** 10. **6.** -88.

§2.10 **1.** (a) $[3, -7, 2]$; (b) $[0, 0, 0]$; (c) $[0, 0, 5]$; (d) $[-4, 1, 8]$.

3. $\left[\dfrac{5}{\sqrt{30}}, \dfrac{2}{\sqrt{30}}, \dfrac{1}{\sqrt{30}}\right]$ or $\left[-\dfrac{5}{\sqrt{30}}, -\dfrac{2}{\sqrt{30}}, -\dfrac{1}{\sqrt{30}}\right]$.

12. $\vec{i} \times \vec{i} = \vec{0}$, $\vec{i} \times \vec{j} = \vec{k}$, $\vec{i} \times \vec{k} = -\vec{j}$, $\vec{j} \times \vec{i} = -\vec{k}$, $\vec{j} \times \vec{j} = \vec{0}$,

$\vec{j} \times \vec{k} = \vec{i}$, $\vec{k} \times \vec{i} = \vec{j}$, $\vec{k} \times \vec{j} = -\vec{i}$, and $\vec{k} \times \vec{k} = \vec{0}$.

13. (a) $9\vec{i} - 19\vec{j} - 11\vec{k}$;

(b) $(y_1 z_2 - z_1 y_2)\vec{i} + (z_1 x_2 - x_1 z_2)\vec{j} + (x_1 y_2 - y_1 x_2)\vec{k}$.

14. (a) 1; (b) 0.   **15.** (a) $\vec{0}$; (b) $\vec{j}$.   **20.** -32.

23. (a) Set of coplanar vectors; (b) not a set of coplanar vectors.

§3.1 **19.** (a) $x + y = 0$; (b) $x = 1$; (c) $y = 1$.

20. $x^2 + y^2 = r^2$, where r is a real number.

21. $y^2 - 12x + 36 = 0$.

§3.2 **1.** $\begin{cases} x = 3 + 2t \\ y = 1 - t. \end{cases}$ **2.** $\begin{cases} x = 2 + 5t \\ y = 4. \end{cases}$

3. $\begin{cases} x = -3 + 3t \\ y = t. \end{cases}$ **4.** $\begin{cases} x = t \\ y = 2t. \end{cases}$

5. $\dfrac{x - 5}{3} = \dfrac{y - 2}{2}$.   **6.** $\dfrac{x + 3}{1} = \dfrac{y}{-5}$.

7. Not possible.   **8.** Not possible.

9. $\begin{cases} x = 5 - t \\ y = 3 + 3t. \end{cases}$ **10.** $\begin{cases} x = 2 + t \\ y = 5t. \end{cases}$ **11.** $\begin{cases} x = -6 - t \\ y = 6 + 3t. \end{cases}$

12. $\begin{cases} x = 3 + 2t \\ y = 2 + t. \end{cases}$ **13.** $\begin{cases} x = 3 \\ y = -2 + t. \end{cases}$

14. (a) $(1 : 0)$; (b) $(1, 1), (2, 1), (3, 1), \ldots$.

15. $\left(\dfrac{3}{5} : \dfrac{4}{5}\right)$.   **16.** $\dfrac{x - 6}{2} = \dfrac{y + 2}{5}$.   **17.** $\left(\dfrac{5}{13} : \dfrac{12}{13}\right)$.

§3.3 **1.** $2x + y - 21 = 0$.   **2.** $x - 3 = 0$.

3. $5x - y - 20 = 0$.   **4.** $x - y + 3 = 0$.

5. $3x + 2y + 2 = 0$.   **6.** $2x - 5y = 0$.

7. $[\tfrac{3}{5}, \tfrac{4}{5}]$ or $[-\tfrac{3}{5}, -\tfrac{4}{5}]$.   **8.** $\left[\dfrac{1}{\sqrt{2}}, -\dfrac{1}{\sqrt{2}}\right]$ or $\left[-\dfrac{1}{\sqrt{2}}, \dfrac{1}{\sqrt{2}}\right]$.

9. $3x - 5y + 17 = 0$.   **10.** $x + y - 7 = 0$.

11. $x - 2y + 5 = 0$.   **12.** $3x + 2y - 21 = 0$.

13. $x + 4y + 6 = 0$.   **14.** $2x - 3y - 6 = 0$.

15. $9x - 7y = 0$.   **16.** $x + 2y - 14 = 0$.

17. $5x + 2y - 4 = 0$.

§3.4 **1.** $2x - 3y - 3 = 0$.   **2.** $2x - y + 2 = 0$.

3. $x + y + 6 = 0$.   **4.** $x - y - 1 = 0$.

5. $\begin{cases} x = -1 + t \\ y = -t. \end{cases}$ **6.** $\begin{cases} x = 7 + 5t \\ y = 3 - 4t. \end{cases}$

§3.4 **7.** $\begin{cases} x = 5 + t \\ y = 1. \end{cases}$ **8.** $\begin{cases} x = 2 \\ y = t. \end{cases}$

9. $P:(\frac{15}{2}, 3)$. **10.** $B:(7, \frac{1}{2})$. **12.** $(3, 2)$.

13. $2x + y - 7 = 0$.

14. $x + 4y - 14 = 0$, $5x - 7y - 7 = 0$, and $7x + y - 35 = 0$.

15. $(-6, 5)$ and $(-2, 7)$. **17.** $3x - y - 13 = 0$.

§3.5 **1.** -1. **2.** 0. **3.** 2. **4.** Undefined.

5. $x - y - 1 = 0$. **6.** $x + y + 1 = 0$.

7. $5x - 3y - 1 = 0$. **8.** $y - 1 = 0$.

9. $3\pi/4$. **10.** $\pi/6$.

11. $\frac{1}{3}$. **12.** $-\frac{8}{5}$. **13.** $\frac{1}{2}$. **14.** $-\frac{2}{3}$.

15. $3x + y - 6 = 0$. **16.** $5x - 8y + 71 = 0$.

17. $x - \sqrt{3}\, y = 0$. **18.** $x - y - 1 = 0$.

19. 3. **20.** $-\frac{2}{3}$. **21.** 2. **22.** -1.

24. $2x + 5y - 20 = 0$; $2x + 5y + 20 = 0$.

§3.6 **1.** (a) 8; (b) 6. **2.** (a) -2; (b) 5.

3. (a) 3; (b) does not exist. **4.** (a) Does not exist; (b) $-\frac{5}{2}$.

5. $3x - 4y + 8 = 0$. **6.** $2x + y - 7 = 0$.

7. $y + 3 = 0$. **8.** $3x - y = 0$.

9. $\dfrac{x}{-3} + \dfrac{y}{3} = 1$. **10.** Not possible.

11. $\dfrac{x}{2/3} + \dfrac{y}{-2} = 1$. **12.** $\dfrac{x}{11} + \dfrac{y}{11/2} = 1$.

13. (a) $y = 2x + 3$; (b) $\dfrac{x}{-3/2} + \dfrac{y}{3} = 1$.

14. (a) $y = -\dfrac{7}{3}x - \dfrac{4}{3}$; (b) $\dfrac{x}{-4/7} + \dfrac{y}{-4/3} = 1$.

15. (a) $y = -\dfrac{3}{2}x + 6$; (b) $\dfrac{x}{4} + \dfrac{y}{6} = 1$.

16. (a) $y = \dfrac{5}{3}x - 5$; (b) $\dfrac{x}{3} + \dfrac{y}{-5} = 1$.

§3.7 **1.** 11. **2.** 8. **3.** 27.

4. $3x + 5y - 15 = 0$. **5.** (a) $-c/a = 3$; (b) $c/a = c/b$.

6. $x + 3y - 5 = 0$.

8. (a) $y = k$, where k is a real number;

(b) $x = k$, where k is a real number.

9. $x + y - 2 = 0$ and $x - y - 4 = 0$.

§3.9 **1.** $5x + 2y - 22 = 0$. **2.** $x = 5$.

3. $3x - 7y - 23 = 0$. **4.** $y - 2 = 0$.

§3.10 **1.** Perpendicular. **2.** Parallel.

3. Parallel. **4.** Perpendicular.

5. Perpendicular. **6.** Neither.

7. Parallel. **8.** Perpendicular.
9. Perpendicular. **10.** Perpendicular.
11. $3x + 2y - 44 = 0$. **12.** $3x - 2y - 11 = 0$.
13. $x = 1$. **14.** $y = 5$. **15.** Yes.
16. $3x - 4y - 13 = 0$, $x - 4 = 0$, and $x + 4y - 3 = 0$.
18. $12x + 14y - 73 = 0$. **19.** $x = 5$.
20. $56x - 44y - 309 = 0$. **21.** $y = 1$.

§3.11 **1.** $\dfrac{1}{\sqrt{5}}$. **2.** $\dfrac{3}{\sqrt{10}}$. **3.** $\dfrac{\pi}{6}$ and $\dfrac{5\pi}{6}$.

4. 0. **5.** $\dfrac{\pi}{4}$ and $\dfrac{3\pi}{4}$. **6.** $\dfrac{\pi}{2}$.

7. $x = 0$; $y = 1$. **8.** $x = 1$; $y = 1$.
9. $3x + y - 3 = 0$; $9x - 13y - 9 = 0$. **10.** $2x - 7y + 6 = 0$.
11. Not perpendicular. **12.** Not parallel.

§3.12 **1.** $x + y - 2\sqrt{2} = 0$. **2.** $x + 1 = 0$.
3. $\sqrt{3}x + y = 0$. **4.** $x + \sqrt{3}y - 12 = 0$.

5. $\dfrac{5}{13}x + \dfrac{12}{13}y - 1 = 0$; 1. **6.** $-\dfrac{4}{5}x - \dfrac{3}{5}y - \dfrac{1}{2} = 0$; $\dfrac{1}{2}$.

7. $\dfrac{1}{\sqrt{2}}x + \dfrac{1}{\sqrt{2}}y = 0$; 0. **8.** $x - 5 = 0$; 5.

9. $-\dfrac{7}{25}x + \dfrac{24}{25}y - 2 = 0$; 2. **10.** $-y - 7 = 0$; 7.

12. $3x + 4y + 15 = 0$, $3x + 4y - 15 = 0$.

§3.13 **1.** 2. **2.** 9. **3.** 1. **4.** 11.
5. -1 or $\frac{13}{2}$. **6.** $-\frac{86}{7}$. **7.** -25. **8.** $\sqrt{5}$.

9. $\dfrac{|c_2 - c_1|}{\sqrt{a^2 + b^2}}$. **10.** 1. **11.** 4.

12. $8x + 6y + 19 = 0$, $8x + 6y - 21 = 0$.
13. $x - 8y + 5 = 0$, $16x + 2y + 15 = 0$.
14. $x - y - 2 = 0$, $2x + 2y - 7 = 0$.
15. $x = 0$, $2y - 1 = 0$.
16. $x - 7y + 24 = 0$, $7x + y = 0$.
19. 20 square units.

§3.14 **1.** $x = 1$, $y = -4$, $z = -2$.
2. $x = 1$, $y = 0$, $z = 1$.
3. (**a**) Consistent; (**b**) independent.
4. (**a**) Consistent; (**b**) dependent.
5. (**a**) Inconsistent; (**b**) independent.
6. (**a**) Consistent; (**b**) independent provided that $b \neq 0$.
7. $x + 4y - 17 = 0$. **8.** $3x + 5y - 6 = 0$.
9. $(-2, 5)$. **10.** $(-\frac{171}{43}, \frac{192}{43})$; $(3, -6)$.

12. $\left(\dfrac{x_1 + x_2 + x_3}{3}, \dfrac{y_1 + y_2 + y_3}{3}\right)$.

§3.15 **7.** $2x + y + k = 0$, where k is a real number.

8. $k_1(x - 6) + k_2(y + 1) = 0$, where k_1 and k_2 are real numbers such that k_1 and k_2 are not both zero.

9. $8x + 3y + k = 0$, where k is a real number.

10. $7x + 11y + k = 0$, where k is a real number.

§4.1 **2.** (a) $(1, \sqrt{3})$;   (e) $(-1, 0)$;

(b) $(-\sqrt{2}/2, -\sqrt{2}/2)$;   (f) $(-1, 0)$;

(c) $(-3, 0)$;   (g) $(0, 0)$;

(d) $(0, 5)$;   (h) $(\sqrt{3}/2, -3/2)$.

3. (a) $(2, 3\pi/4)$;   (e) $(1, 0)$;

(b) $(3\sqrt{2}, \pi/4)$;   (f) $(2, \pi/6)$;

(c) $(2\sqrt{2}, 7\pi/4)$;   (g) $(2, 5\pi/6)$;

(d) $(4, \pi/2)$;   (h) $(2, \pi/3)$.

4. (a) $3\sqrt{2}$;   (b) $\sqrt{5 - 2\sqrt{2}}$;   (c) 5;   (d) $\sqrt{13}$.

11. 10 square units.

§4.2 **1.** $r \cos (\theta - \pi/3) = 2$.   **2.** $r \cos (\theta - \pi) = 1$.

3. $r \sin \theta = -1$.   **4.** $r \cos \theta = 2$.

5. $r \cos \theta = 3$.   **6.** $r \cos \theta = -1$.

8. $r \sin \theta = 2$.   **9.** $r \sin \theta = -3$.

11. $\theta = \pi/4$.   **13.** $r \cos (\theta - \pi/3) = 3 \cos (\pi/12)$.

14. $d = |r_1 \cos (\theta_1 - \phi) - p|$.   **15.** $d = 2\sqrt{3} - 1$.

§4.3 **1.** $x^2 + y^2 - 4x - 8y - 16 = 0$.

2. $9x^2 + 9y^2 + 54x + 18y + 89 = 0$.

3. $36x^2 + 36y^2 - 36x - 24y - 563 = 0$.

4. $x^2 + y^2 - 4 = 0$.

5. $x^2 + y^2 - 4x - 8y = 0$.

6. $x^2 + y^2 + 2x - 2y - 2 = 0$.

7. $x^2 + y^2 - 8x + 6y - 55 = 0$.

8. $x^2 + y^2 - 2\pi x - 2\pi y + \pi^2 = 0$.

9. $C:(4, -1); r = 5$.

10. $C:(0, -2); r = 2$.

11. $C:(-\frac{1}{4}, -\frac{1}{4}); r = \sqrt{2}/4$.

12. $C:(1, 1); r = 2\sqrt{3}$.

13. $x^2 + y^2 - 10x - 14y + 49 = 0$.

14. $x^2 + y^2 - 6x + 8y - 20 = 0$.

15. $k = 13/2$.

16. $x^2 + y^2 - 12x - 4y + 22 = 0$.

17. $x^2 + y^2 - 6x - 6y + 5 = 0$.

19. $2x^2 + 2y^2 - 21x - 23y + 110 = 0$, a circle with center at $C:(\frac{21}{4}, \frac{23}{4})$ and radius $r = 3\sqrt{10}/4$.

20. 3.

21. $x^2 + y^2 - 6x + 4y - 12 = 0$ or $x^2 + y^2 - 4x - 10y + 4 = 0$.

23. (a) $x^2 + y^2 - 10x - 14y + 49 = 0$;
    (b) $x^2 + y^2 - 6x + 8y - 20 = 0$.
24. $x^2 + y^2 + 4x + 10y - 140 = 0$.
25. $x^2 + y^2 + 3x + 10y - 79 = 0$.
28. $3x + y - 16 = 0$.

§4.4   **1.** $x + 3y - 11 = 0$.   **2.** $3x - 2y - 11 = 0$.
      3. $3x + 4y + 7 = 0$.   **4.** $x - y = 0$.
      5. $x + 5y - 26 = 0$.   **6.** $y - 4 = 0$.
      7. $x = 0$.   **8.** $x - y - 2 = 0$.
      9. $x_1(x - x_1) + y_1(y - y_1) = 0$.
      10. $x^2 + y^2 + 2x - 6y + 1 = 0$.
      11. $10x^2 + 10y^2 - 40x - 80y + 31 = 0$.
      12. $12\sqrt{2}$ or $-12\sqrt{2}$.
      13. $3x - 4y - 12 = 0; 3x - 4y + 38 = 0$.
      14. $2x + y + (2 + 4\sqrt{5}) = 0; 2x + y + (2 - 4\sqrt{5}) = 0$.
      16. 4.
      17. $3x + 4y - 2 = 0; 3x - 4y - 34 = 0$.
      18. $x^2 + y^2 - 20x + 75 = 0$.
      19. $x^2 + y^2 + 4x - 4y + 4 = 0$.

§4.5   **1.** $r^2 - 4r \cos (\theta - \pi/6) - 5 = 0$.
      2. $r = 2 \sin \theta$.
      3. $r^2 + 2r \cos (\theta - \pi/3) - 3 = 0$.
      4. $r + 2\pi \cos \theta = 0$.
      5. $r = 4 \cos \theta$.
      6. $r = 4$.
      7. $r^2 - 2 \cos (\theta - \pi/6) - 9 = 0$.
      8. $r^2 - 2r \cos \theta - 8 = 0$.
      9. $r^2 - 6r \cos (\theta - 5\pi/4) - 7 = 0$.
      10. $r^2 - 6r \cos (\theta - 7\pi/4) - 64 = 0$.
      11. $r^2 + 2r \cos \theta - 24 = 0$ is the equation of the locus.
      12. $C:(3, \pi/3); a = 5$.
      13. $r^2 - 8r \cos (\theta - \pi/6) - 12 = 0$.

§5.1 **1.** $\begin{cases} x = -5 + r + 3s \\ y = 4 - 2r - s \\ z = 6 - 3r - 2s. \end{cases}$ **2.** $\begin{cases} x = 1 + 2r + 7s \\ y = 4r - s \\ z = 7 + 2r - s. \end{cases}$

      3. $\begin{cases} x = 1 + 3r + 2s \\ y = 5 + 8r + 5s \\ z = 3. \end{cases}$ **4.** $\begin{cases} x = 3 + r + 3s \\ y = 2 + r \\ z = 4 + r - s. \end{cases}$

      5. $\begin{cases} x = 1 - r \\ y = 1 + r - s \\ z = 1 - r. \end{cases}$ **6.** $\begin{cases} x = 2 + 3r - 2s \\ y = 1 + 4r - 2s \\ z = -1 + r - s. \end{cases}$

      7. $\begin{cases} x = 0 \\ y = 1 - 3r + 3s \\ z = 2 + 2r. \end{cases}$ **8.** $\begin{cases} x = 3 + 2r - 7s \\ y = 4 - 5r - 4s \\ z = 2 + r - s. \end{cases}$

§5.1 **9.** $\begin{cases} x = 2 + 2r \\ y = 5 + r \\ z = 1 - r + s. \end{cases}$ **10.** $\begin{cases} x = 3 + r + 4s \\ y = 6 + 2r + 2s \\ z = 2 + 3r + s. \end{cases}$

§5.2
1. $8x - 3z - 12 = 0.$
2. $4x - y + z - 19 = 0.$
3. $6x + 3y + 2z - 49 = 0.$
4. $x - 9y - 4z + 93 = 0.$
5. $[\frac{1}{3}, -\frac{2}{3}, \frac{2}{3}].$ **6.** $[\frac{5}{13}, 0, -\frac{12}{13}].$
7. $(7t : -2t : 3t)$, where t is any nonzero real number.
8. $\left(\frac{1}{\sqrt{2}} : -\frac{1}{\sqrt{2}} : 0 \right)$ or $\left(-\frac{1}{\sqrt{2}} : \frac{1}{\sqrt{2}} : 0 \right).$ **9.** $\pi/4.$
10. $2x + 2y + z - 4 = 0.$
11. $5x - 10y + 2z - 10 = 0.$
12. (a) $-\frac{d}{a} = 1;$ (b) $\frac{d}{a} = \frac{d}{b};$ (c) $\frac{d}{a} = \frac{d}{b} = \frac{d}{c}.$
14. (a) $by + cz + d = 0;$ (d) $cz + d = 0;$
    (b) $ax + cz + d = 0;$ (e) $ax + d = 0;$
    (c) $ax + by + d = 0;$ (f) $by + d = 0.$
15. $x - 4y + 5 = 0.$ **16.** $z = 5.$

§5.3
1. $y + z - 2 = 0.$
2. $x - 2y + z = 0.$
3. $8x - 21y - 36z + 50 = 0.$
4. $14x - 10y + 9z = 0.$
5. $3x + 12y - 2z - 12 = 0.$
6. $3x - 6y + z + 2 = 0.$
7. $x - z - 1 = 0.$
8. $17x + 3y - 19z + 58 = 0.$
9. $\left[\frac{1}{\sqrt{5}}, -\frac{2}{\sqrt{5}}, 0 \right]$ or $\left[-\frac{1}{\sqrt{5}}, \frac{2}{\sqrt{5}}, 0 \right].$
11. $9x + 5y + 8z - 12 = 0.$
13. The points do not determine a unique plane.
14. $x + 3y - 2z - 19 = 0.$
15. $6x + 3y - z - 12 = 0.$

§5.4
1. $12x - 4y + 7z - 17 = 0.$
2. $3x + 2y + z + 9 = 0.$
3. $x - 3y + 6z - 24 = 0.$
4. $8x - 3y - 29 = 0.$
5. Parallel.   **6.** Neither.
7. Perpendicular.   **8.** Neither.
9. $-1/7.$ **10.** $2x + 2y + 3z - 22 = 0.$

§5.5   **1.** $4/21.$ **2.** $1.$ **3.** $0.$ **4.** $2\sqrt{42}/21.$ **5.** $\pi/4.$ **6.** $0.$

§5.6   **1.** $2.$ **2.** $2\sqrt{6}.$ **3.** $4.$ **4.** $11/3.$ **5.** $9, -2.$ **6.** $-7/3.$

7. $4x - 8y + z + 22 = 0$; $4x - 8y + z - 14 = 0$.

8. $|d|/\sqrt{a^2 + b^2 + c^2}$.   **9.** 3.

11. $-\dfrac{1}{2}x + \dfrac{1}{2}y - \dfrac{\sqrt{2}}{2}z - 2 = 0$; 2.

12. $8x - 4y + z + 18 = 0$; $8x - 4y + z - 18 = 0$.

§5.7 **1.** 6.   **2.** $\sqrt{6}/2$.   **3.** 0.   **4.** 3.

5. $3x + 12y - 4z + 85 = 0$; $3x + 12y - 4z - 71 = 0$.

6. $\dfrac{a_1x + b_1y + c_1z + d_1}{\sqrt{a_1^2 + b_1^2 + c_1^2}} = \pm\dfrac{a_2x + b_2y + c_2z + d_2}{\sqrt{a_2^2 + b_2^2 + c_2^2}}$.

7. $20x + 25y - 5z - 28 = 0$; $8x - 11y - 23z - 28 = 0$.

§5.8 **1.** $x^2 + y^2 + z^2 - 4x - 2y - 10z + 21 = 0$.

2. $x^2 + y^2 + z^2 - 10x + 4z + 28 = 0$.

3. $x^2 + y^2 + z^2 + 2x - 4y - 6z - 11 = 0$.

4. $x^2 + y^2 + z^2 - 2x + 16y - 2z + 50 = 0$.

5. $x^2 + y^2 + z^2 = 9$.

6. $x^2 + y^2 + z^2 - 2z - 3 = 0$.

7. $C{:}(3, 0, 0)$; $r = 3$.

8. $C{:}(0, 1, -2)$; $r = 3$.

9. $C{:}(-2, -1, 1)$; $r = 5$.

10. $C{:}(-\frac{1}{4}, \frac{3}{4}, -\frac{5}{4})$; $r = \sqrt{35}/4$.

11. $C{:}(0, 0, 0)$; $r = 3$.

12. $C{:}(\frac{1}{2}, \frac{1}{2}, \frac{1}{2})$; $r = 1$.

13. $x^2 + y^2 + z^2 - 8x - 6y - 6z - 87 = 0$.

14. $x^2 + y^2 + z^2 - 6x - 2y - 2z - 3 = 0$.

15. $x^2 + y^2 + z^2 - 8x - 6y - 4 = 0$.

17. $x^2 + y^2 + z^2 - 2x = 0$.

18. $x^2 + y^2 + z^2 = 169$.

§5.9 **1.** $y - z + 2 = 0$.   **2.** $2x + 2y + z = 0$.

3. $x + 2y - z - 6 = 0$.   **4.** $y + z - 6 = 0$.

5. $6x - 6y + 7z - 65 = 0$.

6. $x - 4y - 8z + 72 = 0$.

7. $x_1(x - x_1) + y_1(y - y_1) + z_1(z - z_1) = 0$.

8. $2x + 6y + 3z + 3 = 0$; $2x + 6y + 3z - 25 = 0$.

9. 14 and -10.

10. $x^2 + y^2 + z^2 - 4x - 4y + 2z + 5 = 0$.

§5.10 **1.** $\begin{cases} x = 4 + 3t \\ y = 2 + t \\ z = 5 + 2t. \end{cases}$ **2.** $\dfrac{x - 2}{1} = \dfrac{y - 1}{2} = \dfrac{z + 1}{2}$.

3. $\dfrac{x - 4}{6} = \dfrac{y - 3}{-2} = \dfrac{z - 4}{3}$.   **4.** $\begin{cases} x = 6 \\ y = -3 + t \\ z = 1. \end{cases}$

§5.10 **5.** $(2t : -3t : 0)$, where t is any nonzero real number.

    6. $(\frac{6}{11} : \frac{6}{11} : \frac{7}{11})$ or $(-\frac{6}{11} : -\frac{6}{11} : -\frac{7}{11})$.

    7. $\dfrac{x-1}{4} = \dfrac{y+2}{3} = \dfrac{z-7}{1}$.

    8. $\begin{cases} x = 1+t \\ y = t \\ z = 4+2t. \end{cases}$

    9. (a) $\begin{cases} x = 2+3t \\ y = 2-t \\ z = 3+5t; \end{cases}$ (b) $\dfrac{x-2}{3} = \dfrac{y-2}{-1} = \dfrac{z-3}{5}$.

    10. (a) $\begin{cases} x = -2t \\ y = t \\ z = t; \end{cases}$ (b) $\dfrac{x}{-2} = y = z$.

    11. $(0, -4, 19)$.

    12. $\dfrac{x}{x_1} = \dfrac{y}{y_1} = \dfrac{z}{z_1}$.

    13. $c = -5$.

    14. (a) $Aa + Bb + Cc = 0$;   (b) $\dfrac{A}{a} = \dfrac{B}{b} = \dfrac{C}{c}$.

    15. (a) $\dfrac{a_0}{a_1} = \dfrac{b_0}{b_1} = \dfrac{c_0}{c_1}$;   (b) $a_0a_1 + b_0b_1 + c_0c_1 = 0$.

    16. $x + 6y - 5z - 22 = 0$.

    17. $x + 3y - 4z + 6 = 0$.

    18. $10x - 21y + 18z - 81 = 0$.

§5.11 **1.** $\dfrac{x-2}{1} = \dfrac{y+6}{-2} = \dfrac{z}{-1}$.

    2. The symmetric form does not exist.

    3. $\dfrac{x}{8} = \dfrac{y+1}{-5} = \dfrac{z-2}{1}$.

    4. $\dfrac{x}{1} = \dfrac{y-4}{-13} = \dfrac{z-3}{-18}$.

    7. $(-7, 2, 3)$.

§6.1 **1.** Ellipse.   **2.** Hyperbola.   **3.** Parabola.

§6.3 **1.** $10x + 8y - 29 = 0$.

    7. $x = 1$.   **8.** $x = 2$.

    9. $x = 2$ and $y = 3$.

    10. $x = 3$ and $y = 2$.

    11. $x = 0$ and $y = 1$.

    12. $x = -D$ and $y = -E$, provided that $D^2 + E^2 - F \geq 0$.

    14. $(1, -3)$.   **15.** $(2, \frac{3}{2})$.   **16.** $(0, 5)$.

    17. $(0, 7)$.   **18.** $(1, -\frac{1}{4})$.

    19. $(-D, -E)$, provided that $D^2 + E^2 - F \geq 0$.

    25. $p = -12$.   **27.** Odd.   **28.** Neither.

    29. Even.   **30.** Even.   **31.** Even.   **32.** Neither.

§6.5   **5.** $\dfrac{x^2}{9} + \dfrac{y^2}{5} = 1.$ **6.** $\dfrac{(x-5)^2}{61} + \dfrac{(y-4)^2}{25} = 1.$

7. $\dfrac{(x-3)^2}{16} + \dfrac{(y+3)^2}{25} = 1.$ **8.** $\dfrac{x^2}{10} + \dfrac{y^2}{20} = 1.$

9. $\dfrac{(x-1)^2}{25} + \dfrac{(y+4)^2}{9} = 1$ or $\dfrac{(x-1)^2}{9} + \dfrac{(y+4)^2}{25} = 1.$

10. $\dfrac{(x-4)^2}{36} + \dfrac{(y-1)^2}{20} = 1.$

11. $-1 \le k \le 5.$ **12.** $a = b.$

13. $4x^2 + y^2 + 16x - 6y - 75 = 0.$

14. $\dfrac{x^2}{64} + \dfrac{y^2}{16} = 1.$ **15.** $\dfrac{2b^2}{a}.$

16. $0 \le e < 1.$ **17.** $\sqrt{3}/2.$

18. $(a^2 - h^2)x^2 - 2h^2xy + (a^2 - h^2)y^2 = a^4 - 2a^2h^2.$

§6.6   **5.** $\dfrac{x^2}{36} - \dfrac{y^2}{16} = 1.$ **6.** $\dfrac{(x-6)^2}{55} - \dfrac{(y-1)^2}{9} = 1.$

7. $2x^2 - y^2 = 1.$ **8.** $\dfrac{x^2}{16} - \dfrac{y^2}{9} = 1.$

9. $\dfrac{(y-4)^2}{16} - \dfrac{(x-4)^2}{33} = 1.$

13. $k \le -4$ or $k \ge 2.$

15. $x^2 - y^2 - 2y - 2 = 0.$

16. $\dfrac{y^2}{2} - \dfrac{x^2}{8} = 1.$ **17.** $\dfrac{2b^2}{a}.$ **18.** $e > 1.$

§6.7   **5.** $(y+1)^2 = 8(x-4).$ **6.** $(x+3)^2 = -8y.$

7. $x^2 = -3y.$ **8.** $x^2 + 3x - 2y + 10 = 0.$

13. (a) $8x^2 - 72x + 9y^2 + 144 = 0,$ an ellipse;

(b) $3x^2 - 32x + 4y^2 + 64 = 0,$ an ellipse;

(c) $5x^2 - 72x + 9y^2 + 144 = 0,$ an ellipse;

(d) $7x^2 - 128x + 16y^2 + 256 = 0,$ an ellipse.

14. (a) $7x^2 + 72x - 9y^2 - 144 = 0,$ a hyperbola;

(b) $5x^2 + 32x - 4y^2 - 64 = 0,$ a hyperbola;

(c) $3x^2 + 8x - y^2 - 16 = 0,$ a hyperbola;

(d) $8x^2 + 8x - y^2 - 16 = 0,$ a hyperbola.

15. $4p.$ **16.** $(x-2)^2 = 8(y-1)$ or $(x-2)^2 = -8(y-5).$

17. $y - y_1 = \dfrac{2p}{y_1}(x - x_1).$

§6.8

1. Real ellipse.
2. Imaginary parallel lines.
3. Hyperbola.
4. Intersecting lines.
5. Coincident lines.
6. Point.
7. Hyperbola.
8. Imaginary ellipse.

9. Parabola.
10. Point.
11. Parabola.
12. Hyperbola.
13. Real parallel lines.
14. Real ellipse.
15. Real ellipse.
16. Intersecting lines.

§6.9 **1.** $\dfrac{x^2}{20} + \dfrac{(y+2)^2}{36} = 1.$ **2.** $\dfrac{x^2}{20} + \dfrac{(y-2)^2}{36} = 1.$

3. $\dfrac{(y+4)^2}{36} - \dfrac{(x+2)^2}{45} = 1.$ **4.** $\dfrac{x^2}{100} + \dfrac{y^2}{36} = 1.$

5. $\dfrac{x^2}{16} - \dfrac{y^2}{84} = 1.$ **6.** $\dfrac{(x-8)^2}{64} + \dfrac{(y-1)^2}{48} = 1.$

7. $\dfrac{\sqrt{5}}{2}.$ **8.** $\dfrac{1}{3}.$

9. Greatest distance: 94,500,000 miles; least distance: 91,500,000 miles.

10. (a) $(1-e^2)x^2 + y^2 = 0$, a point;   (b) $y^2 = 0$, coincident lines;
(c) $(1-e^2)x^2 + y^2 = 0$, intersecting lines.

§6.10 **17.** $r = \dfrac{12}{3 - 2\cos\theta}.$ **18.** $r = \dfrac{4}{1 + \sin\theta}.$

§7.1 **1.** (a) 2;   (b) 3 by 2;   (c) 2 by 3;   (d) 3.

3. $\begin{pmatrix} -1 & -3 & -5 \\ 2 & 0 & -2 \\ 7 & 5 & 3 \end{pmatrix}.$ **4.** $\begin{pmatrix} 1 & 2 & 3 \\ 2 & 3 & 4 \end{pmatrix}.$

5. (a) Not equal;   (b) equal.

§7.2 **1.** $A + B = \begin{pmatrix} 6 & 2 & 4 \\ -3 & 10 & -2 \end{pmatrix}$; $3A = \begin{pmatrix} 15 & 0 & 3 \\ -6 & 21 & 0 \end{pmatrix}$;

$A - 2B = \begin{pmatrix} 3 & -4 & -5 \\ 0 & 1 & 4 \end{pmatrix}.$

5. (a) $\begin{pmatrix} -1 & -6 \\ 3 & -8 \end{pmatrix}$;   (b) $\begin{pmatrix} -a & -b & -c \\ -d & -e & -f \end{pmatrix}.$

6. $\begin{pmatrix} a_{11} & a_{12} & a_{13} \\ a_{21} & a_{22} & a_{23} \end{pmatrix} = \begin{pmatrix} 8 & 6 & 2 \\ 2 & 15 & 0 \end{pmatrix}.$

§7.3 **1.** $\begin{pmatrix} 1 & -4 \\ 14 & 16 \\ 15 & 14 \end{pmatrix}.$

2. AB, BD, DA, and DC.

7. Yes, if the number of rows of the first matrix is the same as the number of columns of the second matrix.

8. $AB = (2)$; $BA = \begin{pmatrix} 6 & -8 \\ 3 & -4 \end{pmatrix}.$

9. $\begin{pmatrix} \cos(\theta + \phi) & -\sin(\theta + \phi) \\ \sin(\theta + \phi) & \cos(\theta + \phi) \end{pmatrix}.$

12. $AB = BA$.

13. (a) $\begin{pmatrix} 2r & 3r \\ 2s & 3s \end{pmatrix}$, where r and s are any real numbers;

(b) no matrix A exists.

16. $\begin{pmatrix} w & x \\ y & z \end{pmatrix} = \begin{pmatrix} 1 & -\frac{1}{4} \\ -2 & \frac{3}{4} \end{pmatrix}.$

§7.4 **1.** (a) Neither; (b) symmetric; (c) symmetric; (d) skew-symmetric;
(e) symmetric and skew-symmetric;
(f) neither; (g) neither; (h) neither.

$$\textbf{4.}\ \begin{pmatrix} 3 & -1 & 0 \\ 4 & 2 & 1 \\ -2 & 3 & 1 \end{pmatrix} = \begin{pmatrix} 3 & \frac{3}{2} & -1 \\ \frac{3}{2} & 2 & 2 \\ -1 & 2 & 1 \end{pmatrix} + \begin{pmatrix} 0 & -\frac{5}{2} & 1 \\ \frac{5}{2} & 0 & -1 \\ -1 & 1 & 0 \end{pmatrix}.$$

§7.5 **1.** $\begin{pmatrix} \frac{3}{2} & -\frac{7}{4} \\ -2 & \frac{5}{2} \end{pmatrix}.$

2. The inverse does not exist.

$$\textbf{3.}\ \begin{pmatrix} \frac{10}{3} & -\frac{17}{3} & \frac{1}{6} \\ -\frac{5}{3} & \frac{10}{3} & -\frac{1}{3} \\ \frac{1}{3} & -\frac{2}{3} & \frac{1}{6} \end{pmatrix}.\qquad \textbf{4.}\ \begin{pmatrix} 1 & -3 & 10 \\ 0 & \frac{1}{2} & -2 \\ 0 & 0 & \frac{1}{3} \end{pmatrix}.$$

5. $\begin{pmatrix} \cos\theta & \sin\theta \\ -\sin\theta & \cos\theta \end{pmatrix}.$ **6.** $\begin{pmatrix} 0 & -\dfrac{1}{a} \\ \dfrac{1}{a} & 0 \end{pmatrix},$ provided that $a \neq 0.$

7. $\begin{pmatrix} \dfrac{1}{a} & 0 & 0 \\ 0 & \dfrac{1}{b} & 0 \\ 0 & 0 & \dfrac{1}{c} \end{pmatrix},$ provided that $abc \neq 0.$ **8.** $\begin{pmatrix} \frac{2}{3} & \frac{1}{3} & \frac{2}{3} \\ -\frac{2}{3} & \frac{2}{3} & \frac{1}{3} \\ \frac{1}{3} & \frac{2}{3} & -\frac{2}{3} \end{pmatrix}.$

9. $x = -2,\ y = 3.$ **10.** $x = 1,\ y = 0,\ z = 6.$

13. $\begin{pmatrix} \dfrac{d}{ad - bc} & -\dfrac{b}{ad - bc} \\ -\dfrac{c}{ad - bc} & \dfrac{a}{ad - bc} \end{pmatrix}.$

14. $a_{11}a_{22}a_{33} \cdots a_{nn}.$

§7.6 **1.** Proper orthogonal matrix. **2.** Improper orthogonal matrix.
3. Proper orthogonal matrix. **4.** Neither.

6. $\begin{pmatrix} 1 & 0 \\ 0 & 1 \end{pmatrix}$ and $\begin{pmatrix} 0 & 1 \\ 1 & 0 \end{pmatrix}.$

§7.7 **1.** 2. **2.** 2. **3.** 2. **4.** 2.

5. $\begin{pmatrix} 1 & 0 & 0 & -3 \\ 0 & 1 & 0 & 6 \\ 0 & 0 & 1 & 30 \end{pmatrix}.$

6. (a) $\begin{cases} -3x + 5y - 3z = 2 \\ 2x - y + z = 3 \\ -x - 3y + z = -1; \end{cases}$ (b) $\begin{cases} x + y + 2z = 3 \\ 3x + 2z = 2 \\ -x + 2y + 2z = 4. \end{cases}$

7. (a) The first system is inconsistent; the second system is consistent.
(b) The first system consists of independent equations; the second system consists of dependent equations.

8. $(n^2 + n)/2.$

§7.7 **9.** $x = 3$, $y = 4$, and $z = -2$.

10. $w = 5$, $x = 1$, $y = 19$, and $z = 25$.

11. $x = -3t$, $y = (1 + 7t)/-7$, and $z = t$, where t is any real number.

12. The system is inconsistent.

15. (a) A nontrivial solution exists;

(b) a nontrivial solution does not exist.

17. (a) $w = 0$, $x = t$, $y = 0$, and $z = -2t$, where t is any nonzero real number.

19. $\begin{pmatrix} -2 & 0 & 1 & 2 \\ 6 & -2 & 3 & 1 \\ 2 & 3 & 4 & -4 \end{pmatrix}$.

20. $\begin{pmatrix} 0 & 1 \\ 1 & 0 \end{pmatrix}$, $\begin{pmatrix} k & 0 \\ 0 & 1 \end{pmatrix}$, $\begin{pmatrix} 1 & 0 \\ 0 & k \end{pmatrix}$, $\begin{pmatrix} 1 & k \\ 0 & 1 \end{pmatrix}$, and $\begin{pmatrix} 1 & 0 \\ k & 1 \end{pmatrix}$.

21. $\begin{pmatrix} 1 & -4 \\ 0 & 1 \end{pmatrix} \begin{pmatrix} 1 & 0 \\ 0 & -\frac{1}{16} \end{pmatrix} \begin{pmatrix} 1 & 0 \\ -6 & 1 \end{pmatrix} \begin{pmatrix} 0 & 1 \\ 1 & 0 \end{pmatrix}$.

Other sets of elementary row operation matrices exist whose product is the inverse of $\begin{pmatrix} 6 & 8 \\ 1 & 4 \end{pmatrix}$.

§7.8 **1.** (a) Unique point in common;

(b) unique point in common;

(c) unique line in common;

(d) unique line in common.

2. (a) If $k = 8$, the planes have a unique line in common;

(b) the planes have a unique point in common for any real value of k.

§7.9 *In the answers to Exercises 1–4, t is any nonzero real number.*

1. $\lambda^2 - 5\lambda + 4 = 0$; $\lambda_1 = 1$, $(t \quad -2t)^\mathsf{T}$; $\lambda_2 = 4$, $(t \quad t)^\mathsf{T}$.

2. $\lambda^3 - 7\lambda^2 + 14\lambda - 8$; $\lambda_1 = 1$, $(t \quad 0 \quad 0)^\mathsf{T}$;

$\lambda_2 = 4$, $(0 \quad t \quad 0)^\mathsf{T}$; $\lambda_3 = 2$, $(0 \quad 0 \quad t)^\mathsf{T}$.

3. $\lambda^2 - 25\lambda = 0$; $\lambda_1 = 0$, $(4t \quad 3t)^\mathsf{T}$; $\lambda_2 = 25$, $(3t \quad -4t)^\mathsf{T}$.

4. $\lambda^3 - 12\lambda^2 + 45\lambda - 54 = 0$; $\lambda_1 = 6$, $(t \quad -t \quad t)^\mathsf{T}$;

$\lambda_2 = 3$, $(t \quad t \quad 0)^\mathsf{T}$; $\lambda_3 = 3$, $(-t \quad t \quad 2t)^\mathsf{T}$.

§8.1 *In the answers to Exercises 1–8, t is any nonzero real number.*

1. $(3t, 4t, t)$.

2. $(-5t, t, t)$.

3. $(8t, 0, t)$.

4. $(t, -2t, t)$.

5. $(3t, 4t, 2t, t)$.

6. $(5t, 0, t, t)$.

7. $(6t, 3t, -5t, t)$.

8. $(0, 0, 0, t)$.

9. $(6, -2)$.

10. $(\frac{5}{2}, 4)$.

11. $(-4, -3)$.

12. $(0, \frac{1}{2})$.

13. $(1, 3, -1)$.

14. $(5, 0, 7)$.

15. $(1, 3, -2)$.

16. $(-2, 1, 0)$.

§8.2 **1.** $P:(7, 2)$.

2. $P:(2, -4)$.

3. $P:(0, 0)$.

4. $P:(9, -5)$.

5. P_0:$(2, -6, 3)$.   **7.** P_0:$(5, -10, -2)$.

6. P_0:$(0, 0, 0)$.   **8.** P_0:$(-1, -5, 8)$.

9. $\begin{pmatrix} x' \\ y' \\ 1 \end{pmatrix} = \begin{pmatrix} 1 & 0 & 1 \\ 0 & 1 & -2 \\ 0 & 0 & 1 \end{pmatrix} \begin{pmatrix} x \\ y \\ 1 \end{pmatrix}$.

10. $\begin{pmatrix} x' \\ y' \\ z' \\ 1 \end{pmatrix} = \begin{pmatrix} 1 & 0 & 0 & 0 \\ 0 & 1 & 0 & -3 \\ 0 & 0 & 1 & -1 \\ 0 & 0 & 0 & 1 \end{pmatrix} \begin{pmatrix} x \\ y \\ z \\ 1 \end{pmatrix}$.

14. $x'^2 + y'^2 = 1$.   **15.** $3x'^2 + y'^2 = 9$.

16. (a) $(-5, 2)$;   (b) $(1, -4)$.

§8.3   **1.** P:$(4, -3)$.   **3.** P:$(-5, -2)$.

2. P:$(\sqrt{3}, 1)$.   **4.** P:$(0, -2)$.

5. $\begin{pmatrix} x' \\ y' \\ 1 \end{pmatrix} = \begin{pmatrix} \frac{3}{5} & -\frac{4}{5} & 0 \\ \frac{4}{5} & \frac{3}{5} & 0 \\ 0 & 0 & 1 \end{pmatrix} \begin{pmatrix} x \\ y \\ 1 \end{pmatrix}$; $\theta = \arctan(-4/3)$

6. $\begin{pmatrix} x' \\ y' \\ 1 \end{pmatrix} = \begin{pmatrix} -\frac{7}{25} & \frac{24}{25} & 0 \\ -\frac{24}{25} & -\frac{7}{25} & 0 \\ 0 & 0 & 1 \end{pmatrix} \begin{pmatrix} x \\ y \\ 1 \end{pmatrix}$; $\theta = \arctan(24/-7)$.

7. No.   **8.** Yes.

11. $\begin{pmatrix} 1 & 0 & 0 \\ 0 & 1 & 0 \\ 0 & 0 & 1 \end{pmatrix}$.

12. $3x'^2 + 5y'^2 = 50$.   **13.** $x'^2 + y'^2 = r^2$.

16. $\begin{pmatrix} \frac{4}{5} & \frac{3}{5} & 0 \\ -\frac{3}{5} & \frac{4}{5} & 0 \\ 0 & 0 & 1 \end{pmatrix}$.

17. (a) $\pi/4$;   (b) $\frac{1}{2} \arctan \frac{24}{7}$.

§8.4   **1.** P:$(-10, 12, -1)$.   **2.** P:$(-\frac{24}{49}, \frac{40}{49}, -\frac{15}{49})$.

5. No.   **6.** Yes.

7. $a = \frac{3}{5}, b = 0, c = -1, d = 0$.

8. $\begin{pmatrix} \frac{2}{3} & \frac{1}{3} & \frac{2}{3} & 0 \\ \frac{1}{3} & \frac{2}{3} & -\frac{2}{3} & 0 \\ -\frac{2}{3} & \frac{2}{3} & \frac{1}{3} & 0 \\ 0 & 0 & 0 & 1 \end{pmatrix}$.   **9.** $\begin{pmatrix} 0 & 1 & 0 & 0 \\ 0 & 0 & 1 & 0 \\ 1 & 0 & 0 & 0 \\ 0 & 0 & 0 & 1 \end{pmatrix}$.

10. $9x' - 9y' - 4 = 0$.

§8.6   **1.** P: $\left(\dfrac{1 + 7\sqrt{3}}{2}, \dfrac{7 - \sqrt{3}}{2} \right)$.   **2.** P: $\left(\dfrac{4\sqrt{3} - 1}{2}, \dfrac{10 - 3\sqrt{3}}{2} \right)$.

3. $2y''^2 = x''$.   **4.** $2x''^2 - y''^2 = 0$.

5. $3x''^2 + y''^2 = 4$.   **6.** $x''^2 - y''^2 = 2$.

7. P:$(0, 0, 0)$.   **8.** P:$(-2, 0, 0)$.

9. $2x''^2 + 3y''^2 + 2z''^2 + 2zx - 2y = 0$.

10. $x' + y' + z' = 6$.

§8.7 4. (a) $\begin{pmatrix} 1 & 0 & 0 & 0 \\ 0 & -1 & 0 & 0 \\ 0 & 0 & -1 & 0 \\ 0 & 0 & 0 & 1 \end{pmatrix}$; (b) $\begin{pmatrix} -1 & 0 & 0 & 0 \\ 0 & 1 & 0 & 0 \\ 0 & 0 & -1 & 0 \\ 0 & 0 & 0 & 1 \end{pmatrix}$.

§8.9 1. $x'^2 + 6y'^2 - 2 = 0.$ 2. $x'^2 + 4y'^2 - 4 = 0.$
3. $2x'^2 + 10\sqrt{2}y' - 25 = 0.$ 4. $x''^2 + 4y''^2 - 4 = 0.$

§8.11 1. 2.   2. 3.   3. 3.   4. 3.

§9.2 2. $(\pm 3, 0, 0)$, $(0, \pm 2, 0)$, $(0, 0, \pm 3)$; oblate spheroid.
3. $a = 3$, $b = 2$, $c = 3$.   4. None.
5. $x^2 + 4y^2 + 16z^2 = 16.$
6. (a) $x^2 + 3y^2 + 3z^2 = 6$; prolate spheroid;
(b) $x^2 + 3y^2 + z^2 = 6$; oblate spheroid.
7. $\dfrac{(x-1)^2}{6} + \dfrac{(y-1)^2}{4} + \dfrac{(z+4)^2}{12} = 1$;
geometric center $(1, 1, -4)$; semi-axes $\sqrt{6}$, 2, $2\sqrt{3}$.
10. $\dfrac{\pi bc(a^2 - k^2)}{a^2}.$ 11. $5x^2 + 5y^2 + 2z^2 = 72.$

§9.3 2. $\dfrac{x^2}{b^2} + \dfrac{y^2}{a^2} = 1$, $\dfrac{x^2}{b^2} - \dfrac{z^2}{b^2} = 1$, $\dfrac{y^2}{a^2} - \dfrac{z^2}{b^2} = 1.$
3. $\pi ab.$ 4. $x^2 - y^2 + z^2 = k^2.$
5. $9x^2 - 4y^2 = 36$; y axis.   6. Yes.
7. Conjugate axis.   8. $x = -1$, $y = 2$, $z = 2.$

§9.4 3. $|k| \geq c.$
4. Both transverse semi-axes equal to 1 along the x axis and the y axis respectively; conjugate semi-axis equal to $1/\sqrt{2}$ along the z axis.
5. $\dfrac{(x-2)^2}{7} - \dfrac{y^2}{9} + \dfrac{(z-1)^2}{7} = -1.$
6. $4x^2 - 9y^2 = 36$; x axis.
7. (a) $y^2 - x^2 - z^2 = a^2$; (b) $x^2 + y^2 - z^2 = a^2.$
8. $x = 2$, $y = 1$, $z = -3.$

§9.5 2. $25x^2 - 16y^2 - 4z^2 = 0.$ 3. $\dfrac{z^2}{12} - \dfrac{y^2}{18} = 1$, $x = 3.$

4. (a) $\dfrac{y^2}{9} + \dfrac{z^2}{9} = x^2$, cone of revolution;

(b) $9x^2 + 9z^2 = y^2$, cone of revolution.
5. $\dfrac{(x-1)^2}{9} + \dfrac{z^2}{9} = (y-3)^2$; $z = 3(y-3)$, $x = 1$;

$$\begin{cases} x = 1 \\ y = 3 + t \\ z = 0. \end{cases}$$

6. $4x^2 + 3y^2 - z^2 = 0.$ 7. $(0, 4, 0).$

§9.6   2. $x^2 = z$ or $y^2 = z$; z axis.

5. $x^2 + y^2 = 2|z|$; a pair of elliptic paraboloids.

6. $y^2 + z^2 = 4 - kx$; elliptic paraboloid.

7. $(2, 0, 2)$.   8. $9x^2 + 4z^2 = 36y$.

10. (a) $25x^2 - 4y^2 = 0$;   (b) $y^2 + 25z = 0$;   (c) $x^2 - 4z = 0$.

11. Vertex: $\left(k, 0, \dfrac{k^2}{a^2}\right)$; focus: $\left(k, 0, \dfrac{4k^2 - a^2b^2}{4a^2}\right)$.

12. $x^2 + 9y^2 = 72z$.

§9.7   3. $36y^2 - 100z^2 = 225$.

4. (a) $\dfrac{y^2}{16} + \dfrac{z^2}{9} = 1$ or $\dfrac{y^2}{9} + \dfrac{z^2}{16} = 1$;

(b) $\dfrac{x^2}{16} + \dfrac{z^2}{9} = 1$ or $\dfrac{x^2}{9} + \dfrac{y^2}{16} = 1$;

(c) $\dfrac{x^2}{16} + \dfrac{y^2}{9} = 1$ or $\dfrac{x^2}{9} + \dfrac{y^2}{16} = 1$.

5. $x^2 + z^2 = k^2$.   6. $x^2 = 4 - 4z$.

8. $x^2 + y = 0$ or $y^2 - 8x = 0$.

9. $bx - ay = 0$ and $bx + ay = 0$.

§9.9   1. Real ellipsoid.   2. Cone of revolution.

3. Imaginary elliptic cylinder.   4. Cylinder of revolution.

5. Elliptic paraboloid.   6. Sphere.

7. Hyperboloid of two sheets.   8. Oblate spheroid.

9. Elliptic paraboloid.   10. Hyperbolic paraboloid.

11. Hyperboloid of revolution of one sheet.

12. Intersecting planes.   13. Hyperbolic cylinder.

14. Cylinder of revolution if $k > 0$; line if $k = 0$; imaginary elliptic cylinder if $k < 0$.

15. Sphere.   16. Oblate spheroid.

17. Prolate spheroid.   18. Cone of revolution.

19. Hyperboloid of revolution of one sheet.

20. Cone of revolution.   21. Cylindrical surface.   22. Prolate spheroid.

23. Hyperboloid of revolution of two sheets.   24. Cylinder of revolution.

25. Hyperboloid of revolution of one sheet.

26. Paraboloid of revolution.   27. Oblate spheroid.

28. $x^2 + y^2 + 16z = 0$.

29. $7x^2 + 7y^2 + 7z^2 - 104x + 104y - 104z - 384 = 0$.

30. Any point on the z axis.   31. Hyperboloid of two sheets.

32. Elliptic paraboloid.   33. Hyperboloid of one sheet.

34. Hyperbolic paraboloid.   35. Quadric cone.   36. Oblate spheroid.

37. Sphere if $k < 1$; plane if $k = 1$; sphere if $k > 1$.

§10.2   1. Cone of revolution.   2. Elliptic paraboloid.

3. Hyperboloid of one sheet.   4. Hyperbolic paraboloid.

5. Quadric cone.   6. Cone of revolution.

§10.2 7.
$$\begin{pmatrix} -\frac{2}{3} & \frac{2}{3} & -\frac{1}{3} & 0 \\ \frac{1}{3} & \frac{2}{3} & \frac{2}{3} & 0 \\ \frac{2}{3} & \frac{1}{3} & -\frac{2}{3} & 0 \\ 0 & 0 & 0 & 1 \end{pmatrix}.$$

8. $x + 2yz = 0.$ **9.** $x^2 + y^2 - z^2 - 9 = 0.$

§10.4 1. 3.   **2.** 3.   **3.** 3.   **4.** 4.   **5.** 3.   **6.** 4.

§10.5 2. Either det $\Delta < 0$, det $D > 0$, $ab + bc + ca - f^2 - g^2 - h^2 > 0$, and $a + b + c > 0$; or det $\Delta < 0$, det $D < 0$, $ab + bc + ca - f^2 - g^2 - h^2 > 0$, and $a + b + c < 0$.

3. Either det $\Delta > 0$, det $D > 0$, $ab + bc + ca - f^2 - g^2 - h^2 > 0$, and $a + b + c > 0$; or det $\Delta > 0$, det $D < 0$, $ab + bc + ca - f^2 - g^2 - h^2 > 0$, and $a + b + c < 0$.

4. Det $\Delta > 0$, det $D = 0$, and $ab + bc + ca - f^2 - g^2 - h^2 < 0$.

5. Det $\Delta < 0$, det $D = 0$, and $ab + bc + ca - f^2 - g^2 - h^2 > 0$.

6. Either det $\Delta > 0$, det $D < 0$, and $a + b + c > 0$; det $\Delta > 0$, det $D < 0$, $ab + bc + ca - f^2 - g^2 - h^2 < 0$, and $a + b + c \leq 0$; det $\Delta > 0$, det $D > 0$, and $a + b + c < 0$; or det $\Delta > 0$, det $D > 0$, $ab + bc + ca - f^2 - g^2 - h^2 < 0$, and $a + b + c \geq 0$.

7. Either det $\Delta < 0$, det $D > 0$, and $a + b + c < 0$; det $\Delta < 0$, det $D > 0$, $ab + bc + ca - f^2 - g^2 - h^2 < 0$, and $a + b + c \geq 0$; det $\Delta < 0$, det $D < 0$, and $a + b + c > 0$; or det $\Delta < 0$, det $D < 0$, $ab + bc + ca - f^2 - g^2 - h^2 < 0$, and $a + b + c \leq 0$.

INDEX